STUDENT WORKBOOK
for use with

BUSINESS LAW AND
THE REGULATORY ENVIRONMENT

CONCEPTS AND CASES

Eighth Edition

METZGER ■ MALLOR ■ BARNES ■ BOWERS ■ PHILLIPS

PREPARED BY
ARLEN W. LANGVARDT   LAURA GINGER
both of
INDIANA UNIVERSITY

IRWIN
Homewood, IL 60430
Boston, MA 02116

© Richard D. Irwin, Inc., 1970, 1974, 1978, 1982, 1986, 1989, and 1992

ISBN 0-256-08892-6

Printed in the United States of America

1 2 3 4 5 6 7 8 9 0 VK 8 7 6 5 4 3 2 1

CONTENTS

CHAPTER 1

THE NATURE OF LAW

True-False - Circle T for True and F for False.

T F 1. The *Restatements* set forth statutory rules that bind courts across the country.

T F 2. Constitutions not only set up the branches of government and their powers, but also restrict governmental actions.

T F 3. Even if the words of a statute seem clear and unambiguous, a court engaging in statutory interpretation is not required to apply the statute according to the plain meaning of the statutory language.

T F 4. If a case is instituted in court by the government, the case must be a criminal proceeding because the government is not a private party.

T F 5. American legal realists typically assert that questions of morality are beyond the province of the law and that legal rules "on the books" should therefore be obeyed in all instances, without regard for whether society's moral sensibilities are offended by the law.

T F 6. Administrative rules or regulations and administrative agency decisions are valid even though they are not made by a legislature or a court.

T F 7. A statute making armed robbery a crime is an example of procedural law.

T F 8. Law serves a variety of societal functions, some of which may be in conflict in certain instances.

T F 9. *Ejusdem generis* is the doctrine that has served as the major shaping force in the development of American common law.

T F 10. A natural law thinker regards morality as an essential component of a valid law.

Multiple Choice - Circle the best answer.

11. Judge Dullard, an old family friend, is a trial judge in Indiana. He needs help in deciding Case A, which is now pending in his court. Because he knows that you are not yet failing your business law course (the semester is far from over, however), he has called you for advice. Judge Dullard stated the following:

"I'm really in a quandary over Case A. There's an Indiana statute, passed in 1982, that directly addresses the specific issue in the case, but I've found several Indiana Supreme Court cases from the 1960s and 1970s. All of those cases apply a common law rule that is the opposite of the rule stated in the statute. I've thought this over carefully, and I'm convinced that the rule contained in the statute makes for horrendous public policy, and that the common law rule is better. Can I decide Case A according to the common law rule?"

What should you tell the judge?

a. That he is bound by the statute because in instances of conflicts between different types of law, the more recent statement of the applicable rule controls.

b. That he is free to apply the common law rule, in view of the judiciary's power to make and apply common law that is consistent with sound policy.

c. That he is bound by the statute because the common law cannot apply if there is an applicable statute.

d. That he must develop a new rule appropriate to Case A, because the conflicting common law and statutory rules cancel each other out.

12. A person who follows the American Legal Realism school of jurisprudence:

a. views law as a social ordering process that reflects current American society's dominant interests and values.

b. believes that unjust or immoral laws do not deserve to be regarded as law, and should not be enforced or obeyed.

c. would advocate obedience to any properly enacted law, regardless of whether that law is just or moral.

d. defines law as the behavior of those persons and institutions charged with enforcing and applying the law, rather than the law as it appears in written form.

13. The common law:

a. exists only at the federal level.

b. applies only in situations that are governed by statutes or other positive law.

c. will prevail over a conflicting constitutional provision.

d. is judge-made law that controls if no other type of law applies.

14. For purposes of statutory interpretation, the term *legislative purpose* refers to:

a. the overall aim or objective the legislature was trying to achieve by enacting the statute.

b. the meaning that the legislature intended certain words in the statute to have.

c. widely accepted general notions of sound public policy that serve as a backdrop against which a statute should be interpreted.

d. each of the above.

15. Rules of procedural law:

a. set up standards of conduct for people to follow as they deal with each other in society.

b. govern the behavior of governmental bodies as they make and enforce rules of substantive law.

c. seek to define the essence of law.

d. include statutes forbidding the sale and use of controlled substances.

16. Assume that in 1978, State X amended its constitution by adopting a provision specifying that State X-based trucking firms engaged in interstate commerce could not be required to have mudflaps of any kind on their trucks, at least while the trucks were located in State X. Also assume that in 1989, Congress enacted a federal statute stating that any trucking firm engaged in interstate commerce must at all times have its trucks equipped with Type PDQ mudflaps, regardless of the trucks' location. Bigrig Trucking Co., which is based in State X, regularly engages in the transportation of goods in interstate commerce. In view of the facts just stated, which of the following accurately sets forth Bigrig's rights or obligations in connection with the mudflaps issue?

a. Bigrig need not install the mudflaps called for by the federal statute, because the statute is not controlling in states having constitutional provisions such as State X's.

b. Bigrig must comply with the federal statute because of the rule that in a conflict between the types of law present in the facts, the type of law that went into effect later states the controlling rule.

c. The constitutional provision controls because of the rule that the type of law taking effect first controls when types of law conflict; therefore, Bigrig need not install the mudflaps.

d. The federal statute controls here because state law must yield to federal law in the event of a conflict between the two; therefore, Bigrig must comply with the statute.

17. The following statements pertain to equitable remedies. Which statement is accurate?

a. The equitable remedy known as an injunction may consist of a court order that a party not do a certain thing, but cannot consist of an order that a party do a particular thing.

b. An equitable remedy may be appropriate if an award of money damages would not provide adequate relief to a party entitled to a remedy.

c. The equitable remedy known as reformation allows a court to effectively "rewrite" a contract in a manner contrary to the parties' real intentions, so that a fair result may be reached.

d. An award of suitable money damages to an injured party is the most common equitable remedy granted by courts.

2

18. In 1989, Dave Derelict pleaded guilty in State X to a charge of felony theft. Because of an over-sight, however, the court never formally entered a judgment of guilty on the charge. In 1990, after a policeman discovered that Derelict had a handgun in his coat pocket, Derelict was arrested and convicted for violating a State X statute that makes it a crime for a person who has been con-victed of a felony to possess a handgun. Derelict appealed his conviction, arguing that he did not violate this statute because he had not actually been convicted of a felony as of the time he was caught with the gun in his pocket. The appellate court disagreed, stating that debate on the floor of the State X legislature had "made it clear that in enacting the statute barring convicted felons from possessing handguns, the legislature was intent on preventing those with criminal back-grounds from possessing firearms." Which method of statutory interpretation did the appellate court use?
    a. Plain meaning
    b. Legislative intent
    c. Legislative purpose
    d. Prior interpretations

19. Assume that in 1968, the Supreme Court of State X decided *Groovy v. Peace N' Love*. In that case, the court established a common law rule that if a plaintiff claims a loss of hearing as a result of attending a musical concert, the plaintiff has no legal cause of action for money damages against the musicians whose concert he attended. Another case presenting essentially the same facts and legal issues has made its way through State X's court system and is now before the Su-preme Court of State X. The present case, *Sleazy v. Pervasive Stench*, cannot be distinguished from the *Groovy* case. In deciding the *Sleazy* case, the Supreme Court of State X:
    a. is bound by the *Groovy* precedent and has no choice but to decide *Sleazy* in accordance with it, because the doctrine of *stare decisis* demands absolute adherence to precedent.
    b. cannot overrule the *Groovy* decision because a court is prohibited from overruling its own ear-lier decision unless it can distinguish it from the case now at hand.
    c. may overrule the *Groovy* decision and develop a new common law rule in *Sleazy*, if, after careful reflection, the court concludes that the rule stated in *Groovy* is no longer good policy.
    d. is free to disregard the *Groovy* decision and develop a new common law rule for application in *Sleazy*, because the doctrine of *stare decisis* applies only to trial courts, not to appellate courts.

20. Administrative agencies have the power to make law because:
    a. Congress or a state legislature has delegated this power to them.
    b. the state and federal constitutions give them this power.
    c. the English common law tradition dictates that they have this power.
    d. of the increasing tendency of courts to defer to the expertise of agencies under the *ejusdem ge-neris* doctrine.

Short Essay

21. Assume that since 1903, the following statute has existed in State X:

"Any state government employee who makes personal use of state-owned paper or writing instru-ments, or of other similar state-owned supplies, shall be punished by having three fingers severed from each of his or her hands, and by being tarred and feathered and paraded in such condition down the main street of the town of his or her residence at 12:00 noon on the first Monday of the month following the state employee's conviction for such offense."

In addition, assume that even though the legislature of State X has left the statute in the Official Statutes of State X instead of repealing it, police and prosecutors in State X have never enforced it against any state government employee. Examine this statute, the foregoing facts, and the issues they suggest from the perspectives of each of the four schools of jurisprudence described in the text. For each school, briefly discuss: the general approach that school would likely take to the ex-amination of this statute (including the thing or things about the statute that would be the most in-teresting, important, or worthy of careful attention); and how an adherent to that school would view the validity or invalidity of the statute, including whether there is a duty to obey it (if that school of jurisprudence would make such a judgment).

22. Explain how the doctrine of *stare decisis* not only produces stability and predictability in the common law, but also enables the common law to evolve to meet changing social conditions.

23. Assume that a statute of State A contains this sentence: "No employer whose principal office is in this state shall discriminate against, between, or among prospective or existing employees on the basis of their race or color of skin, when making decisions on employment-related matters of whatever nature." Also assume that the statute was passed during the late 1960s in response to public pressure for legislation to alter employment practices that kept non-Caucasian persons from being hired or from advancing suitably in their employment after being hired. Average, Inc., whose principal office is in State A, decided on its own to implement an affirmative action plan in 1990. One portion of this plan specified that when Average made its 1990 and 1991 selections of ten existing employees for participation in the company's management training program, at least four of the ten slots available each year would go to non-Caucasian employees. Selection of employees for the program was to be based on the employees' performances on certain tests, although non-Caucasians who did not fare as well on the tests as Caucasian employees could be selected anyway if doing so was necessary to have at least four non-Caucasians among the selected group. Larry Livid, a Caucasian employee of Average, was not selected for the management training program this year even though his test scores were seventh highest overall and were higher than those of the four non-Caucasians who were selected. Livid has sued Average for appropriate legal relief on the theory that Average's affirmative action plan violated the above-quoted statute of State A. What statutory interpretation technique will Livid assert that the court should apply here? What technique will Average ask the court to apply? Explain your reasoning.

24. You remember Judge Dullard, the old family friend whose request for your advice on a case was the subject of question #11, above. Besides asking you about that case, Judge Dullard asked you about Case B, which is also pending in his court. He stated the following during your recent conversation:

"Case B is governed by the common law. My exhaustive research has revealed the existence of an apparent precedent case. It's a 1985 decision of the Indiana Supreme Court, the highest court in Indiana. I don't think the rule stated in that case is a very good rule, however. Do I have to apply it in deciding Case B? Is there some way I can get around it? If so, how?"

How should you respond to Judge Dullard's questions?

CHAPTER 2

THE RESOLUTION OF PRIVATE DISPUTES

True-False - Circle T for True and F for False.

T F 1. A court that lacks subject matter jurisdiction cannot render a judgment that is binding on the parties to the case.

T F 2. Any lawsuit between citizens of two different states can be decided under the federal courts' diversity jurisdiction.

T F 3. A small percentage of the cases that come to the U.S. Supreme Court fall within the Court's certiorari jurisdiction, under which the court has discretion whether to hear the appeal.

T F 4. As a general rule, appellate courts decide questions of law rather than questions of fact.

T F 5. If the filing of a suit in a given court is inconsistent with the venue requirements established by state law, the court cannot have *in personam* jurisdiction over the parties.

T F 6. Jurisdiction may be limited geographically, by subject matter, or by the amount of damages that a court is empowered to award.

T F 7. The discovery process affords a party to a civil suit the opportunity to obtain substantial amounts of information from the other party prior to trial.

T F 8. The defendant who fails to file a counterclaim is deemed to have admitted the allegations in the plaintiff's complaint.

T F 9. One of the purposes of the pretrial conference is to get the parties to stipulate to facts that are not in dispute.

T F 10. When the trial judge decides to have the jury return a special verdict, the jury will declare which party wins the case and the relief, if any, to be awarded.

Multiple Choice - Circle the best answer.

11. Cornelius Husker, an elderly Nebraska resident, believes that Jay Hawk, a Kansas resident, committed the tort of battery upon him. The incident giving rise to Husker's claim took place in Memorial Stadium in Lincoln, Nebraska, just after the University of Nebraska eked out a narrow 59-3 football triumph over the University of Kansas. Husker has filed his battery claim against Hawk in a Nebraska trial court. Nebraska has a long arm statute containing the typical provisions described in the text. On these facts,

    a. the Nebraska court has *in rem* jurisdiction even though Hawk is a Kansas resident, because the incident took place in Nebraska.

    b. the long arm statute has not been satisfied, because nothing in the facts indicates that Hawk transacted business in Nebraska or otherwise availed himself of the protections of Nebraska law.

    c. the Nebraska court will likely conclude that the long arm statute and the "minimum contacts" doctrine have been satisfied, making it proper for the court to exercise jurisdiction over Hawk.

    d. the Nebraska court should dismiss the suit because under the facts, Husker must sue Hawk in either state or federal court in Kansas.

12. Douglas has brought a civil suit against Haney. Douglas:

    a. may win the suit even if he does not prove the elements of his claim beyond a reasonable doubt.

    b. may obtain an enforceable judgment against Haney if the court has either subject matter jurisdiction or *in personam* jurisdiction.

    c. must win the the suit if he proves that the greater weight of the evidence, in terms of quantity, supports the elements of his claim.

    d. must wait until the time of trial to obtain under-oath testimony from Haney.

13. The following statements set forth supposed attributes of arbitration. Which statement is *inaccurate*?
    a. Disputes usually may be resolved more quickly than in court.
    b. Disputes often may be resolved more cheaply than in court.
    c. Disputes often are settled by someone who is an expert in the subject matter of the dispute.
    d. Disputes usually are resolved through recognition of the full protections of the rules of evidence.

14. By granting which of the following motions does the trial judge decide the case herself instead of allowing the jury, which has heard and seen the evidence presented at trial, to make the decision?
    a. Motion to dismiss for failure to state a claim
    b. Motion for directed verdict
    c. Motion for summary judgment
    d. Motion for judgment notwithstanding the verdict
    e. Motion for restroom break

15. Of the following statements about jurisdiction, which is/are accurate?
    a. Subject matter jurisdiction has to do with whether the court has the power to decide the type of controversy being presented.
    b. If a plaintiff from Indiana files suit in a Delaware court, the Delaware court has *in personam* jurisdiction over the plaintiff even though she is not a resident of Delaware.
    c. A court of a certain state has *in personam* jurisidiction over defendants who reside in that state only when the state's long arm statute is satisfied.
    d. Both a and b.
    e. Both a and c.

16. Popular television evangelist Ariel Goldmine, a resident of Tennessee, has filed a product liability suit against Industrial Strength Facial Makeup Corp., a Missouri firm. Goldmine seeks several hundred thousand dollars worth of damages because of alleged breaches of warranty by Industrial Strength. Of the following statements about the suit, which is/are accurate?
    a. If Goldmine filed the suit in an appropriate federal court, Industrial Strength may elect to have it removed to an appropriate state court.
    b. If Goldmine filed the suit in an appropriate state court, Industrial Strength may elect to have it removed to an appropriate federal court.
    c. Goldmine must have filed the suit in a appropriate state court, because the fact that her suit does not involve a federally based right means that a federal court could not hear the case.
    d. Both a and b.

17. Which of the following does an appellate court have the power to do when deciding a case?
    a. Grant a summary judgment in favor of the appellant.
    b. Grant a directed verdict in favor of the appellant.
    c. Consider and correct errors of law made by the trial court.
    d. Consider new testimony and other new evidence offered by the appellant.

18. The courts' power to declare the actions of the legislative and executive branches of government unconstitutional is the power to:
    a. exercise judicial review.
    b. issue a declaratory judgment.
    c. exercise *in rem* jurisdiction.
    d. exercise *stare decisis*.

19. Pungent Corp., which was incorporated in Illinois and has its principal offices there, produces a popular men's cologne known as "Evening in Peoria." A particular batch of Evening in Peoria, sent by Pungent into the stream of commerce, was defective and unreasonably dangerous as of the time it left Pungent's control because the cologne in that batch was unusually flammable. Butch Studley, an unsuspecting Wyoming resident, purchased a bottle of Evening in Peoria from a Wyoming retailer. The bottle purchased by Studley was part of the defective batch. Studley took the Evening in Peoria home, applied it liberally, and then lit a cigarette. Studley immediately became engulfed in flames. He was burned so severely that his medical expenses alone totaled $96,000. Studley intends to bring a tort claim against Pungent. Assume that Wyoming has a long arm statute containing the typical provisions described in your text. Which of the following provides the most accurate and most complete listing of the courts in which Studley may properly bring suit?

   a. An appropriate state trial court in Illinois or an appropriate federal district court in Illinois.
   b. An appropriate state trial court in Wyoming or an appropriate federal district court in Wyoming.
   c. An appropriate state trial court in Wyoming or an appropriate state trial court in Illinois.
   d. An appropriate state trial court in Wyoming or Illinois, or an appropriate federal district court in Wyoming or Illinois.

20. Alf has obtained a judgment against Biff. Alf wishes to partially satisfy the judgment by obtaining funds that Biff has on deposit at Nearly Insolvent Savings & Loan. In order to reach the deposited funds, Alf should obtain a:

   a. writ of execution.
   b. writ of garnishment.
   c. demurrable counterclaim.
   d. judicial determination that Biff is not judgment-proof.

Short Essay

21. An appellate court is faced with deciding the case of *Pyle v. Dorf*. At the trial court level, the jury returned a verdict in favor of the defendant, Dorf. Pyle appealed. She wishes to present to the appellate court certain evidence that she neglected to present at the trial. She believes that this additional evidence would show that she should win the case, and that in the interest of justice the evidence should be considered by the appellate court. Alternatively, Pyle argues that the appellate court should reverse the decision below and remand the case for a new trial because, in Pyle's view, the trial judge erroneously sustained an objection made by Dorf's attorney. As a result, according to Pyle, she was not allowed to present certain other evidence that could reasonably have caused the jury to find in her favor rather than in Dorf's. Will the appellate court allow Pyle to present the additional evidence she now wishes to present in the interest of justice? Why or why not? As for Pyle's alternative argument, is it a proper basis for seeking a reversal and remand? Explain your reasoning.

22. Consider the following potential cases:

Case #1—John, a New Hampshire resident, wishes to bring a breach of contract suit against Gratis Air Travel Corp., a Virginia firm. John expects to seek $39,000 in damages because he had to pay that amount out of his own pocket for travel that, under his contract with Gratis, was not to have cost him anything.

Case #2—Mike, a Massachusetts resident, wishes to sue the State of Massachusetts in an effort to have one of its statutes held to be in violation of various provisions of the U.S. Constitution. Assume that the statute bars former governors and previously unsuccessful candidates for national political office from seeking to be elected to any state office except that of State Dog-Catcher. Mike does not intend to seek any money damages. He will ask only for a declaration that the statute is unconstitutional.

Putting aside any consideration of whether the respective plaintiffs would ultimately win their cases, which of the two cases could properly be *brought* in federal court? Explain your reasoning.

23. What common characteristic is shared by *in personam* jurisdiction and *in rem* jurisdiction? What is the crucial difference between these types of jurisdiction?

CHAPTER 3

BUSINESS AND THE CONSTITUTION

True-False - Circle T for True and F for False.

T F 1. A state law that unduly stands in the way of the fulfillment of purposes of a federal law is likely to be preempted by the federal law.

T F 2. The Fifth and Fourteenth Amendments to the Constitution prohibit the federal and state governments from taking the private property of citizens.

T F 3. Supreme Court interpretations of the Commerce Clause have allowed Congress to rely on the clause as effectively a "police power" basis for regulating on seemingly noncommmercial matters.

T F 4. A state law that bars parties from entering into certain types of contracts after a certain future date is likely to violate the Contract Clause.

T F 5. If a government action's constitutionality is tested according to the rational basis test, the court will inquire whether the government action is necessary to the fulfillment of a compelling government purpose.

T F 6. The government's firing of an untenured public employee normally will trigger due process rights on the part of the terminated employee.

T F 7. The states have broad police power to legislate and otherwise regulate in an effort to protect the health, safety, and welfare of the public.

T F 8. Although the main purpose of the federal government's taxing power is to raise revenue for the government, the taxing power may also be used as a regulatory device.

T F 9. If federal regulation on a subject is pervasive, a state regulation on that subject may be regarded as preempted even though the state regulation does not expressly contradict any particular federal regulation.

T F 10. The Constitution allows the federal and state governments to take private property for any purpose, if they pay the property owner suitable compensation.

T F 11. In recent years, the Supreme Court appears to have taken a stricter approach when examining state laws that impair the state's own contracts than when examining state laws that impair private contracts.

T F 12. When a statute is tested under the full strict scrutiny analysis, the court will ask whether the statute is reasonably related to the fulfillment of a legitimate government interest.

Multiple Choice - Circle the best answer.

13. Recent medical studies have indicated that excessive consumption of caffeinated coffee may increase one's risk of developing coronary problems. Another recent medical study has indicated that excessive consumption of decaffeinated coffee may raise one's cholesterol level and thereby increase his risk of having a heart attack. Assume that Congress, motivated by these studies and acting out of concern for the public health, enacts a statute prohibiting televised advertisements for coffee (both caffeinated and decaffeinated). Also assume that the statute is challenged on first amendment grounds in a suit filed by various coffee producers and coffee drinkers against the United States government. In view of the most recent applicable decisions of the Supreme Court, which of the following is an accurate statement about the essential issues in the case?

   a. The statute will be held constitutional even if it does not directly advance the government's underlying interest, so long as the court does not consider the statute absurd.

   b. The statute will be held invalid because of one simple fact: Congress has not outlawed the sale and consumption of coffee, which means that the statute's attempt to ban advertisements for coffee is unconstitutional.

c. The plaintiffs should succeed in their attempt to have the statute declared unconstitutional by arguing these two points: that Congress cannot show that it was acting to further a compelling purpose here; and that nonmisleading commercial speech cannot be restricted by the government.

d. The statute may be upheld by the court even if it concludes that the statute was not the least restrictive means by which the government could have furthered the purpose underlying the statute.

14. Assume that a state has enacted a statute abolishing the "absentee" and "mail-in" ballots that previously were available to physically handicapped persons. The statute also states that any registered voter wishing to vote in any election must actually come to the appropriate polling place and cast his or her vote there. The statute has been challenged, on equal protection grounds, in a suit filed by a group of persons who allege that their severe physical handicaps make it impossible for them to come to a polling place on election day. What analysis is the court hearing the plaintiffs' equal protection case likely to apply to the statute, and why?

a. The court is likely to employ the rational basis test because of the latitude given to states concerning how their elections are to be conducted.

b. The court is likely to employ the full strict scrutiny analysis because the statute discriminates with regard to the exercise of a fundamental right.

c. The court is likely to apply the rational basis test because physically handicapped persons are not considered a suspect class.

d. The court is likely to employ an intermediate scrutiny analysis because of the nature of the voting right affected by the statute.

15. Shoddy Construction Co. fired construction worker Chuck Tubafore without giving him an explanation for the termination. Tubafore has sued Shoddy, alleging that he was denied due process of law when Shoddy failed to give him a hearing at which he could contest the firing. Which of the following facts will be the most useful to Shoddy when it seeks a quick dismissal of Tubafore's suit?

a. That Tubafore has a drinking problem.

b. That it would be an unreasonable burden for employers such as Shoddy to have to provide a hearing each time they fire someone.

c. That Shoddy is a private corporation.

d. That Tubafore sexually harassed a building inspector.

16. The following statements pertain to First Amendment issues applicable to parties engaged in business. Which statement is accurate?

a. Nonmisleading commercial speech receives full First Amendment protection, but misleading commercial speech receives only an intermediate degree of constitutional protection.

b. Corporate political speech receives an intermediate degree of First Amendment protection, rather than the full First Amendment protection given to individual persons' political speech.

c. Although commercial speech was once considered to be outside the scope of First Amendment protection, commercial speech is now given the same level of First Amendment protection given to political speech.

d. Despite the extension of First Amendment protection to commercial speech, even nonmisleading commercial speech about lawful matters may be regulated constitutionally by the government.

17. The Commerce Clause:

a. sets forth a Congressional power that must yield to state power to regulate when the matter to be regulated has both interstate and intrastate facets.

b. has become, through judicial interpretations, an increasingly narrow source of power that Congress rarely can rely on effectively as a constitutional basis for enacting a statute.

c. has been interpreted by the courts so as to justify Congressional action dealing with largely intrastate activities that nonetheless affect interstate commerce in some meaningful sense.

d. sets forth a broad Congressional power but does not serve to limit the states' expansive authority, under their police powers, to regulate business activities connected with interstate commerce.

18. Supreme Court precedent appears to indicate that if speech being regulated by the government possesses both commercial and noncommercial components,
    a. the predominating component is likely to determine the level of First Amendment protection given to the speech as a whole.
    b. the presence of the noncommercial component means that the speech as a whole is treated as noncommercial speech for purposes of First Amendment analysis.
    c. the commercial component of the speech receives First Amendment treatment that is different from the First Amendment treatment given to the noncommercial component of the same speech.
    d. the presence of the commercial component means that the speech as a whole is treated as commercial speech for purposes of First Amendment analysis.

19. A court would be very likely to strike down, on due process grounds, state legislation that:
    a. dispensed with the right to a trial in criminal prosecutions for alleged misdemeanor offenses.
    b. established a minimum age for obtaining employment.
    c. regulated the number of hours employees could work during a week.
    d. did any of the above.

20. Assume that Congress became concerned about the harmful health effects of a diet that is too high in saturated fats. Also assume that in 1991, Congress therefore enacted (and the President signed into law) a statute banning the sale of food products containing saturated fat contents above a certain level specified in the statute. The statute specified that it would go into effect on Jan. 1, 1993. In early January 1992, Lardco, Inc., a shortening manufacturer, filed suit in an effort to have the statute declared unconstitutional on equal protection grounds. Much of the shortening produced and sold by Lardco would exceed the saturated fat level established in the statute and therefore would violate the statute if it were allowed to take effect. Which of the following is an accurate statement about Lardco's equal protection suit?
    a. In view of the effect the statute would have on Lardco's business, the court will require the government to prove that the statute is necessary to the fulfillment of a compelling government purpose.
    b. Because engaging in one's chosen business is a fundamental right in our society, the court will apply at least intermediate scrutiny to the statute.
    c. Because Congress's underlying interest in protecting the public health is clearly not illegitimate, Lardco will lose unless it convinces the court that the statute is not reasonably related to the underlying government interest.
    d. Recent trends indicate that the court will be likely to treat Lardco's claim as if it were a substantive due process claim, meaning that the court will strike down the statute as an unwarranted incursion into private business decisionmaking.

21. Assume that in an effort to enhance public safety, the legislature of State X passed a statute limiting semi-trucks, but no other motor vehicles, to a speed of 45 miles per hour on two-lane State X highways. In addition, assume that the law of each surrounding state allows semi-trucks to be operated at a maximum speed of 55 miles per hour on two-lane highways in those states. The following observations pertain to a suit brought by a group of affected truckers who do business in State X and in the surrounding states and who question the validity of the State X statute. Which of the statements is accurate?
    a. The truckers should prevail in the suit if they argue that the statute violates the Equal Protection Clause, because there is no logical reason for the legislature to treat semi-trucks differently from other motor vehicles.
    b. The truckers have a strong argument that the State X statute is invalid because it amounts to a violation of substantive due process.
    c. The truckers should prevail in the suit if they argue that the State X statute is preempted by the conflicting statutes of the surrounding states.
    d. The truckers have a possibly meritorious argument that the State X statute is invalid because it amounts to a burden on commerce.

11

22. Which of the following is *not* an accurate statement about the Takings Clause of the Fifth Amendment?

    a. The protection it affords has been held to be incorporated within Fourteenth Amendment due process.

    b. It bars the government from taking privately owned property for public use.

    c. The protection it affords may be triggered even when the government has not used formal condemnation procedures.

    d. Extensive government regulation may sometimes constitute a taking within the meaning of the constitutional provision.

23. A state workers' compensation statute requires employers or their insurers to pay death benefits to the surviving family members of employees killed while on the job. The statute specifies that the death benefit is to be $50,000 if the deceased employee was male and $40,000 if the deceased employee was female. A suit challenging the constitutionality of the statute has been filed by the surviving family members of a female employee who was killed while performing the duties of her employment. Their claim is that the statute violates the Equal Protection Clause. In deciding the case, the court will:

    a. apply the intermediate scrutiny analysis because of the statute's apparent discrimination on the basis of sex.

    b. apply the full strict scrutiny analysis because sex is a suspect basis of classification.

    c. defer to the legislature's judgment and uphold the statute under the rational basis test.

    d. employ a substantive due process analysis to determine whether the legislature validly exercised its power.

Short Essay

24. While the two of you were studying for an exam, your fellow student, Everett Blowhard, Jr., stated the following:

"I have engaged in a careful reading of the actual language of the First and Fourteenth Amendments to the U.S. Constitution. After completing that endeavor, I came to the irrefutable conclusion that Professor Schmuck committed a grievous error in class yesterday when he asserted that the Constitution's freedom of speech and press clauses and its equal protection clause restrict actions by all levels of government. That, alas, cannot be so. The freedom of speech and press clauses are part of the First Amendment, whose literal language restricts only *federal government* action. The equal protection clause appears in the Fourteenth Amendment, which speaks only of restrictions on actions by *the states*. I am greatly dismayed by this regrettable state of constitutional affairs, but that feeling pales at my disgust over Professor Schmuck's having dispensed blatant nonsense to unsuspecting students."

Assuming that you like Blowhard, how should you respond to his statement?

25. Assume that in response to recent product tampering scares, Congress enacts a statute containing extremely specific and extensive packaging requirements for medications, prescription and non-prescription alike. A group of manufacturers of medications files suit in a effort to have the statute struck down on equal protection grounds. The manufacturers' argument is that they are denied equal protection, in that they have been singled out for special treatment, whereas manufacturers of food products (which have also been tampered with), have not had comparable requirements imposed on them. What legal test will the court employ in deciding the equal protection claim? Why will that test be applied? Will the manufacturers succeed with their claim? Why or why not?

26. Assume that Congress, acting to protect the public health, safety, and welfare, enacts an outright ban on all commercial advertising of cigarettes. In addition, assume that various cigarette manufacturers, media interests, and consumers file suit in an effort to have the statute struck down as a violation of the First Amendment. As to which of the four questions set forth below would a "*NO*" answer by the court be the *most damaging* to the government with regard to its position that the advertising ban is constitutional and should be upheld? Explain your reasoning.

A—Will the advertising in which the cigarette manufacturers wish to engage be misleading?

B—Will the advertising ban reduce the amount of cigarette use by the public?

C—Is the advertising ban the least restrictive means of promoting the government's substantial interest?

D—Do the cigarette manufacturers wish to advertise any product whose sale is unlawful?

13

BUSINESS ETHICS, CORPORATE SOCIAL RESPONSIBILITY, AND THE CONTROL AND GOVERNANCE OF CORPORATIONS

True-False - Circle T for True and F for False.

T F 1. Most modern subscribers to rights-based theories of ethical behavior place considerable emphasis on economic rights such as property rights and freedom of contract.

T F 2. Critics of corporations tend to concede one point as undeniably true: large corporations promote economic efficiency.

T F 3. Causes for concern about the power of modern corporations include the fact that they are not subject to constitutional checks and the probability that outside forces will have virtually no influence on the selection of corporate directors and officers.

T F 4. Some defenders of the modern corporation argue that profit maximization is in fact socially responsible corporate behavior because it maximizes society's economic welfare by efficiently allocating society's scarce resources.

T F 5. The "groupthink" phenomenon is likely to cause a group of corporate decisionmakers to be overly concerned about the potential problems to be encountered if a given corporate venture were undertaken.

T F 6. The term "iron triangle" refers to the formation of a mutually beneficial relationship among a government agency, the industry it regulates, and the congressional subcommittee controlling the agency.

T F 7. "Risky shift" means that a group of people reaching a consensus on an acceptable level of risk often decide on a level of risk that is lower than the risk they would accept as individuals.

T F 8. Some corporate reformers assert that improved information-flow procedures should lead to more responsible corporate decisionmaking because "bad news" would stand a better chance than it now does of "getting to the top."

T F 9. One possible conception of ethical corporate behavior—that the ethical corporation must act in the best interests of all of its various constituencies—is problematic in actual practice because the interests of these constituencies often conflict.

T F 10. Market forces are more likely to be effective in influencing corporate behavior when the corporation has been producing unsafe products than when the corporation has been bribing mid-level officials of foreign governments.

Multiple Choice - Circle the best answer.

11. Which of the following is *not* an accurate statement about utilitarianism?
    a. It is classified as a deontological theory because it judges the moral worth of an action by the consequences it produces.
    b. It is generally consistent with the notion of "the greatest good for the greatest number."
    c. It may tend to sacrifice personal interests in order to maximize collective utility.
    d. It is sometimes criticized as unworkable because of the difficulties associated with measuring societal utility.

12. Some commentators argue that the only ethical obligation corporate managers should have is to maximize profits and, by doing so, achieve the efficient allocation of scarce resources. A flaw in this argument is that:
    a. corporations cannot in fact allocate resources efficiently.
    b. profit-maximization behavior does not result in the efficient allocation of scarce societal resources.
    c. there may sometimes be other values that are as important as, if not more important than, allocational efficiency.
    d. allocational efficiency is not an important social value in the first place, and is therefore not a sufficient justification for profit maximization.

13. Why are market forces and pressure by consumers not always effective to influence corporations to behave in a socially responsible manner?
    a. Because corporations cannot always be counted on to respond rationally to pressures brought to bear by market forces and private consumer action.
    b. Because consumers may not be aware of where to apply pressure in an effort to influence corporate behavior, or may not be properly situated to apply pressure.
    c. Because those being harmed by corporate behavior may not be aware of the injury until long after the corporate behavior takes place.
    d. All of the above.

14. The main weakness in the theory that corporate social responsibility can be increased by increasing shareholders' power to influence corporate policy is that:
    a. most shareholders are not sophisticated enough to make good business judgments.
    b. shareholders are likely to be at least as interested in profit maximization as corporate managers are, if not more so.
    c. shareholders already have great power to influence corporate policy.
    d. shareholders as individuals are not sufficiently ethical to make desirable decisions about ethical corporate behavior.

15. Of the following statements about rights-based theories of ethical behavior, which is/are accurate?
    a. They concede that rights-based claims must yield to utilitarian claims when the two conflict.
    b. They are teleological in nature because they determine the moral worth of an action without taking into account its consequences.
    c. They tend to give considerable importance to negative rights such as freedom of expression and the right of privacy.
    d. All of the above.

16. Why are so-called industry codes of conduct objectionable to those who favor increased corporate social responsibility?
    a. Because they regard these codes as self-serving efforts that merely give the appearance of requiring ethical behavior.
    b. Because they feel that such codes impose unfairly high standards of behavior on the firms subject to them.
    c. Because they feel that such codes discourage profit-maximization by the firms in the industry.
    d. Because such codes have the force of law and therefore trigger "good" behavior by compulsion, rather than by instilling a sincere desire in corporate management to engage in ethical behavior.

17. The law is not always an effective device for controlling corporate misbehavior because:
    a. business often uses its significant voice in determining the content of law to shape the law so that it reflects corporate interests.
    b. corporations sometimes consciously decide to break the law if the benefits to be gained by doing so are great and the adverse consequences of doing so are small in comparison.

c. some of the dangers posed by "improper" corporate behavior are unknown or even unknowable and therefore are not prohibited at the time the behavior takes place.

d. of each of the above reasons.

18. Which of the following is the most important reason why the board of directors often has little influence on corporate policy?

a. Directors are not adequately paid for their services.

b. Modern boards of directors pay undue attention to the wishes of shareholders.

c. Many board members do not have enough time, expertise, or energy to carefully consider corporate decisions.

d. Boards of directors have so many constituent directors of varying viewpoints that agreement on a proposed course of action is rare.

19. Those who study corporate behavior:

a. believe that corporations are always rational actors.

b. have found that often, bad news does not reach top managers.

c. tend to argue that "risky shift" causes corporate decisionmakers to be less comfortable taking risks as a group than they would be as individuals.

d. tend to argue that when corporate decisionmakers act as a group in deciding on a highly profitable venture, they are likely to be more sensitive to problems that would be associated with the venture than if they were making the decision outside the group setting.

20. Which of the following is the strongest argument *against* profit-maximization as the sole standard for evaluating corporate behavior?

a. That a profit-maximization objective is virtually guaranteed to lead to disputes among corporate directors, officers, and shareholders.

b. That profit-maximization is an inherently unethical notion.

c. That a profit-maximization strategy invariably leads to greater disparities of wealth among different segments of our society, and invariably causes corporations to take improper advantage of those who are outside the corporate circle.

d. That profit-maximization is a shortsighted approach under which short-term profits are emphasized at the expense of long-term allocational efficiency and long-term societal objectives.

Short Essay

21. OK Furniture Corp. manufactures numerous items of wood furniture. The table saws it uses in the production process comply with existing federal safety standards. Even so, OK officials know that approximately once a month, an employee using a table saw will suffer a serious cut that requires stitches. OK's injury reports indicate that approximately every six months, an employee will be injured even more seriously, such as by having a finger severed, while using a table saw. (Obviously, it is not the same employee each time.) These injuries occur even when the employees are using proper care in operating the saws. Safer table saws with elaborate protective guards are available and, if purchased by OK, would eliminate nearly all of the injuries just mentioned. The "catch" is that the safer table saws are extremely expensive. In addition, the presence of the protective guards on the more expensive table saws makes them slower and less precise than the table saws OK now uses. OK management has concluded that the increased costs and losses of efficiency associated with the safer table saws would translate into considerable reductions of furniture output and sales. These reductions, OK fears, would lead to significant decreases in corporate profits (even considering the reduced workers' compensation expenses OK would realize if its employees were no longer being injured by table saws). OK is also concerned that reduced corporate profits would bring about a need to reduce the OK workforce. How would *utilitarians* resolve the question whether OK should purchase the safer table saws?

22. Review the facts of question #22. How would a *modern rights-based theorist* resolve the question whether OK should purchase the safer table saws?

23. You are a high-ranking officer of Griese Corp., which operates a large chain of fast food restaurants. Griese restaurants "deep fry" a variety of foods in beef tallow. The same is true of numerous other competing fast food restaurants. A few competitors, however, have ceased using beef tallow in response to scientific studies indicating that regular consumption, over a period of years, of foods deep fried in beef tallow may be harmful to the health of some persons. Assume, for purposes of this question, that the conclusions drawn in the scientific studies are correct. Also assume that thus far, there has been only moderate public attention devoted to the beef tallow issue, and that the cost of using something other than beef tallow for frying would necessitate price increases on Griese food items. Do you urge your fellow officers to authorize a shift away from the use of beef tallow? State the reasons for your answer.

24. You are an executive of a tobacco company whose cigarettes are sold throughout the United States and in various other countries. Approximately 18% of your firm's cigarette sales during 1991 were made in Nation X. Your company's competitors also sell large amounts of cigarettes in that country. Although all packages of cigarettes sold in the United States must bear certain health-related warnings as specified by federal law, neither United States law nor the law of Nation X requires that packages of cigarettes sold in Nation X carry any warnings about the health hazards posed by smoking. During the past several years, your company's sales in Nation X have increased significantly. Overall cigarette consumption in that country (including not only your company's cigarettes but also those sold by your competitors) has increased dramatically during the same time frame. You are faced with deciding whether your firm should voluntarily begin placing health-related warnings on packages of cigarettes sold in Nation X. What constituencies stand to be affected, and how are they likely to be affected, by a decision either way on this issue? What course of action do you believe should be taken? Why that course of action?

CHAPTER 5

CRIMES

True-False - Circle T for True and F for False.

T F 1. Warrantless searches by law enforcement personnel do not necessarily violate the Fourth Amendment.

T F 2. In states that require a preliminary hearing for felony cases, the prosecutor must convince a magistrate at this hearing that there is probable cause to believe the accused committed a felony.

T F 3. A corporation may prevent the use of corporate records in a criminal prosecution against it by asserting its Fifth Amendment privilege against self-incrimination.

T F 4. Evidence obtained in violation of the defendant's Fourth Amendment right to be free from unreasonable searches and seizures may never be used in a criminal prosecution against him.

T F 5. Strict criminal liability ordinarily involves holding a party criminally liable without proof that she committed any wrongful act.

T F 6. Voluntary intoxication may reduce the defendant's criminal liability, but it cannot provide a complete defense to such liability.

T F 7. The power of courts to develop the common law does not extend so far as to allow judicial creation of common law crimes.

T F 8. Most states now require the prosecution to meet the preponderance of the evidence test in order for the defendant to be found guilty of a crime.

T F 9. A corporation may be held criminally liable for the crimes of its employees if they were acting within the scope of their employment and for the benefit of the corporation, even if their acts contravened corporate policy or instructions.

T F 10. If Behavior X has not previously been illegal in State Y, but State Y's legislature enacts a statute that takes effect on March 1, 1992 and purports to criminalize any exercise of Behavior X on March 1, 1992 or thereafter, the statute is vulnerable to attack as an *ex post facto* law.

Multiple Choice - Circle the best answer.

11. The following statements deal with the supposed operation and effect of the Fifth Amendment. Which statement is accurate?

   a. The Fifth Amendment is not necessarily violated by the prosecution's use of evidence of the defendant's post-arrest but pre-*Miranda* warning silence, if the evidence is intended to impeach the defendant's trial testimony.

   b. The Fifth Amendment has been violated if the defendant waived his *Miranda* rights and confessed to the crime without first being informed by police that an attorney retained for him by a relative was seeking to contact him.

   c. The Fifth Amendment entitles the sole proprietor of a business to resist a subpoena of his business records if the records were private in nature, regardless of whether the act of producing the records would be incriminating.

   d. The Fifth Amendment language is more detailed than many constitutional amendments, in that it expressly states the particulars of what has come to be called the *Miranda* warning.

12. Which of the following police actions is *least* likely to be a Fourth Amendment violation?

   a. Warrantless and unconsented entry of the defendant's unlocked garage, in which the police found evidence of criminal activity, if the garage was located 15 feet behind the defendant's house rather than being attached to it.

   b. Warrantless and unconsented exposing of the defendant's luggage to a narcotics detection dog in a public area of a municipal airport, with the eventual result being that narcotics were discovered in the luggage.

c. Warrantless and unconsented aerial surveillance of the defendant's industrial complex by means of satellite technology that reveals evidence of criminal activity, if the technology employed was not available to the general public.

d. Warrantless and unconsented placement of a hidden video camera in bushes near the patio behind the defendant's house, with the result being that evidence of criminal activity was recorded on videotape.

13. Sweatshop Corp. employee Walt Wembley died after several weeks of exposure to certain toxic chemical fumes at the Sweatshop plant. The chemicals were in open vats and could not reasonably be avoided by Wembley and other Sweatshop employees. The local prosecutor filed criminal charges against Sweatshop, its president, and its plant manager in connection with Wembley's death. The prosecutor alleges that Sweatshop's president and plant manager knew of the dangerous nature of the fumes but neither warned Wembley and other Sweatshop employees nor took other action to lessen the danger. Which of the following is an accurate statement?

a. Sweatshop cannot be held criminally liable for the acts of the president and the plant manager if they were acting within the scope of their employment and for the benefit of the corporation.

b. Sweatshop cannot be held criminally liable for Wembley's death because a corporation cannot form a criminal intent.

c. The president and the plant manager could be held criminally liable for Wembley's death under theories of strict and vicarious liability.

d. If Sweatshop can prove that it used due diligence in trying to prevent the president and the plant manager from committing a crime, the corporation will have a defense to criminal liability.

14. Which of the following makes unconstitutional a criminal statute that does not define the prohibited conduct with sufficient clarity to put an ordinary person on notice of the behavior that would violate the statute?

a. The Equal Protection Clause of the Fourteenth Amendment.

b. The Fourth Amendment, as interpreted by the Supreme Court in the *Dow Chemical* case.

c. The First Amendment.

d. The Due Process Clauses of the Fifth and Fourteenth Amendments.

15. Which of the following is an accurate statement about the insanity defense?

a. A defendant who is found "guilty but mentally ill" is set free after the jury renders such a verdict.

b. If a defendant who has been sentenced to death is found to be legally insane at the time he is to be executed, he may not be executed until his sanity is restored.

c. A defendant who is found to be legally insane at the time of sentencing may still be sentenced, but the sentence cannot carried out until her sanity is restored.

d. The *M'Naghten* rule provides that a criminal defendant is not responsible by reason of insanity even though he knew the nature and quality of his act and knew that the act was wrong, if mental disease caused an irresistible impulse to commit the crime.

16. In which of the following situations could the RICO statute properly be used?

a. In a civil suit filed by the federal government to force dissolution of the defendant corporation.

b. In a criminal prosecution brought by the federal government to punish suspected organized crime figures for arsons they have committed in the past.

c. In a civil suit filed by a private citizen asking for treble damages and attorney's fees from an accounting firm that defrauded him several times over a ten-year period.

d. Each of the above.

17. The following statements pertain to differing views on the purpose or purposes of the criminal sanction. Which statement(s) is/are *inaccurate*?
    a. The deterrence theory of criminal punishment focuses on both special deterrence (when punishment of the convicted offender deters him from committing further crimes) and general deterrence (when punishment of the convicted offender deters others from committing similar crimes).
    b. Critics of the rehabilitation focus urged by some analysts of the criminal justice system commonly point to high rates of recidivism as evidence of the general failure of our rehabilitation efforts to date.
    c. Those who take the utilitarian view of the criminal sanction regard retribution—the infliction of deserved suffering on those who violate society's fundamental rules—as the sole proper purpose for imposing criminal penalties.
    d. a, b, and c.

18. Which of the following pieces of evidence would a court be required by the Fifth Amendment to exclude from the evidence allowed at trial?
    a. Routine business records that were voluntarily kept by the defendant and that contain incriminating information.
    b. Samples of the defendant's hair, clipped from his head by the arresting officers without his consent.
    c. The defendant's confession, which occurred after he was arrested and advised of his *Miranda* rights.
    d. None of the above.
    e. Both a and b.

19. Shady Corp. is the defendant in a criminal prosecution. Potentially the most damaging evidence against Shady is contained in business records that Shady was required by federal law to keep. May these records be used against Shady in the criminal prosecution?
    a. Yes, because the records are not protected by any Fifth Amendment privilege against self-incrimination.
    b. No, because it would violate Shady's due process rights to allow the use of incriminating records that Shady probably would not have kept if not for the requirements of federal law.
    c. No, because their use would violate Shady's Fifth Amendment privilege against self-incrimination.
    d. Yes, because corporations have no Fourth Amendment rights.

20. The Sixth Amendment contains:
    a. a clause barring the imposition of cruel and unusual punishment on convicted criminal defendants.
    b. a provision entitling criminal defendants to confront and cross-examine the witnesses against them.
    c. a "double jeopardy" clause that protects criminal defendants from multiple prosecutions for the same offense.
    d. all of the above.

21. Country western legend Diddly Squat has filed a civil RICO suit against Fold, Spindle & Mutil-
     ate, Inc. (FSM), a securities firm that formerly represented him in commercial investment matters.
     Squat's complaint alleges (among other things) that during the preceding decade, FSM engaged in
     what amounted to mail fraud on several different occasions and that he sustained business losses
     as a result. His complaint contains no allegation that FSM was ever convicted of a crime, how-
     ever. Neither does it allege that FSM has organized crime connections. The absence of these alle-
     gations squares with the facts: FSM has never been convicted of a crime and is not connected
     with organized crime in any usual sense in which the term is used. Is Squat's suit properly before
     the court? Explain your reasoning.

22. Although the exclusionary rule has served as the basic device for enforcement of Fourth Amend-
     ment rights, the Supreme Court has in recent years recognized instances in which evidence ob-
     tained in violation of the defendant's Fourth Amendment rights may nonetheless be introduced at
     trial. What are these instances?

23. Sham Corp., whose business ostensibly is the importing of various foreign food products, is the
     target of a federal grand jury probe into alleged smuggling of cocaine into the United States. Jus-
     tin Alterego is Sham's president and majority shareholder. He also has custody of the
     corporation's business records. A grand jury subpoena demands that certain Sham business re-
     cords be made available to the grand jury. Assume that the records contain information that poten-
     tially would incriminate both Sham and Alterego. May either Sham or Alterego resist the
     subpoena on Fifth Amendment grounds? If so, which one(s) may do so, and why? If not, why
     not?

CHAPTER 6

INTENTIONAL TORTS

True-False - Circle T for True and F for False.

T F 1. Assuming that a wrongdoer intended only to threaten someone else with harmful contact but did not intend for the actual contact to occur, the wrongdoer has committed a battery if the harmful, though unintended, contact actually takes place.

T F 2. If the constitutional aspects of defamation law require the plaintiff to prove *actual malice* in order to prevail in her defamation suit, the plaintiff satisfies that requirement by proving the defendant's feeling of ill will or hatred toward the plaintiff.

T F 3. If a party who was found not guilty in a criminal proceeding bases a later malicious prosecution suit on that criminal proceeding, the issue of his guilt in the incident giving rise to the criminal proceeding may be retried in the malicious prosecution suit.

T F 4. Plaintiffs in slander cases are not required to prove special damages unless the case was one of slander per se.

T F 5. In an attempt to resolve conflicts between invasion of privacy law and constitutionally protected freedoms of speech and press, courts have made it less difficult for public officials and public figures to win public disclosure of private facts cases than it is for private figures to win those cases.

T F 6. If A intends to make harmful contact with B and attempts unsuccessfully to make such contact, A has not committed a battery and, depending on the facts, may not have committed an assault.

T F 7. Because some intentional torts involve behavior that may also be criminal in nature, plaintiffs in civil suits over intentional torts must prove the elements of their claim beyond a reasonable doubt.

T F 8. Because of the legal system's increasing sensitivity to emotional distress claims, a plaintiff today is generally allowed to recover damages from a defendant whenever any intentional act by the defendant caused the plaintiff to experience emotional distress.

T F 9. Even if Party B won an earlier suit brought against Party A, Party B may be sued successfully by Party A for abuse of process, if Party B's earlier suit against Party A was brought for a primary purpose other than the one for which such suits are designed.

T F 10. Because tortious interference with property rights is generally treated as an offense against the right of possession, the owner of property is not always the proper plaintiff in a suit over the defendant's harm to rights associated with that property.

Multiple Choice - Circle the best answer.

11. In an interview that was aired on WJRK-TV, an Indianapolis television station, WJRK sports director Ed Soboorish asked Indianapolis Dolts linebacker Jake Pitbull what he thought about the rumors that the Dolts were trying to acquire quarterback Vinnie Primadonna and offensive tackle Hugh Mongous from another team. Pitbull said this about Primadonna: "I hope we don't trade for him. The guy's overrated. His last name says it all." The portion of the interview concerning Mongous went this way:

Soboorish: "Jake, my man, what do you think about Hugh Mongous? Can he help the Dolts?"

Pitbull: "Mongous is a great player, Ed, but I can't help wondering how he added so much bulk during the past couple of years. In my opinion, it's gotta be 'roids."

Soboorish: "Just to clarify things a little, Jakester, you mean use of steroids, not having hemorrhoids. Right?"

Pitbull: "Yeah, Ed, steroids. I've got no idea about the hemorrhoids, but if he's got those too, I feel sorry for the dude."

Primadonna and Mongous have filed separate defamation suits against Pitbull. Which plaintiff should have a better chance of winning his suit, and why?

a. Mongous, even though Pitbull was simply expressing his opinion, because the reference to hemorrhoids could prove embarrassing to Mongous.

b. Primadonna, because the entire statement about him was negative, whereas in the statement about Mongous, Pitbull acknowledged that Mongous was "a great player."

c. Mongous, because Pitbull's statement of "opinion" about him was not the pure opinion found in the statement about Primadonna.

d. Primadonna, because his "stock" in the eyes of the Dolts' management may be lowered as a result.

12. Paul E. Ester has filed a false imprisonment suit against Doubleknit Duds, Inc., a clothing store. His suit arises out of an incident in which Doubleknit personnel detained him in order to determine whether he had shoplifted. The detention resulted in a conclusion that Ester had not in fact shoplifted. The state whose law controls Ester's case has enacted a typical shopkeepers' statute of the sort described in the text. On these facts, Doubleknit:

a. will win the case because the existence of the shopkeepers' statute gives merchants complete protection against liability for false imprisonment.

b. will lose the case because the fact that Ester did not shoplift makes the protection of the shopkeepers' statute inapplicable.

c. may win the case, but only if Doubleknit personnel gave Ester the *Miranda* warning and offered to call an attorney for him.

d. may lose the case, depending upon the length and manner of the detention, even if Doubleknit personnel had a reasonable basis for believing that Ester had shoplifted.

13. As part of a televised documentary dealing with teenage unwed mothers, reporter Gerald O. Unfaira revealed that Wanda N. Deanna, now age 34, had a child out of wedlock when she was 15 and gave the child up for adoption. Unfaira reported this information without Deanna's consent. His report was true. Unfaira acquired the information from private hospital records supplied to him by an unnamed employee of the hospital where Deanna gave birth. Deanna, now a resident of a tiny Indiana town and known only by her family and a few close friends, had been successful at the keeping the matter of the teenage pregnancy and ensuing adoption a closely guarded secret—until Unfaira's report. She became quite upset when the report aired. Which of the following statements contains an accurate legal analysis of the facts?

a. Deanna should win a defamation suit against Unfaira if she can prove that Unfaira made the report out of ill will toward her or for other improper purposes.

b. Deanna has an arguably meritorious public disclosure of private facts claim, to which the truth of Unfaira's statement would not be a defense.

c. Deanna has a meritorious false light publicity claim, because Unfaira's report portrayed her in a manner different from how other persons customarily perceived her.

d. Deanna should be able to win a commercial appropriation of name or likeness suit against Unfaira because he used her name for commercial purposes without her consent.

14. Emmett Bezzler, a long-time loan officer at Nearly Insolvent Savings & Loan (NISL), was informed by NISL's president that he (Bezzler) was being fired for embezzlement of NISL funds. In fact, Bezzler had done no such thing. Bezzler telephoned his friend, Dee Falcation, director of personnel at Usurious National Bank, to see whether Usurious National needed to hire a loan officer. As soon as he heard Falcation say "Hello, this is Dee Falcation," Bezzler stated: "Dee, they just told me I've been fired for embezzling money. I'm innocent. Does Usurious National need a loan officer?" Falcation replied by stating that there was a loan officer's position open and that prior to Bezzler's telephone call, she would have considered him eminently qualified for the job. She added, however, that "there is no way we can hire you, Em, with that embezzlement cloud hanging over your head." Bezzler has filed a defamation suit against NISL. Which of the following is an accurate observation about the case?

a. The compelled self-publication doctrine applies because of the employment termination context; therefore, the common law elements of defamation are present in the facts.

b. The falsity of the accusation leveled at Bezzler by NISL's president clearly damaged Bezzler; therefore, Bezzler will win the suit regardless of whether NISL's president had a reasonable basis for believing the accusation to be true.

c. On the facts given, NISL would have a strong argument that it should not be held liable because the necessary element of publication did not occur.

d. On the facts given, NISL should argue that even though there was publication, NISL should not be held liable because Falcation will probably continue to be Bezzler's friend anyway.

15. Chicago resident Abner Mality is not well-known except by members of his family and a few close friends. He has filed a defamation suit against a newspaper, the *Chicago Tribulation*, on the basis of a *Tribulation* investigative reporter's story that labeled Mality as the purported leader of a massive criminal enterprise consisting of drug smuggling and other unlawful activities of considerable public concern. Mality actually had no involvement whatsoever with the criminal activities. In view of the constitutional aspects of defamation law, which of the following is an accurate statement about Mality's suit?

a. Mality will not be entitled to recover punitive damages unless he proves that the reporter who prepared the story acted with knowledge of its falsity or with reckless disregard for its truth or falsity.

b. Mality cannot win the suit unless he proves the degree of fault set forth in the preceding answer.

c. If Mality proves that the reporter who prepared the story was negligent in failing to ascertain the falsity of the statement about Mality, he will win the suit and will recover both compensatory and punitive damages.

d. Because Mality is a mere private figure, the constitutional aspects of defamation law have no application to the case; therefore, he will not be required to prove fault on the defendant's part.

16. English professor Kingsley Lear was upset because a student, Hamlet, was eating a Macbeth (a sandwich sold by a well-known fast food restaurant chain) during class. Lear therefore hurled a hardbound copy of *Shakespeare's Collected Plays* at Hamlet. The book missed Hamlet, who was so intent on devouring his Macbeth that he did not realize the book had been thrown. The book instead struck Othello, who was deep in thought and did not see the airborne book before it struck him. Othello was not physically harmed, but was outraged at what had transpired. When class ended, Lear noticed that as usual, star-crossed lovers Romeo and Juliet were locked in a steamy embrace. An irritated Lear waited until all students except Romeo and Juliet had left the second-floor classroom. He then locked the room's only door, leaving Romeo and Juliet inside. A few minutes later, Romeo and Juliet realized that the door was locked. The room had two open windows, but Romeo and Juliet decided not to attempt an exit through either of them. They remained in the room for an hour, until a custodian noticed they were there, unlocked the door, and let them out. On these facts, what torts has Lear committed?

a. Assault as to Hamlet and assault and battery as to Othello.

b. Assault as to Hamlet, battery as to Othello, and false imprisonment as to Romeo and Juliet.

c. Battery as to Othello and false imprisonment as to Romeo and Juliet.

d. Assault as to Hamlet, as to Othello, and as to Romeo and Juliet.

17. The following statements pertain to intentional torts that cause interference with property rights. Which statement is accurate?

a. If a person enters upon another's land under the mistaken belief that his entry was legally justified, he may be held liable for trespass despite the existence of his mistaken belief.

b. A major difference between *conversion* and *trespass to personal property* is that conversion generally involves a less substantial interference with another person's property rights than does trespass to personal property.

c. If a highly unpleasant odor consistently emanates from Party #1's land and interferes with Party #2's enjoyment of Party #2's land, Party #2 probably has a meritorious conversion claim against Party #1.

d. One cannot be held liable for trespass to land unless her initial entry upon the land was unlawful or improper.

18. Lee Ayatollah is the well-known president of Crisisler Motor Corp. For the past 15 years, Ayatollah's name has been a household word throughout the United States, primarily because of his highly visible role in helping to bring Crisisler back to a position of prominence after it teetered on the brink of bankruptcy. At one time (not long before the events about to be described), Ayatollah was identified by 53% of the participants in a Gallstone poll as "the private-sector figure that I would most like to see as a candidate for national political office." On December 24, 1991, the *Detroit Informer* (DI), a nationally circulated and well-respected newspaper, published a story stating that Ayatollah would soon be entering a drug treatment program because of a longstanding addiction to various mind-altering drugs. The source for the story was a highly credible U.S. Senator, Seymour Pacmoney, who told a DI reporter that he had innocently overheard a telephone conversation in which Ayatollah revealed such information. With a publication deadline rapidly approaching, DI editors decided to run the story because of the credibility of the source. If DI personnel had done further checking with other sources, it would have become apparent that Sen. Pacmoney had misinterpreted the telephone conversation and that Ayatollah had neither a drug problem nor any plans to enter a drug treatment program. Convinced that his reputation was tarnished by the story, Ayatollah has sued the DI for defamation. Should Ayatollah win his suit?

a. Yes, because the DI editors who decided to run the story without further checking of sources were clearly negligent.

b. No, because he will be unable to prove actual malice on the part of the defendant.

c. Yes, because his reputation was harmed by a reckless defendant from whose behavior the requisite ill will toward Ayatollah may be inferred.

d. No, because Sen. Pacmoney is the party who should have been sued.

19. Roger Miller was employed as a cook at the Griese Grill. Gil Griese, the restaurant's owner, tagged Miller with the nickname "King of the Road" because of the 1960s-era song of the same name by entertainer Roger Miller (no relation to the Miller referred to in this problem). Each time he saw Miller, Griese would greet him by calling him "King." Miller became extremely depressed because of how uncomfortable Griese's repeated use of the nickname made him feel. He filed an intentional infliction of emotional distress suit against Griese on the basis of the facts just stated. Miller should:

a. win the suit because Griese's repeated use of the nickname was intentional action that caused him to experience severe emotional distress.

b. lose the suit because a defendant cannot be held liable for intentional infliction of emotional distress unless he also committed battery or some other tort.

c. win the suit because Griese's statements and actions indicate the existence of actual malice on Griese's part.

d. lose the suit because Griese's statements, though intentional, probably would not be considered outrageous and beyond all bounds of decency.

20. Zeke Fungus was the lead singer for the heavy metal band Rancid Meat, which was immensely popular during the late 1970s. Although Fungus retired from the music scene when Rancid Meat broke up in 1981, his unusual singing voice remains immediately recognizable to the public when any one of the numerous Rancid Meat hits is played. Fungus provided the lead vocals on all of Rancid Meat's songs. In a recent TV commercial for its low-calorie frozen dinners, PDQ Co. used a variation of the old Rancid Meat hit "Kidneys, Liver, or Even Gall Bladder." PDQ had asked Fungus to sing a version of the song for its commercial, but he declined. Because PDQ had already obtained the consent of the owner of the copyright on "Gall Bladder" (XYZ, Inc.), PDQ decided to use a version of the song in the commercial anyway, but with a singer other than Fungus. The tune of the song in the PDQ commercial was the same as that of "Gall Bladder," but the lyr-

ics were changed (to "turkey, liver, you won't get much fatter") to make them more appropriate for a low-calorie frozen dinner commercial. As requested by PDQ, the commercial's singer (who did not appear on camera) imitated the unusual singing voice of Fungus in performing the commercial's version of the song. Much of the public believed that Fungus did the singing in the commercial. Claiming that "his" voice effectively was used without his consent, Fungus has brought a right of publicity suit against PDQ. Which of the following statements is accurate?

a. Although there is a question about whether federal copyright law preempts Fungus's claim, the court will conclude that his claim is not preempted and may therefore may be pursued if the court follows the lead of the most applicable precedent case.

b. Fungus is likely to lose his suit because neither his name nor his physical likenss was used in the PDQ commercial.

c. Applicable precedent indicates that PDQ will defend the case successfully on the basis of the First Amendment protection extended to commercial speech.

d. None of the above.

21. In which of the following alternative fact situations has the element of *publication* occurred?

a. In a telephone conversation between George and Dan, George says he believes that Dan bribed the dean of the university from which Dan graduated in order to be able to graduate. Understandably upset by this unfounded accusation, Dan telephones his friend Lloyd and reveals what George has said in order to obtain Lloyd's opinion on how to respond to George. Dan has now sued George for defamation.

b. An important horseshoe-pitching tournament caused George to be unavailable for a previously scheduled speech at the annual convention of the American Pork Rind Producers' Organization. Therefore, George asked his employee, Dan, to appear on his behalf and to deliver the speech George had prepared. Dan did so, reading the speech to a packed convention hall. Although some of the two- and three-syllable words caused Dan some difficulty, he accurately read the following line from the speech: "I know for a fact that Mike is a card-carrying member of the Communist Party." Mike has now sued George and Dan for defamation.

c. George fired his employee, Dan. In a conversation between the two of them when the firing occurred, George told Dan that he was being fired because he was spending nearly all of his time playing golf instead of working. Dan needed a job, so he interviewed for a position as assistant to Mike, the head dog-catcher in a prominent eastern state. When Mike asked Dan why he had lost his last job, Dan revealed the reason asserted by George and then attempted to explain to Mike that what George had said was inaccurate. Mike did not hire Dan for this sensitive position, however. Dan has now sued George for defamation.

d. Both fact situations b and c, but not a.

e. Fact situations a, b, and c.

22. Spike and Bambi live next door to each other. Their respective parcels of property are approximately one-half acre in size. Which of the following is *least* likely to provide a valid basis for a trespass suit by Spike against Bambi?

a. Bambi's placement of a 1,000-pound statue of Elvis Presley just across her lot line and on Spike's property, with Bambi's placement of the statue there being the result of an honest mistake on her part about where her property ended and Spike's began.

b. The virtually nonstop barking of Bambi's Rottweiler, Maynard, which curtails Spike's ability to use and enjoy his property.

c. Bambi's daily practice of burning large amounts of garbage in open fires in her backyard, with the results being a persistent foul odor in the air over Spike's property and a very-hard-to-remove coating of ash and soot on Spike's house.

d. Bambi's deliberate and successful use of an electric cattle prod to inflict injury on Spike's pit bull, Jaws.

23. Lucy Inthesky resigned from her job as turnstile operator for Kaleidoscope Eyes, Inc. (KE). KE officials, including personnel manager Lennie Mac Cartney, were relieved when she resigned because for several months, they had suspected her of having made personal use of KE funds. There was a strong factual basis that reasonably seemed to support these suspicions. In reality, however, Inthesky had never used KE funds for personal purposes. When Inthesky later was under serious consideration for a job at Diamonds, Inc., Diamonds' personnel manager, John Elton, telephoned Cartney and asked him what sort of employee Inthesky had been when she worked for KE. Cartney responded by stating his (and KE's) belief that she had used KE funds for her own purposes. Upon hearing this, Elton concluded that there was no future for Lucy Inthesky with Diamonds. He therefore did not hire her. Inthesky has now filed a defamation suit against Cartney and KE. Who should win the suit? Why?

24. Lotta Graft was attending a taping of the popular TV game show "Steal a Fortune," on which former executives of insolvent savings and loan institutions compete to see which one can line his pockets quickest with government-supplied money. The taping was open to anyone who wished to be part of the studio audience. When amiable host Chuckles Keating announced that it was time for the contestants to begin the "billion dollar bailout round" of the show, an excited Graft stood up, began waving her arms wildly, and screamed, "Big money, big money. Let's increase that national deficit." A reporter and photographer for the nationally circulated newspaper *USA 2 Nite* were on the scene during the taping. The photographer snapped a picture of Graft just as she was screaming the words just quoted. Without Graft's consent, *USA 2 Nite* later used the photograph (which most readers would consider amusing) as a "human interest" item to accompany a feature story on the Steal a Fortune show. Graft became extremely embarrassed and distressed after the photograph was published. As it turned out, *USA 2 Nite*'s sales of the issue containing Graft's photograph were greater than its usual sales. Graft has sued *USA 2 Nite* on six alternative theories: defamation; false light publicity; intrusion on solitude; public disclosure of private facts; commercial appropriation of name or likeness; and intentional infliction of emotional distress. Briefly discuss Graft's chances of success on each of these theories.

25. Eddie Eager, manager of the P-Mart department store, suspected that a customer, Oma Gosch, was attempting to shoplift a purple scarf. He was suspicious because he saw Gosch place a purple-colored item in the pocket of her coat as she looking at the P-Mart display of purple scarves. Eager followed Gosch to the front door of the store and then courteously asked her to accompany him to his office. When they arrived there, Eager calmly informed Gosch of his suspicion. Gosch denied the accusation and pulled a purple scarf from her pocket. She claimed that she had purchased the purple scarf at another store earlier that day, and that if Eager examined it, he would realize it was different from the purple scarves sold by P-Mart. Gosch claimed that she had taken the previously purchased scarf out of her pocket to compare it to the ones for sale at P-Mart, and that she had placed it back in her pocket once she had completed the comparison. She also took the other store's receipt out of her purse and offered to telephone the other store to verify the purchase. Eager politely but firmly refused to examine the scarf and the receipt. He also refused to allow her to call the other store. He telephoned the police and informed Gosch that she would have to remain in his office until the police arrived. Ninety minutes later, a police officer arrived. The officer quickly ascertained that Gosch had not shoplifted anything. Gosch has now filed a false imprisonment suit against Eager and P-Mart. The state whose law controls the case has in force a shopkeepers' statute of the sort discussed in the text. Should Eager and P-Mart be held liable for false imprisonment? State each reason to support your answer.

26. Consider the fact situations set forth below in light of the constitutional aspects of defamation law.

   A.—Madulla is an internationally known singer and movie star whose every move commands attention from the press and the public. She has brought a defamation suit against a newspaper, *The National Tantalizer*, because of its untrue story stating that while Madulla was married to her former husband, actor Shaw Porn, she was having an affair with singer Barry Manornot.

   B.—Priscilla Sincere, a resident of Smalltown, North Dakota, is not widely known by most of the general public. Through her own efforts during the past two years, however, she has become the leader of a large anti-abortion group in North Dakota. She has also become an outspoken participant in public debate over whether the Supreme Court's controversial *Roe v. Wade* decision should be overruled. Sincere's defamation suit, brought against *Rustler* magazine, is based on a false *Rustler* story stating that she had an abortion six months ago.

   What fault requirement must Madulla prove in order to win her suit? Why that fault requirement? What fault requirement must Sincere prove in order to win her suit? Why that fault requirement?

CHAPTER 7

NEGLIGENCE AND STRICT LIABILITY

True-False - Circle T for True and F for False.

T F   1.   Proximate cause exists whenever the plaintiff's injury would not have occurred if not for the defendant's breach of duty.

T F   2.   If an unforeseeable act, force, or event occurs after the defendant's negligence and contributes to the plaintiff's injuries, the defendant generally will not be held liable for the consequences stemming from the later act, force, or event.

T F   3.   In a state that adheres to the traditional contributory negligence rule, if the plaintiff's own negligence contributed substantially to the causation of her injury, the defendant will have a complete defense to liability even though the defendant's negligence was a greater causative factor than the plaintiff's was.

T F   4.   Even if a preexisting physical characteristic of the plaintiff made the injuries resulting from the defendant's negligence more severe than they would have been if the plaintiff had not had such a characteristic, the negligent defendant is liable for the full extent of the plaintiff's injuries.

T F   5.   As a general rule, if a negligent defendant injures the plaintiff and the plaintiff's injury is then made worse by the negligence of health care providers, the originally negligent defendant is liable only for the original injury and not for the worsened condition stemming from the negligence of the health care providers.

T F   6.   All states have now dispensed with the physical injury requirement formerly imposed on plaintiffs in negligent infliction of emotional distress cases.

T F   7.   If an activity's social utility overshadows its dangerousness, courts are likely to conclude that those engaged in the activity should be held liable only on a showing of fault rather than on strict liability grounds.

T F   8.   The special relationship existing between landlords and tenants has caused some courts to impose upon landlords a duty to take reasonable steps designed to protect tenants against the foreseeable criminal acts of others.

T F   9.   The "reasonable person" standard of negligence law is an objective standard under which the actions or inactions of real persons are judged according to what the hypothetical reasonable person would have done or would not have done.

T F 10.   If the plaintiff proves that the defendant's behavior amounted to recklessness instead of mere negligence, what ordinarily would be considered assumption of risk by the plaintiff does not constitute a valid defense upon which the defendant may rely.

Multiple Choice - Circle the best answer.

11.   Thirteen years ago, when Ned Barth was 10 years old, his father died. Cecil Nimrod, a long-time friend of Ned's father, then became effectively a father figure to Ned. Ned and Cecil had spent great amounts of time together until the events about to be described. Recently, Ned was walking down the street with Cecil. Ned stopped to tie his shoes, but Cecil kept walking and soon was approximately 40 feet ahead of Ned. Ned finished tying his shoes, looked up, and saw Cecil fall to the sidewalk at essentially the same time he (Ned) heard the sound of a gunshot. Ned rushed to aid Cecil, but Cecil was already dead. Cecil had been shot accidentally as he walked past the doorway of Don's Firearms, a gun shop owned by Don Derelict. What had occurred was that one of Derelict's minimum-wage employees, Lemuel "Lemme" Wastem, was performing his usual job of showing a customer how to aim and pull the trigger of a handgun. Assuming that the gun was not loaded but negligently failing to check to be sure, Wastem pointed the gun at the open front door of the business and pulled the trigger. The gun indeed was loaded, and the hapless

Cecil met his untimely death as a result. Ned has filed a negligence suit against Wastem and Derelict in an effort to collect damages for the severe emotional distress he experienced as a result of the incident just described. Assume that courts of the state whose law controls apply the "foreseeability" approach (as set forth in the *Mazzagatti* case in the text) in cases of this nature. Which of the following is likely to provide the biggest obstacle to Ned's winning the suit?

a. The fact that Ned and Cecil had no legal relationship.

b. The fact that Ned was not in the zone of danger at the time Cecil was shot.

c. The fact that Wastem is a minimum-wage employee with virtually no assets.

d. The fact that neither Wastem nor Derelict intended to cause any harm to Cecil or Ned.

12. Used car dealer Skip Hardsell acquired a 1985 Chevrolet Cheapette automobile, which he intended to resell in the usual course of his business. Assume that Hardsell negligently failed to inspect the car for major defects before making it available to prospective purchasers for test drives. Also assume that if Hardsell had conducted a reasonable inspection, he would have discovered that this Cheapette's steering mechanism was seriously defective and capable of rendering the car uncontrollable. Prospective purchaser Bambi LaFawn became quite interested in the Cheapette as soon as she saw it on Hardsell's car lot. Therefore, with Hardsell's permission, she took the car for a test drive. At the time of the test drive, LaFawn was aware that used cars are not always in perfect condition and may sometimes have defects in them. Shortly after LaFawn left Hardsell's place of business in the Cheapette, the car crashed into a utility pole. LaFawn, who was severely injured, has filed a negligence suit against Hardsell. The state whose law controls adheres to traditional principles of contributory negligence and assumption of risk. Which of the following statements is/are accurate?

a. If the accident was the result of the defective steering mechanism, LaFawn will be regarded as having assumed the risk of injury and will therefore lose the suit.

b. If the major reason the accident occurred was the defective steering mechanism but a significant, though secondary, reason was LaFawn's negligent failure to apply the brakes when the car began going out of control, LaFawn will win the suit but will not recover the full amount of damages she would have recovered had she not contributed to the causation of her injuries.

c. If the reasons the accident occurred were as stated in answer b, LaFawn will lose the suit.

d. Both a and c.

13. Insurance agent Ralph Overbearing was injured while walking through a parking lot owned by Big Deal Discount Store, Inc. The parking lot is adjacent to the Big Deal store and is designated for use by its customers during the hours the store is open. Overbearing's injury occurred when his leg slipped partially into a hole in the parking lot's pavement. The hole, located near the center of the parking lot, was 12 inches in diameter and 12 inches in depth. It had existed for three months. Despite its size, the hole was not readily visible to persons driving or walking through the parking lot. For two months prior to and at the time of Overbearing's injury, Big Deal had a large sign at the entrance to the parking lot. The sign read: "Attention, Big Deal shoppers. Potentially dangerous hole in center area of parking lot. Be careful." Overbearing, who did not read the sign when he entered the lot, has filed a negligence suit against Big Deal. Assume that the state whose law is controlling adheres to the traditional classifications of persons who are on property owned or possessed by another party. Under which of the following alternative versions of important additional facts would Overbearing have an excellent chance of winning the suit?

a. If, during regular Big Deal business hours, Overbearing entered the parking lot through the entrance where the sign was, parked his car, and, when injured, was walking toward the store, where he intended to convince Big Deal's store manager to purchase life insurance for herself.

b. If, during regular Big Deal business hours, Overbearing entered the parking lot through the entrance where the sign was, parked his car, and, when injured, was walking toward the store, where he intended to purchase a new 100% polyester leisure suit while Big Deal still had them on sale for the fabulous price of $29.99.

c. If Overbearing entered the parking lot on foot at 2:00 a.m. (when Big Deal was closed) at a point other than where the sign was, and, when injured, was walking though the lot as a short-cut to the No-Tell Motel, where he intended to conduct an important business transaction of an unspecified nature.

d. Each of the above.

14. The following statements pertain to tests used by courts in order to determine the existence or absence of proximate cause. Which of the statements is/are accurate?

a. When the "scope of foreseeable risk" test is applied, proximate cause will not be found to have existed if the injury to the plaintiff was not a foreseeable consequence of the defendant's failure to use reasonable care.

b. When the "natural and probable consequences" test is applied, proximate cause will be found to have existed in each situation in which the harm to the plaintiff would not have resulted but for the defendant's failure to use reasonable care.

c. When the "highly extraordinary" test is applied, proximate cause will not be found to have existed unless the plaintiff's injury was an exceedingly unusual consequence of the defendant's failure to use reasonable care.

d. All of the above.

15. Todd Punk attended a concert at an auditorium owned by Bigshow Co. Even though Bigshow had used all reasonable care to keep the auditorium reasonably safe for concert attendees and even though Punk was exercising reasonable care for his own safety, Punk tripped over an empty bottle that was on one of the steps leading down from the auditorium's balcony. As a result, Punk fell down a long flight of stairs and in the process sustained a fractured skull and two broken arms. Worse yet, from Punk's standpoint, the fall ruined an expensive coiffure he had just had performed on his hair. If Punk brings a negligence suit against Bigshow on the basis of the facts just stated,

a. Punk will win the suit because he sustained severe injuries that did not result from fault on his part.

b. Bigshow will defend the suit successfully because of Punk's failure to discover the presence of the bottle on the step.

c. Punk will win the suit despite his own negligence, in view of Bigshow's being liable on strict liability grounds.

d. Bigshow will defend the suit successfully despite the severity of the injuries sustained by Punk.

16. Of the following statements regarding the doctrine of strict liability, which is accurate?

a. When the doctrine of strict liability applies, the defendant may be held liable even though he, she, or it exercised all reasonable care under the circumstances.

b. The doctrine of strict liability applies in all cases involving defendants engaged in dangerous activities.

c. The doctrine of strict liability applies in cases of activities involving a risk of harm that may be eliminated by the exercise of reasonable care.

d. When the doctrine of strict liability applies, the defendant is not allowed to employ the plaintiff's own behavior as a defense.

17. Geoff Chaucer was the only passenger who survived the crash of a Canterbury Airlines jumbo jet. He sustained serious injuries, however. All crew members perished in the crash. What remained of the plane following the disaster revealed nothing about the probable cause of the crash. Investigators at the crash site could not find the "black box" that sometimes contains the recording of a pilot's statements immediately prior to a crash. Although Chaucer has vivid tales to tell about his awful experience on the Canterbury flight, none of them sheds light on the cause of the crash. If Chaucer sues Canterbury in an effort to collect damages for his injuries, he:

a. will be unable to prove any specific way in which Canterbury employees were negligent, meaning that he cannot win a negligence claim.

b. should be able to win a strict liability claim, because commercial aviation is a hazardous activity.

c. should rely on the res ipsa loquitur doctrine as a means of establishing inferences of the elements of a negligence claim.

d. will be likely to lose a negligence claim, because any person who reads the newspaper or watches the news on television is well aware that there are dangers associated with travel by air.

18. Seedy Motel owner Dale Discreet was remodeling a motel room in honor of his best customer, television evangelist Timmy Haggard. Discreet invited Haggard and an unidentified companion (soon to be the subject of a photo essay in *Repenthouse* magazine) to stop by and see how the remodeling was going. Before he went to the Seedy, Haggard had an abstract awareness that accidents sometimes happen at construction or remodeling sites. As Haggard entered the room where Discreet was working, Discreet—hammering all the while—urged Haggard to "be sure you watch your step, T.H." Heeding this warning, Haggard was cautiously walking toward Discreet when a mirror fell from the ceiling and struck Haggard's head. The mirror fell because of Discreet's failure to use reasonable care: he had neglected to remove the mirror from the ceiling before hammering with great force on a nearby wall. The impact of the mirror with Haggard's head caused Haggard such severe injuries that he was unable to continue as a TV star. His lucrative "ministry of the airwaves" soon folded. Haggard has filed a negligence suit against Discreet, who argues, in defense, that Haggard assumed the risk of injury. Is Discreet correct?

    a. Yes, because Haggard was aware that accidents may happen at remodeling sites.

    b. Yes, because Haggard deliberately proceeded into the room in spite of Discreet's warning.

    c. No, because the facts indicate that Discreet failed to use reasonable care.

    d. No, because the facts do not indicate that Haggard knew the nature and extent of the risk.

19. Ace, an amateur scientist, negligently mixed two chemicals he should not have mixed. As a result, a massive explosion occurred on his property. The explosion knocked down power lines, interfered with the normal flow of electrical current, and caused a surge of electricity at the home of Betty, who lived one mile from Ace's property. The surge of electricity started a substantial fire at Betty's home. Clyde, an octogenarian whose many years of smoking cigarettes had left him with emphysema, lived next door to Betty. The smoke from the fire at her home caused Clyde to experience a lengthy coughing fit, after which he suffered a fatal heart attack. Clyde's estate has now brought a negligence suit against Ace, on the theory that Ace's negligence set off the disastrous chain of events that ended with Clyde's death. Which of the following is the *strongest* argument for Ace to make in an attempt to avoid being held liable?

    a. That he did not intend to cause any harm to Clyde—let alone Clyde's death.

    b. That by smoking cigarettes for so many years, Clyde assumed the risk of dying as he did.

    c. That Clyde's death was too remote a consequence to be regarded as proximately caused by Ace's negligence.

    d. That the initial explosion described above was a superseding cause, which should relieve Ace from liability.

20. Little Richard Pennyman went to Miss Molly's Market after receiving his allowance. While walking through the store on his way to the candy aisle, Richard slipped on a pool of melted Good Golly brand tutti frutti ice cream, which had oozed out of a carton located on the floor. Richard fell to the floor and sustained a broken leg as a result. Of the following statements about the legal issues suggested by the facts, which is accurate?

    a. The only duty Miss Molly's owed to Richard while he was at the store was to warn him of dangerous conditions he would be unlikely to discover.

    b. Even if no Miss Molly's employee actually knew the melted ice cream was on the floor, Miss Molly's could be held liable on a negligence theory for damages associated with Richard's injury.

    c. Even if Miss Molly's was negligent, Miss Molly's will not be held liable because the facts reveal Richard's assumption of the risk of injury.

    d. Regardless of whether any Miss Molly's employee knew the melted ice cream was on the floor, Miss Molly's is liable to Richard because store owners are insurers of the safety of customers within the store.

21. Assume that a Mississippi statute reads as follows: "It is unlawful for a tavernkeeper or operator of a package liquor store to sell alcoholic beverages to a person who is younger than 21 years of age at the time of purchase." According to the statute's legislative history, one of its purposes was to lessen the frequency of alcohol-related traffic accidents involving drivers under the age of 21. Assume that the age specified in the statute had been raised from 18 to 21 because of numerous traffic fatalities and injuries caused by intoxicated drivers aged 18-20. After the above-quoted statute was in effect, Cheap Liquor Sales Co. (which sold alcohol for consumption off the premises) sold a 12-pack of Generic brand beer to Biff Redneck, an 18-year-old high school dropout. At the time of the purchase, Redneck showed the Cheap salesclerk a fake i.d. Besides appearing to be genuine, the i.d. represented Redneck as a 25-year-old. Judging from Redneck's appearance, the salesclerk reasonably thought that Redneck looked nearly 30 years old. After purchasing the 12-pack, Redneck drove his car to a city park. There, while sitting behind the wheel, he consumed 10 of the 12 beers. An intoxicated Redneck then drove out of the park and promptly caused (because of his intoxication) an accident in which pedestrian Pauline Polk was severely injured. Profoundly and predictably peeved, plaintiff Polk has sued Cheap on a negligence per se theory. Polk is likely to:

    a. lose the suit because the Cheap salesclerk did not have reason to believe that Redneck was younger than 21.

    b. lose the suit because Redneck's responsibility for her injuries was more direct and more substantial than Cheap's responsibility was.

    c. win the suit despite the lack of fault on Cheap's part, because the court will easily recognize that Cheap has a better ability to pay money damages than Redneck would have.

    d. win the suit despite the salesclerk's belief regarding Redneck's age, because of the operation of the negligence per se doctrine and the presence of sufficient causation.

Short Essay

22. During a command performance at the Cow Chip Lounge by the mother-daughter country western duo "The Dudds," Iama Dudd (the mother) slipped on an unidentified substance that Cow Chip employees had negligently allowed to remain on the stage for a substantial length of time. In her resulting fall to the floor, Iama suffered a severe brain concussion and was knocked unconscious. She remained unconscious for several weeks. Iama's daughter, Uara Dudd, was also on the large Cow Chip stage when her mother fell. At that time, Uara was standing approximately 25 feet from the substance on which Iama slipped. Uara saw the entire slip-and-fall incident, as well as the obviously injured state of Iama after the fall. Uara experienced extreme and lingering emotional distress as a result of the incident. She also developed an ulcer, which expert medical testimony will attribute to her emotional distress and her considerable amount of worrying about Iama. Uara has now filed a negligence suit against the Cow Chip's owner in order to seek damages for the severe emotional distress she experienced after seeing what happened to her mother. The state whose law controls the case follows the foreseeability approach (as set forth in the *Mazzagatti* case in the text) in cases such as Uara's. Should Uara win her suit? Why or why not?

23. King Corp. owns a souvenir shop known as Elvis R Us (ERU). The shop is located in a high-crime area. Various rough-looking characters have been known by King officials to frequent ERU. Several acts of extreme violence (known about by King officials) have been committed upon customers there within the past year. Reasoning that hiring uniformed security personnel would not be worth the cost, King instead posted, on an ERU wall, a prominently-displayed sign that stated: "Attention, customers. Store owner assumes no liability for injuries you may suffer while on premises." Ernie Doubleknit, a real estate broker who moonlights as an Elvis impersonator, came to ERU to purchase a sequined jumpsuit for use in his Elvis act. As Doubleknit was admiring a pastel blue 100% polyester beauty, he was attacked by an unknown assailant (not an employee of King) and was beaten nearly to death. Although Doubleknit later learned that it was small-time thug Mitzi "Rambo" Stallone who inflicted the severe beating, he has instead sued King for negligence in an effort to collect damages for his injuries. Should Doubleknit win the suit? Why or why not?

24. McLean Donaldson used all reasonable care as he drove his Chevy toward his intended destination, the levee. Agood Oldboy, who had been drinking whiskey and rye while behind the wheel of his eastbound car, negligently allowed his vehicle to sideswipe Donaldson's eastbound Chevy when he (Oldboy) attempted to pass in a no passing zone. The impact dented the driver's side of Donaldson's car and caused it to go into a spin. The Chevy ended up positioned sideways across the eastbound lane of the highway. Donaldson was dazed but was not seriously injured. Before Donaldson could regain his faculties and get his car off the roadway, an eastbound pickup truck driven by an inattentive and lonely teenager, Broncin' Buck, crashed into the Chevy. The collision between Buck's truck and the Chevy resulted in the Chevy's being totally demolished and in Donaldson's sustaining a broken collarbone and severely bruised vocal cords. Donaldson has filed a negligence suit against Oldboy, in an effort to recover appropriate compensation for all damages to his Chevy and for all of his personal injuries. Is Oldboy liable to Donaldson for the property damage and personal injuries stemming from the collision between Buck's truck and Donaldson's car? Why or why not?

25. Prince has brought a negligence suit against Duke in a state that has a comparative negligence statute. On the basis of the evidence presented, the jury has concluded that Duke's negligence accounted for 30% of the reason Prince was injured, and that Prince's own negligence supplied the other 70 % of the reason for his injuries. Under appropriate instructions from the trial judge, the jury has also concluded that if Prince had not been negligent and if Duke's negligence had been the sole cause of Prince's injuries, Prince would have been entitled to recover $80,000 in compensatory damages from Duke. What should be the result if the statute establishes a pure comparative negligence rule? What should be the result if the statute establishes a mixed comparative negligence rule? Explain the reasons for each of your answers.

CHAPTER 8

INTELLECTUAL PROPERTY, COMPETITIVE TORTS, AND UNFAIR COMPETITION

True-False - Circle T for True and F for False.

T F 1. Although the Lanham Act is the federal trademark statute, section 43(a) of the statute may be employed in a variety of contexts that do not involve trademark rights.

T F 2. As part of the application for a patent, the party seeking the patent must submit a specification containing sufficient detail and clarity to enable any person of average intelligence to make and use the invention.

T F 3. If the plaintiff in a copyright infringement action believes that she has proved nonwillful infringement, damages of $18,000, and infringer's profits of $13,000, she would be well-advised to elect statutory damages instead of the basic monetary remedy because the court could award her as much as $100,000.

T F 4. The defendant's use of product analysis to discover the plaintiff's trade secret will give rise to a valid misappropriation of trade secret suit in favor of the plaintiff.

T F 5. Proof by the plaintiff that the defendant's work was substantially similar to the plaintiff's copyrighted work will not be sufficient to enable the plaintiff to win an infringement suit if the plaintiff does not also prove that the defendant had access to the plaintiff's work.

T F 6. If A and B have a contract and C simply offers B a better deal, C could end up being liable to A in an interference with contractual relations suit.

T F 7. In trademark law, a mark has *secondary meaning* if, instead of serving to identify the source of a particular product, it serves the secondary function of being the name by which the public customarily refers to a type of product made and sold by various manufacturers.

T F 8. A 1988 amendment to section 43(a) of the Lanham Act prohibits the section's use in competitor vs. competitor cases in which the plaintiff alleges that the defendant made false statements about the plaintiff's product.

T F 9. The owner of a patent on a process is able to invoke trade secret law as a means of preserving her exclusive right to make, use, or sell the process once the patent expires.

T F 10. In order to win an injurious falsehood suit, the plaintiff must prove fault on the part of the defendant, but the requisite degree of fault varies among courts.

Multiple Choice - Circle the best answer.

11. At a Sept. 20, 1991 meeting, Garish Co. management decided that Garish should expand its product line by manufacturing 100% polyester leisure suits (doubleknit, of course) in a range of pastel colors. (In making this decision, Garish anticipated an upcoming realization of many Americans' worst fears: that the dreaded disco plague of the mid-to-late 1970s would re-emerge.) Garish management also decided at the meeting that the leisure suits would be sold nationally under the "Knit-Wit" brand name beginning Jan. 1, 1992. You are a part-time Garish employee, but you have been promised a promotion from your current mailroom position to Vice-President for Marketing once you complete the degree for which you are now studying. Garish's CEO, Wally Dorfman, contacted you earlier today because he knows that you are well-versed in trademark law. Dorfman informed you of the decisions made at the Sept. 20 meeting, and asked you various questions concerning the protection of "Knit-Wit" as a trademark. Which of the following would be a legally sound statement for you to make to Dorfman?

a. "Can we get the leisure suits on the market any sooner than Jan. 1? We can't seek to get 'Knit-Wit' registered at the federal level until we've started using the mark publicly."

b. "Once we start using 'Knit-Wit' on Jan. 1, we won't have any trademark protection for it if we don't seek to have it registered as a trademark under federal law."

c. "We can go ahead and seek federal trademark registration for 'Knit-Wit' now, even though we haven't yet started to use it as a trademark."

d. "If the U.S. Patent & Trademark Office regards 'Knit-Wit' as a suggestive mark, we can't get it federally registered until we can prove that the public associates 'Knit-Wit' with us."

12. Geezer Corp. produces blue hair tint that is sold at grocery and discount stores throughout the United States. Geezer markets the product under the "Aunt Gert" brand name. Aunt Gert hair tint has been the nation's top-selling product hair tint for approximately 15 years. Elderly customers like it because it is the only blue hair tint designed for application at home, rather than at a hairstyling salon. When the Aunt Gert name is used on hair tint labels or in advertisements, it appears in cursive lettering. Geezer has had the Aunt Gert mark (in cursive lettering) registered on the Principal Register since 1974. Irreverent, Inc. publishes *Irreverent* magazine, which is sold in grocery and discount stores in every state, as well as by subscription. The September 1991 issue of *Irreverent* contained a series of mock advertisements for "products we'd like to see." One of these ads was for a product known as "Aunt Kurt." According to the ad, "Aunt Kurt is the only pastel blue hair tint designed specifically for use by transsexuals (but you transvestites can use it too)." Whenever the Aunt Kurt name appeared in the ad, it was in cursive lettering. Geezer has now sued Irreverent for trademark infringement. Geezer should:

a. lose the suit because trademark infringement liability cannot be imposed on defendants who use a substantially similar version of the plaintiff's mark, as opposed to an identical version.

b. win the suit because the defendant's parody of the plaintiff's trademark would logically have offended Geezer and could offend Aunt Gert purchasers.

c. lose the suit because the context and content of the Aunt Kurt "ad" would prevent the existence of a basic element of trademark infringement.

d. win the suit because the length of time Aunt Gert has been registered makes the mark incontestable.

13. In January 1991, Eddie Poe wrote a movie script. Although he had placed the script in typewritten form by January 20, 1991, he showed it to no one until July 12, 1991, when he made copies of the script available to various movie studio executives so that they could determine whether to purchase it. Each of the copies of the script contained a proper notice of Poe's claim to copyright protection. Poe soon learned, from one of the movie studio executives, that his studio had already purchased a nearly identical script from Charlene Dickens. Convinced that Dickens had stolen his script, Poe had his copyright registered with the federal Copyright Office on August 23, 1991, and brought a copyright infringement suit against Dickens on August 30, 1991. On these facts, any copyright protection to which Poe is entitled should be considered effective as of:

a. August 30, 1991.

b. August 23, 1991.

c. July 12, 1991.

d. January 20, 1991.

14. Which of the following inventions may be eligible for patent protection?

a. An industrial process that, among other things, involves use of a mathematical equation and application of a scientific principle.

b. A revolutionary mechanical device that was invented in 1988, has been sold publicly by the inventor (and by no one else) since that year, and is the subject of a patent application filed in 1991 by the inventor.

c. A machine referred to in a patent application filed by Ruth, who began making and selling the machine after its inventor, Mary, expressly abandoned the invention and disavowed any claim to a patent on it.

d. None of the above.

15. Ruby Tuesday, an employee of Tumbling Dice, Inc. (TD), invented a process of treating rolling stones so that they will gather moss. Tuesday invented the process during her regular work hours, and used TD laboratory equipment in doing so. She has now obtained a patent on the process. Which of the following is an accurate statement about the rights of Tuesday and TD?

   a. Regardless of the purpose or purposes for which Tuesday was hired, TD is entitled to insist that Tuesday transfer ownership of the patent to it.

   b. Assuming that the purposes for which Tuesday was hired did not include doing inventive work of any sort, Tuesday may license the use of the process to parties other than TD.

   c. Assuming that the purposes for which Tuesday was hired did not include doing inventive work of any sort, TD is entitled to have ownership of the patent transferred to it, but in that event TD must grant Tuesday a royalty-free license to use the process.

   d. Assuming that the purposes for which Tuesday was hired did not include doing inventive work of any sort, TD is entitled to an exclusive license to use the process.

16. Fawndonna Co. is the manufacturer of an unpatented rice cereal known as *Shredded Rice*. The company has had *Shredded Rice* registered as a trademark on the Principal Register for four years. During that time, Fawndonna's rice cereal has become exceedingly popular. As a result, other manufacturers have begun producing rice cereals. Consumers frequently use the term "shredded rice" to refer to the various rice cereals produced by the different companies. North-Hart, Inc. recently began using *Shredded Rice* as the name of its rice cereal. Fawndonna has brought a trademark infringement suit against North-Hart. Which of the following is the strongest argument for North-Hart to make in its attempt to avoid liability?

   a. That Fawndonna's failure to obtain a patent on its cereal justified competitors in producing similar rice cereals.

   b. That no North-Hart personnel had actual knowledge of Fawndonna's federal registration of the mark *Shredded Rice*.

   c. That *Shredded Rice* is a generic term to which trademark protection should no longer attach.

   d. That any use by North-Hart of the *Shredded Rice* name is protected under the fair use doctrine.

17. Ex-talk show host Morton Downandout, Jr. was the subject of a "profile" story in *Overbearing*, a magazine sold in thousands of stores throughout the United States. *Overbearing*'s publisher holds a valid copyright on the story, which, among other things, contained considerable biographical information about Downandout. After the story appeared in print, TV personality Geraldo Unbearable financed, wrote, produced, and hosted a nationally telecast documentary titled "The Rise and Fall of Downandout: An American Tragedy." In the documentary, Unbearable relied heavily on the *Overbearing* article for numerous pieces of information about Downandout's life. Unbearable clearly used most of the biographical data that the *Overbearing* reporter had gone to the trouble of gathering, although Unbearable consistently rewrote the information so that it would fit his personal style. *Overbearing*'s publisher has now used Unbearable for copyright infringement because of his use of the biographical data. The plaintiff:

   a. should win the suit because Unbearable made considerable use of the "fruits" of the labors of the plaintiff's reporter.

   b. should not win the suit unless Unbearable failed, in the documentary, to cite the *Overbearing* article as a source used by him.

   c. is likely to the win the suit because there is no serious question about whether Unbearable had access to the copyrighted article when he prepared the documentary.

   d. is unlikely to win the suit because any borrowing by Unbearable from the *Overbearing* article apparently was not a borrowing of material protected by the copyright.

18. Liability for patent infringement:

   a. cannot be imposed if the defendant's actions did not involve exact reproduction of the plaintiff's patented item.

   b. includes responsibility for paying damages in an amount at least as great as what would have been a reasonable royalty for the use made by the infringer.

c. may be imposed on one whose actions induced another person to commit patent infringement, regardless of whether the party whose actions produced that effect knew of the plaintiff's patent or intended that the infringement occur.

d. means that the infringer automatically is held liable for three times the actual damages sustained by the plaintiff.

19. Chad Shark, an attorney, is also the owner-operator of a fast food restaurant known as the Bun-n-Run. Representing himself, Shark has filed an injurious falsehood suit against a competitor whose advertisements contained grossly false and disparaging statements about the supposed meat content of Bun-n-Run hamburgers. Shark has at his disposal solid evidence that the statements were false and that the competitor made them with knowledge of their falsity. Although he does not have proof that the false statements have caused or will cause him to suffer any economic loss in connection with his business, Shark will be able to prove that he suffered considerable emotional distress as a result of the competitor's false advertisements. On these facts, should Shark win the suit?

a. Yes, because the facts indicate that the competitor, who made the false statements knowing of their falsity, did not act in good faith.

b. Yes, because the competitor's false statements damaged Shark's personal reputation and therefore injured him.

c. No, because the competitor's statements, though false, will be considered protected by the privilege to make unfavorable comparisons.

d. No, because Shark did not sustain special damages and therefore will be unable to satisfy a basic element of his claim.

20. Nixon Corp. produces fertilizer spreaders. Carter sells fertilizer spreaders in his retail business. For the years 1983 through 1991, Nixon and Carter entered into a series of one-year contracts under which Nixon was to supply Carter, and Carter was to purchase from Nixon, all of the fertilizer spreaders Carter required for his business that year. Reagan Co. began making fertilizer spreaders in 1989. Reagan officials were aware that Nixon and Carter has entered into a contract of the sort just described for the year 1991. Eager to enhance Reagan's competitive position in the fertilizer spreader market, Reagan officials approached Carter on June 1, 1991 and offered to charge him $20 less per spreader than the price set in his contract with Nixon, if Carter would buy from Reagan all of the spreaders he needed for the remainder of 1991. Carter in fact did so for the remainder of the year, purchasing no more from Nixon. On June 5, 1991, officials of Ford, Inc. (another fertilizer spreader manufacturer) contacted Carter and made him an offer that was extremely favorable from his standpoint. The Ford offer was for the supplying of Carter's spreader requirements for the year 1992. When this offer was made, Ford officials knew that Carter's contract with Nixon ran through 1991. Carter was certain that no one else could match the terms Ford offered. Therefore, Carter contracted with Ford for 1992. Of the following statements, which is accurate?

a. If Nixon sues Ford for interference with prospective advantage, Ford's offer to Carter will not be classified as improper even though it was made at a time when Nixon and Carter had a contract.

b. If Nixon sues Reagan for interference with contractual relations, Reagan is likely to prevail by arguing that it merely offered Carter a better deal in order to enhance its competitive position.

c. If Nixon sues Ford on the theory referred to in answer a and Reagan on the theory mentioned in answer b, Nixon is likely to win both claims.

d. None of the above.

21. Assume that Greasy Records, Inc. holds the relevant copyrights on the song "Hound Dog," which the late Elvis Presley made into a hit during the 1950s. Popular comedian Alec Smart recently wrote and recorded a song called "Ground Dog," which is both a deliberate take-off on "Hound Dog" and a satiric comment on the supposed ingredients in the hamburgers sold by a certain nationwide chain of fast food restaurants. At least half of the melody of "Ground Dog" is virtually identical to the melody of "Hound Dog." Several lines in the lyrics of "Ground Dog" bear easily recognizable resemblance to lines in "Hound Dog." Greasy has sued Smart and Shifty Records, Inc. (the company on whose label Smart recorded the song) for copyright infringement. The defendants have raised the defense of fair use. Which of the following statements is accurate?

    a. Greasy will be able to establish the basic elements of copyright infringement (substantial similarity and access); as a result, the defendants cannot claim the protection of the fair use doctrine.

    b. In arguing that the fair use defense should protect them, the defendants should stress that their work of satire will not substitute for the original, i.e., that anyone who wants "Hound Dog" would not be content to have "Ground Dog" instead.

    c. In order to win the suit, Greasy will have to prove that the defendants' actions created a likelihood of confusion regarding the sources or origins of the songs discussed in the facts.

    d. None of the above.

Short Essay

22. During the summer of 1991, you had an internship with Rancid Corp., an up-and-coming manufacturing firm based in North Carolina. You no doubt recall that Mac E. Avellian, Rancid's Vice-President for Marketing, was immensely impressed with your abilities and judgment. He is very interested in having you work for Rancid after you complete the degree for which you are now studying. Knowing the Rancid reputation for excellence, you of course aspire to become a Rancidite. Avellian knows that you are familiar with trademark law. He therefore wrote you a letter in which he outlined a legal problem on which he would like your comments. Your possible future as a Rancidite may depend heavily on how well you analyze the problem. In his letter, Avellian stated:

    "We're planning to come out soon with a new deodorant for dogs. We don't know for certain what we'll call the product, but whatever name we choose, we'll want to try to get it registered for federal trademark protection as soon as we can. We're mulling over three possible names for the dog deodorant: 1. *Odor Eradicator*; 2. *Confident Hound*; and 3. *Carolina Pine-Fresh*. What I want to know from you are these things: (1) *In terms of probable speed and ease in getting it registered for trademark protection, which one of the three names would be the easiest to get registered and therefore the best one for us to choose?*; and (2) *Why would that name be the best one and why would the other two not be as good?*"

    Answer Avellian's questions.

23. Roy Bob Smedley owns a popular southern Indiana restaurant known as "U 8 Yit?". In 1988, Smedley developed a formula for a soft drink that is made and sold at the restaurant. He calls the drink the "Nun [sic] Better." Since 1988, he had sold huge quantities of the drink to U 8 Yit? customers, who may quaff as many Nun Betters as they please on the premises and then take home a six-pack or two for later consumption. After developing the revolutionary formula for Nun Better, Smedley attempted to preserve it as a trade secret. Until the events about to be described, no one else in the world had developed or sold a soft drink that was even remotely similar to Nun Better. On Aug. 15, 1991, Edna Sue Mumford opened her own business after quitting her job as Smedley's Nun Better production coordinator. Out of necessity, Mumford had been given access to the details of the Num Better formula when she worked for Smedley. Although she knew that the formula was a trade secret, her written employment contract with Smedley did not contain any express provision barring her from using such information once her employment relationship with Smedley ceased. Mumford's new business features the sale of a soft drink made with the same formula used for Nun Better. Smedley filed a misappropriation of trade secret suit against Mumford on Sept. 9, 1991. He seeks appropriate injunctive relief and damages. On Sept. 16, 1991, Smedley filed an application for a patent on the Nun Better formula. On these facts, should Smedley succeed in his suit against Mumford? Explain your reasoning. Should Smedley be granted a patent on the formula? Why or why not?

24. For many years, Huge Co. has had the name *Derngood* registered as a trademark on the Principal Register. It uses *Derngood* as the name of the frozen pies it sells throughout the midwestern portion of the United States. Bulky, Inc., a kitchen appliances manufacturer whose products are distributed throughout the country, has begun using the name *Derngood* for its trash compactors. Huge has filed a trademark infringement suit against Bulky because of Bulky's use of the name *Derngood*. What must Huge prove in order to establish trademark infringement? Is Huge likely to succeed in its suit? Why or why not?

25. Mitzi Ritzy, who served as assistant to the assistant to the social secretary for President and Mrs. Reagan during the former President's first term in office, wrote the manuscript of an unpublished book about her experiences as a White House employee. A major publishing company, Aquarius Co., had committed itself to publishing the manuscript, but the publication process had not yet begun. Ownership of a copyright on the manuscript still rested with Ritzy. Although the lengthy manuscript dealt with many incidents involving the Reagans, the portion likely to be of greatest potential interest to the public was a three-page discussion of Ritzy's knowledge of the Reagans' reliance on the advice of astrologers. A copy of the unpublished manuscript was placed, by some unknown person, on the desk of a reporter for *Newstime*, a nationally circulated magazine. *Newstime*'s editors reviewed the manuscript and then published a story referring to it and quoting approximately 350 words from the three-page astrology discussion noted above. When the *Newstime* story was published, Acquarius reneged on its commitment to publish Ritzy's book. Ritzy then sued *Newstime* for copyright infringement. *Newstime* has raised the fair use defense. Should the fair use defense protect *Newstime* from liability? State the reasons for your answer.

CHAPTER 9

INTRODUCTION TO CONTRACTS

True-False - Circle T for True and F for False.

T F 1. When a contract calls for a party to provide goods and perform services, the presence of the "sale of goods" component in the contract does not necessarily mean that the contract is governed by Article 2 of the Uniform Commercial Code.

T F 2. A bilateral contract is one in which an act is exchanged for a promise.

T F 3. Modern contract law features more legislative and judicial intervention into private contractual relationships than classical contract law did.

T F 4. A plaintiff may recover damages under a quasi-contract theory only if both parties have shown an intent to enter into a binding contract.

T F 5. A contract resulting from one party's use of fraud upon the other party is not void.

T F 6. Labeling a contract "express" is not necessarily an indication that the contract has been reduced to writing.

T F 7. If neither party to a contract for the sale of goods is a merchant, the contract is not governed by Article 2 of the UCC.

T F 8. A voidable contract is one in which at least one party has the legal right to cancel her obligations under the contract.

T F 9. In order for two parties to be bound contractually to each other, they must have expressly stated and agreed upon the terms that will govern their dealings with each other.

T F 10. An executory contract is one in which both parties have fully performed their respective contractual duties.

Multiple Choice - Circle the best answer.

11. Tuesday owned a vacant commercial building in downtown Honky Tonk, Alaska. On June 1, 1991, she promised her friend, Flash, that on Dec. 15, 1991, she would give Flash legal ownership of the building. She did not ask Flash to promise or do anything in return. Flash decided that he would like to use the building, once it became his, to fulfill his longstanding dream: the operation of a retail business featuring the sale of records, tapes, and compact disks. He therefore began making preparations to engage in that business. Flash spent $800 to have the building's red doors painted his favorite color—black—and obligated himself on contracts for the purchase of $15,000-worth of albums, tapes, and CDs, so that he would have suitable inventory from which customers could make choices. He also contracted to purchase $4,000-worth of shelves and racks to hold his inventory. When Dec. 15, 1991 arrived, Tuesday refused to deed the property to Flash because she had decided to use it for another purpose. After realizing that he could get no satisfaction out of trying to reason with Tuesday, Flash sued her in an attempt to recover the amounts referred to above. The following statements purport to state the "best" legal theory for Flash to use in his suit. Which statement is accurate?

    a. Quasi-contract would be the best theory for Flash to use because when Tuesday failed to confer the expected benefit on Flash, he was unjustly harmed.

    b. Breach of contract would be the best theory for Flash to use because Tuesday made an offer that Flash obviously intended to accept.

    c. Promissory estoppel would be the best theory for Flash to use because Flash took action in detrimental reliance on a promise that Tuesday should have foreseen as likely to induce reliance.

    d. The best theory for Flash to use would be that the parties had an executory contract, in view of Tuesday's failure to live up to the terms of her promise.

12. Vic Ditale telephoned his pal, Hugh Lenson, to discuss Ditale's plan for a possible business venture involving the two of them. Ditale stated the following to Lenson: "Hugh, babyyyy, I've decided to do something I've always had a secret desire to do—open a hairstyling salon. With your flair for hair, I know you'd be a great drawing card in terms of attracting customers. What I want to do is to employ you as chief hairstylist and to call the shop 'The Hugh-Do.' We would call you 'Mr. Hugh.' I'd own the business, but I can assure you I'd pay you top dollar for your incomparable services." Ditale went on to describe numerous other details of the planned business venture, including the sorts of "specials" that would be offered to customers and the notion that the salon would have a sports-oriented theme. Ditale then asked Lenson whether he would be interested in pursuing the outlined plan. Lenson declined. A month later, Lenson resigned his position as head tiddly winks coach at a major university and opened a hairstyling salon called "The Hugh-Do." Lenson, who served as chief hairstylist at the salon, began calling himself "Mr. Hugh." Lenson's salon featured a sports-oriented theme and the same sorts of specials Ditale had described to Lenson. Various other details of "The Hugh-Do" corresponded to those previously mentioned by Ditale. Ditale recently sued Lenson for breach of contract. Which of the following is an accurate observation?

    a. This case is governed by the UCC, whose provision requiring parties to act in good faith was violated here by Lenson; therefore, Ditale will win his suit.

    b. Ditale's chances of success on a breach of contract theory are not as great as they would have been if, in his telephone call to Lemson, Ditale had stated that he was disclosing the details of his plan for the purpose of offering it for sale to Lenson.

    c. A better theory (from Ditale's standpoint) than breach of contract would be promissory estoppel, because Ditale would justifiably have assumed that Lenson meant what he said when he stated that he was not interested in pursuing Ditale's plan.

    d. None of the above.

13. Which of the following is *not* a characteristic of 20th century contract law?

    a. An interventionist, "hands-on" judicial posture toward private contracts.

    b. An increasing judicial concern with just results in cases where one contracting party uses its superior bargaining power to disadvantage another.

    c. A general tendency not to interfere with private contracts and, instead, to simply enforce whatever deal the parties made.

    d. Broad, fuzzy, discretionary rules.

14. Ned Dorfman took his green 1975 AMC Gremlin automobile to Auto Hospital, Inc. (AH) and informed an AH employee that he wanted a new set of rear brakes put on the car. Dorfman left the premises, stating that he would return later in the day to pick up the car. As it happened, there was another 1975 Gremlin at AH that day. That Gremlin's owner had brought his car there in order to have AH personnel paint it red, at an agreed cost of $1,000. Nearly all other reputable car painters in the area would have charged no more than $600 for such a paint job. Confused AH employees mistakenly painted Dorfman's Gremlin red and installed the new rear brakes on the other Gremlin. AH discovered the mistake when the owner of the Gremlin that was to have been painted refused to pay for a paint job he did not get. When Dorfman returned to AH to pick up his car, he learned of the mixup. AH demanded that Dorfman pay $1,000 for the paint job from which he had benefited. Dorfman refused, even though the paint job made his Gremlin look far better than it had ever looked. On these facts, AH:

    a. has a meritorious quasi-contract claim for $1,000 against Dorfman, because the paint job was a benefit that he accepted and retained.

    b. has a meritorious quasi-contract claim against Dorfman for the reason stated in answer a, but only to the extent of $600.

    c. has a meritorious $600 implied contract claim against Dorfman, because it would be unjust not to find that Dorfman made an implied promise to pay for the benefit he received.

    d. has neither a meritorious quasi-contract claim nor a meritorious implied contract claim against Dorfman.

15. To which of the following contracts is Article 2 of the UCC most likely to apply?
    a. A contract for the sale of a mobile home.
    b. A contract by an artist to paint a portrait.
    c. A contract to give a car's engine a tuneup.
    d. A contract for the sale of a house.

16. Porter tells Dolly that he will sell her his stereo system in one week if she agrees now to pay him $400 at that time. Dolly agrees to buy the stereo system on Porter's terms. The contract between Porter and Dolly is:
    a. unilateral, executory, and valid.
    b. unilateral, executed, and voidable.
    c. bilateral, executory, and express.
    d. bilateral, executory, and void.

17. In which of the following situations is there a contract that would properly be classified as *unenforceable*?
    a. Despicable and Dastardly entered into a supposed contract designed to ahcieve an objective that clearly violates state law.
    b. Acme breached a valid contract to which Acme and Generic were parties. Generic did not file a breach of contract suit against Acme until after the statute of limitations expired.
    c. Nondescript and Ordinary entered into a contract as the result of Nondescript's use of duress upon Ordinary.
    d. Each of the above.
    e. Both a and b, but not c.

18. Don Dim is induced by Sue Shrewd's fraud to enter a contract with Shrewd. The contract between Dim and Shrewd is:
    a. void.
    b. implied.
    c. quasi.
    d. voidable.

19. The *Restatement (Second) of Contracts*:
    a. reflects the influence of both legal realism and the UCC.
    b. is a positivist attempt to formulate a system of black letter rules of contract law.
    c. has been enacted into statutory form in nearly all states.
    d. displaces the common law in contracts for the furnishing of services.

20. In which of the following situations is there a contract that is unilateral in nature?
    a. Shark Loan Co. loans Carl Clod $5,000. In return, Clod makes the promise desired by Shark: a promise to repay the $5,000 plus interest at the highest rate allowed by law.
    b. Nikki Lenin promises to pay Karla Marx $10,000 on Dec. 31, 1991 in order to purchase Marx's entire collection of books dealing with the virtues of capitalism. In return (and as requested by Lenin), Marx promises that she will deliver the collection to Lenin on Dec. 31, 1991.
    c. Jo Stalin promises to pay her nephew, Lee Ontrotsky, $500 if Ontrotsky drives her to the town of Siberia, Montana. Onstrotsky gives Aunt Jo the requested ride to Siberia.
    d. Both a and c.

21. On Nov. 1, 1991, oil magnate Tex Crude promised his boyhood friend, Bobby Bill Hardluck, that on Dec. 1, 1991, he would give Hardluck full ownership of one of his 100 oil wells. Crude did not ask Hardluck to do or promise anything in return. During the period from Nov. 1 to Dec. 1, Hardluck daydreamed about what things would be like once he owned the oil well and, in general, counted on the notion that Crude would live up to the terms of his promise. When Dec. 1 rolled around, however, Crude informed Hardluck that he had reconsidered and that he would not be giving Hardluck an oil well after all. Both disappointed and angry, Hardluck has sued Crude on a promissory estoppel theory. In view of the facts, who should win the suit? Why that party?

22. Stan Short owed Brutish Finance Co. $3,000 on a loan whose repayment date was past due. When Short received a $3,300 check from Leviathan Insurance Co. in settlement of a claim he had made, Short telephoned the Brutish collections manager and stated that he would stop by within the next few days to pay off the $3,000 debt with part of the money he had received from the insurance company. On the following evening, Short's house was burglarized by Nelson Nasty. Among the items stolen by Nasty was the $3,300 check Short had received from Leviathan. Nasty later forged Short's endorsement on the check, succeeded in getting it cashed, and spent all of the money. After Nasty was apprehended by the police, Brutish learned what had happened. Brutish has filed a quasi-contract suit against Nasty, on the theory that Nasty pocketed money which had been promised by Short to Brutish. Should Brutish win its suit? Explain your reasoning.

23. What is the fundamental difference between the doctrine of quasi-contract and the doctrine of promissory estoppel?

CHAPTER 10

THE AGREEMENT: OFFER

True-False - Circle T for True and F for False.

T F 1. As a general rule, an offer may be revoked at any time prior to acceptance, even if the offeror promised to hold the offer open for a certain length of time.

T F 2. The UCC may supply various terms that parties to a contract have omitted, but a sales contract that omits a price term is unenforceable even under the UCC.

T F 3. The death of the offeror terminates the offer even if the offeree does not know of the death.

T F 4. An offer that contains no duration term is open for a reasonable time.

T F 5. When an auction is advertised as being "without reserve," the seller is treated as having made an offer to sell the goods to the highest bidder.

T F 6. For a binding contract to exist, it must be proved that the parties subjectively intended to contract with each other.

T F 7. Although a rejection terminates the offer, a counteroffer does not have that effect.

T F 8. As a general rule, a newspaper ad stating the price of the advertised goods is not an offer to sell the goods at the stated price.

T F 9. Revocations of offers are effective when received, but rejections of offers are effective when mailed.

T F 10. Under modern contract law, only those terms of which the offeree had actual notice are considered to be part of the offer (and hence part of the contract if the offer has been accepted).

Multiple Choice - Circle the best answer.

11. Pooh Benson owns The Pooh-Do, a shop at which he sells toupees and wigs. After noticing that he was overstocked on Cosell brand toupees, Benson decided to take special action to get them sold. Therefore, Benson sent his friend Nick Witale a signed letter on Dec. 9, 1991. In the letter, Benson offered to sell Witale a Cosell brand toupee for the bargain-basement price of $999, and stated that the offer would be held open until Dec. 24, 1991. On Dec. 16, 1991, Benson telephoned Witale and stated that the offer was revoked. Later that same day, Witale telephoned Benson and stated: "Pooh, my man, you're a hardnosed retailer with a genuine flair for quasi-hair, but I'm not the empty-headed fool I appear to be. You gave me until Dec. 24 to decide. I want that Cosell 'rug' for 999 clams, just as you promised." Benson, however, refused to sell Witale the toupee for $999. Witale has sued him for breach of contract. Should Witale win?

    a. No, because Benson revoked the offer before Witale attempted to accept it.
    b. Yes, because Benson made a valid firm offer that was properly accepted by Witale.
    c. No, because the facts do not indicate that Benson separately signed the assurance term in the offer.
    d. Yes, because Benson's power to revoke was suspended until Witale had had a reasonable amount of time within which to decide whether to accept.

12. Gus Griese and Sortafast, Inc. had negotiated for some time over the possibility of Griese's acquiring a franchise for a Sortafast oil change shop. If he obtained a Sortafast franchise, Griese intended to open the business in Gnaw Bone, Indiana. Although the details of any agreement between Sortafast and Griese had not yet been worked out, Sortafast executives promised Griese on various occasions that he would be awarded a Sortafast franchise which he could operate in Gnaw Bone, and that the terms of the agreement would be arrived at later. In response to Sortafast's statement that it liked its franchisees to have had experience in the oil change business, Griese quit his job as a high-fashion model in Indianapolis and went to work on a temporary basis as an oil changer for another Gnaw Bone shop. He also moved himself and his family (at his own

expense) from Indianapolis to Gnaw Bone. As it turned out, the details of an agreement between Sortafast were never arrived at by Sortafast and Griese, and Sortafast later refused to award Griese a franchise. Which of the following is an accurate statement about the facts?

a. If Griese sues Sortafast, most courts would fully enforce Sortafast's promises by granting Griese damages that would include the profits Griese expected to make and all other sums Griese expected to realize once the promised franchise was awarded to him.

b. If Griese sues Sortafast, he should rely on a quasi-contract theory because Sortafast was unjust in its treatment of him, and because Sortafast's failure to award him the promised franchise caused him not to experience the enrichment he expected.

c. Griese's best chance of success in a suit against Sortafast would be on a promissory estoppel theory, under which a court could award him damages based on out-of-pocket losses that he incurred in relying on Sortafast's promises.

d. Griese should have a valid breach of express contract claim against Sortafast because the parties expressly agreed that he should have a franchise, even though they failed to agree on various details and terms.

13. Which of the following parties will normally be classified as an offeror who is making an offer?

a. A person who places an advertisement of a reward in the newspaper.

b. A general contractor who requests bids on a construction project.

c. An auctioneer who conducts an auction of goods.

d. A seller who takes out a newspaper advertisement stating the price of certain goods.

14. A offers to buy some TV tubes from B. The purchase order is complete and certain as to all material terms except price, which is not mentioned at all. There is a readily ascertainable market price for the tubes. B accepts all terms of the offer. The parties:

a. do not have a contract.

b. have a contract only if it can be proved that the parties specifically discussed the market price.

c. have a contract only if B contacts A and they agree on a price for the tubes.

d. have a contract.

15. After suffering through 13 consecutive winless seasons on the gridiron, Bagby College's president and board of trustees fired longtime head football coach Lester Singlewing. The president and the board then joined in a letter offering the position to former All-Pro linebacker Doberman "Dobie" Rottweiler. The letter, dated Nov. 11, 1991, informed Rottweiler that "if you wish to accept, you must do so by Nov. 25, 1991." The properly addressed letter was mailed on Nov. 11 but because of a postal worker's error, it did not reach Rottweiler until Dec. 2, 1991. Rottweiler contacted Bagby's president the following day and stated that he wished to accept the offer. Which of the following contains the best legal analysis of the facts?

a. Rottweiler and Bagby have a contract because Bagby failed to revoke its offer prior to Rottweiler's acceptance of it.

b. Rottweiler has made an offer that Bagby is free to accept or reject.

c. Rottweiler made a prompt and proper acceptance of Bagby's offer, because it was not his fault that the letter was so slow in arriving.

d. Rottweiler made a timely acceptance of Bagby's offer, because the time for acceptance is customarily measured from the date the offeree receives the offer.

16. Kyle sent Ted a letter offering to sell Ted his car. Ted left the letter on his desk and his roommate, Bill, saw it. Bill then wrote to Kyle and stated that he wanted to accept Kyle's "most excellent" offer. Which of the following statement(s) is/are accurate?

a. Bill's letter is a valid acceptance of Kyle's offer.

b. Kyle is now bound to sell the car to Bill.

c. There is no contract between Kyle and Bill because Kyle did not communicate his offer to Bill.

d. Ted and Kyle have a contract for the purchase of Kyle's car.

e. Both a and b.

17. On Dec. 16, 1991, Ariel Oldbag made a written offer to sell Marginal State University her palatial estate, Oldbag Manor, for $500,000. On that same date, Oldbag also extended Marginal State a written option to buy the property at the offered price until April 1, 1992. Marginal State paid Oldbag $2,500 (the amount specified by her) for the option. Which of the following is an accurate statement?

    a. If Oldbag notifies Marginal State in writing on February 15, 1992 that she does not want to sell, she will be acting in a manner consistent with the mutuality of obligation reasonably contemplated by the option.

    b. Marginal State has no legal obligation to purchase the property from Oldbag.

    c. Oldbag may revoke her offer to sell the property at any time before Marginal State accepts, so long as she refunds the $2,500.

    d. If Marginal State decides not to purchase Oldbag Manor, Oldbag will have a valid breach of contract claim against the school.

18. Ace Deuce owns a new business known as Ace Deuce Hardware. To announce the grand opening of his business, Deuce placed an advertisement in the local newpspaer. The ad quoted prices on various items, including a Massacre brand chainsaw. The grand opening was much more successful than Deuce had imagined it would be. He was unable to satisfy all consumer demand for certain items. After Deuce had sold all of the Massacre chainsaws he had in stock, customer Howard Surly demanded that he be sold a Massacre chainsaw at the advertised price. When Deuce did not comply, Surly sued him (in small claims court) for breach of contract. How should the court rule?

    a. That no contract was formed because Deuce did not accept Surly's offer.

    b. That Deuce is liable for breach of a contract formed when Surly demanded a chainsaw at the advertised price.

    c. That Deuce's having run out of Massacre chainsaws amounted to a revocation of his offer.

    d. That Deuce's advertisement was an offer, but only if Surly actually read the advertisement before coming to the store.

19. In a newspaper advertisement, Able listed $100,000 as the price at which she would sell her home. On April 1, Bumstead personally delivered to Able a written and signed offer to buy the house for $90,000. Bumstead's offer stated that it would be held open until April 6. On April 2, Able sent Bumstead a letter proposing to sell him the house for $95,000. Bumstead received the letter but made no response. On April 5, Able personally delivered to Bumstead a letter in which she stated that she was pleased to accept his earlier offer to buy the house for $90,000. Able's April 5 letter:

    a. was an acceptance because it reached Bumstead within the duration that he had expressly placed on his offer.

    b. created a contract to sell the house to Bumstead for $90,000.

    c. was an offer that Bumstead is not obligated to accept.

    d. was superfluous because Bumstead's failure to respond to Able's April 2 letter created a contract calling for a $95,000 purchase price.

    e. is correctly characterized in answers a and b.

20. Sam Drucker, a retailer, sent Hooterville Manufacturing Co. (HMC) a purchase order requesting the shipment of wringer-style washing machines. Although the purchase order reasonably reflected Drucker's apparent intent to enter into a legally binding relationship with HMC, the purchase order did not contain a certain term one would ordinarily expect in a transaction of this nature. HMC sent Drucker (and Drucker received) its standard acknowledgement form, which stated that "we gott yer ordur & we'll bee tickled pink to phil it fer ya rite kwik hear." HMC later had a change of heart and refused to deal with Drucker, who has now sued HMC for breach of contract. Which of the following statements is accurate?

    a. If the term missing from Drucker's purchase order was a price term, Drucker will lose the suit because the absence of such an important term means that he did not make a valid offer.

    b. Although purchase orders are often offers, Drucker's was not because of his failure to include a term one would ordinarily expect in this sort of transaction; therefore, Drucker will lose the suit.

    c. The common law strictly adheres to the rule that what was intended as an offer is not an offer if it is too indefinite; therefore, Drucker will lose the suit.

d. If the term missing from Drucker's purchase order was a term on when delivery was to take place, Drucker should win the suit because the absence of such a term did not prevent the creation of a valid contract.

Short Essay

21. An important piece of equipment at Bayhcorp, Ltd.'s manufacturing plant broke down on Dec. 2, 1991. Evan Waxman, Bayhcorp's operations manager at the plant, contacted Quayleco, Inc. to see whether Quayleco would be interested in submitting a proposal for repair of the equipment. Dan Vice, Quayleco's service manager, responded by stating that he would perform a free inspection of the equipment as soon as he finished an emergency golf game, and would then submit a repair proposal. Vice followed through, submitting a written proposal that stated the nature of the problem with the equipment and what Quayleco would plan to do in order to fix it. Under the proposal's terms, Quayleco would be supplying certain parts for the equipment, but the supplying of parts was clearly secondary and incidental to the services that Quayleco would be performing in repairing the equipment. The proposal also indicated that Quayleco would be ready to begin work on Dec. 9, 1991. The Quayleco proposal said nothing about what Bayhcorp would be expected to pay in return for Quayleco's performance. On Dec. 4, 1991, Waxman reviewed the Quayleco proposal and faxed this message to Quayleco: "The repair proposal looks OK. We'll see you on the 9th. /s/ Evan Waxman, for Bayhcorp, Ltd." On Dec. 6, 1991, Waxman telephoned Vice and told him that Quayleco's services would not be needed after all because another firm had been enlisted to do the repair work. Quayleco has filed a breach of contract suit against Bayhcorp on the basis of the above facts. Who should win the suit? Explain your reasoning.

22. Feeble Co. manufactures a wide range of products. Walt Schlemiel, a retailer, contacted Feeble's sales manager, Naomi Nimrod, because he was interested in ordering certain Feeble products for resale in the usual course of his business. Nimrod supplied Schlemiel with a form that Feeble had prepared for purchasers of its products to use when making purchase ordwers. She asked Schlemiel to use the form when he submitted his order. Schlemiel did so, filling in important information concerning the particular goods he wanted, the quantity desired, the price he proposed to pay, and so forth. He signed the form and accurately dated it Sept. 23, 1991. On the back side of the form was this clause: "Offeror hereby promises to hold open the offer set forth in the purchase order for a period of 30 days from the date of the offer." Schlemiel hand-delivered the completed purchase order form to Nimrod on Sept. 23. On Sept. 26, 1991, before Feeble had delivered the goods or expressed an intent to do so, Schlemiel telephoned Nimrod and stated that the offer contained in the Sept. 23 purchase order was revoked. Nimrod responded by expressing Feeble's willingness and intent to provide the goods. Nimrod followed up the conversation with a letter to the same effect, adding a handwritten "We've got a deal, Schlemiel" at the bottom. When Schlemiel continued to refuse to purchase the goods on the terms he had offered, Feeble sued him for breach of contract. On the facts given, who should win the suit? Why that party?

23. Assume that an offeree tries to accept an offer for a unilateral contract by beginning performance of the act requested, but the offeror attempts to revoke the offer before the offeree completes performance. What approaches do courts take to protect the offeree in this situation?

24. A prominent executive of Stench, Inc., acting within his authority, contacted country western singer Conroy Ditty and made this statement: "Conroy, good buddy, we're developing a new advertising campaign for our cologne, *Real Man*, and we want to feature you as the *Real Man* spokesdude in our print media ads and TV commercials. We'll contact you later to work out the details of what we reckon will be a humdinger of a deal for you, but right now we just want you to know how important you are in our plans." After this statement was made by the Stench executive, Ditty purchased several 100% polyester leisure suits and an assortment of polka dot shirts and colorful string ties, all of which he intended to wear in the advertisements and commercials. Ditty normally did not dress so stylishly and would not have bought these clothing items if the above statements had not been made to him. As it turned out, Stench and Ditty never agreed on any specific terms, and Stench eventually scrapped its plans involving Ditty. Ditty now wishes to sue Stench. What legal theory should he use? Why that theory? If Ditty were to succeed on that theory, what relief should he be granted? Explain your reasoning.

CHAPTER 11

THE AGREEMENT: ACCEPTANCE

True-False - Circle T for True and F for False.

T F 1. UCC section 2-207 requires courts to employ the "mirror image" test for whether an offeree's response is an acceptance.

T F 2. A contract will become binding at the moment the parties agree on all material terms, even if they intend to write down those terms later in order to be prudent but never do so.

T F 3. The common law treats a "grumbling acceptance" as a counteroffer rather than as an acceptance.

T F 4. In order to accept an offer to enter into a bilateral contract, the offeree must perform the requested act.

T F 5. In some settings involving offers for unilateral contracts, the *Restatement Second*'s approach would impose, on the offeree, an obligation to inform the offeror that the requested performance has begun.

T F 6. Offerees who accept an offeror's performance knowing what the offeror expects in return have impliedly accepted the offeror's terms.

T F 7. If a merchant's offer for the sale of goods is responded to by a merchant-offeree who intended the response as an acceptance, the presence in the response of any terms in addition to those stated in the offer will prevent the parties from having an enforceable contract.

T F 8. Some acceptances are effective upon dispatch, even if the offeror never receives them.

T F 9. If two parties appear to have agreed on essential terms for a contract but have also agreed that they will not be bound to each other until a written version of the agreement has been signed, a later failure of the written agreement to come into being would mean (absent other relevant factors) that the parties do not have an enforceable agreement.

T F 10. Under traditional contract principles, an acceptance by a nonauthorized means is not effective even on receipt.

Multiple Choice - Circle the best answer.

11. On Dec. 9, 1991, Dr. Mason Dixon, president of Y'all State University (a prominent Southern institution) sent criminal law expert Zsa Zsa Abore a letter offering to pay her $10,000 if she would agree to give the commencement address at the school's graduation ceremony in May 1992. (Assume that Dixon had full authority to act on behalf of Y'all State regarding such matters.) The letter stated that Abore "may respond by mail" and that the offer would be held open until Jan. 2, 1992. On Dec. 10, 1991, Dixon learned that business ethics expert Ivan Boesky would be willing to give the commencement address for free. Therefore, that same date (Dec. 10), Dixon sent Abore a letter stating that the offer was revoked. Abore mailed Dixon a letter of acceptance on Dec. 11, 1991. She received Dixon's letter of revocation on Dec. 12, 1991. Dixon received Abore's letter on Dec. 13, 1991. Do Y'all State and Abore have a contract?

a. No, because Dixon revoked the offer (on behalf of Y'all State) before it was accepted by Abore.

b. Yes, because Abore's acceptance was effective on dispatch.

c. No, because Abore received the revocation letter before the university received her acceptance letter.

d. Yes, because Dixon made a firm offer on behalf of Y'all State.

12. On Thursday, Graham made Bell an offer in which she stated that "if you choose to accept, you must communicate that decision by means of a telephone call to me at my office prior to 2:00 p.m. tomorrow." Bell, never one to rely on the telephone as a means of communicating important information, had a telegram of acceptance dispatched before 2:00 on Friday. The telegram was delivered to Graham's office at 2:15 p.m. Do Graham and Bell have a contract?

    a. Yes, because Bell dispatched the telegram prior to 2:00.

    b. No, because Bell's use of a telegram amounted to a revocation of Graham's offer.

    c. Yes, because Bell's communication of acceptance substantially complied with the terms of the offer.

    d. No, because Bell's supposed acceptance was both untimely and in improper form.

13. Wanda Sue sent Jim Bob a letter stating that "I have a '79 Chevy half-ton pickup, which I will sell you for $1950, cash on the barrelhead. If I don't hear from you before Sunday, I will assume that you want it and will expect payment from you on Monday." Jim Bob received the letter but did not answer it. He refused to pay Wanda Sue anything and would not accept delivery of the truck when Wanda Sue attempted to deliver it on Monday. Which of the following is an accurate statement?

    a. Wanda Sue and Jim Bob do not have a contract.

    b. Silence never constitutes an acceptance.

    c. Wanda Sue's letter was not an offer.

    d. Jim Bob is estopped from denying the existence of a contract.

14. A and B are widget merchants. A wrote to B as follows: "I will sell you one carload of widgets for $5000." B responded with this letter: "I accept. You are to pay the freight to my place of business and I will have 30 days in which to pay." The shipment and payment terms noted by B in his response are customary in the widget industry. Which of the following is an accurate statement?

    a. Because this case would be governed by the common law, A and B do not have a contract.

    b. Under the UCC, a contract exists.

    c. B's inclusion of terms beyond those in A's offer will be construed as a material alteration; therefore, the additional terms will not apply to the parties' transaction.

    d. There is no contract unless A contacts B and expresses agreement to the additional terms.

15. SBC, Inc., a major television network, was concerned that its long-running program, "36 Minutes (After Commercials)" was losing its reputation for hard-hitting investigative reporting. SBC decided that Doug Lleweeney (famous for the probing questions he asks of litigants at the close of "trials" on the "Frivolous Claims Court" program) would provide the rejuvenation 36 Minutes needed. Therefore, SBC sent Lleweeney a letter that set forth, in great detail, the terms of an offer under which Lleweeney (if he accepted) would become a 36 Minutes correspondent. The latter, dated Sept. 6, 1991, stated that the offer would be held open until Sept. 13, 1991, and that Lleweeney should "feel free to send us a letter if you wish to accept." On Sept. 9, 1991, Lleweeney sent appropriate SBC officials a telegram of acceptance. After Lleweeney did this but before SBC received the telegram, a high-ranking SBC official telephoned Lleweeney and informed him that the offer was revoked. SBC received Lleweeney's telegram shortly after the conclusion of the telephone conversation—long before an acceptance by mail would have arrived. Lleweeney has sued SBC for breach of contract. Which of the following statements is accurate?

    a. If the court deciding the case adheres to the *Restatement Second*'s approach to cases of this nature, Lleweeney will lose the suit because the court will conclude that there was no contract.

    b. If the court deciding the case adheres to the traditional rule governing cases of this nature, Lleweeney will win the suit because the court will conclude that there was an enforceable contract.

    c. Lleweeney will lose the suit because only if this case were governed by the UCC (which it isn't) could the court conclude that the parties had an enforceable contract.

    d. None of the above.

16. Lane sent Rigby a letter containing an offer. The letter said nothing about an appropriate means for communication of acceptance. Rigby first sent Lane a letter of rejection. Before Lane received this letter, Rigby reconsidered and mailed Lane a letter of acceptance. Lane then received the rejection letter. A day later, Lane received the acceptance letter. When Lane refused to deal with her, Rigby filed a breach of contract suit. Rigby should:
    a. win the suit because she dispatched her acceptance before Lane received the rejection letter.
    b. lose the suit because her rejection was effective on dispatch and therefore prevented a contract from arising.
    c. win the suit because her acceptance letter reached Lane within a reasonable time.
    d. lose the suit because her rejection letter reached Lane before her acceptance letter did.

17. Influential State University (ISU) sent country western legend Conroy Ditty a detailed letter in which ISU offered to engage Ditty to perform a concert as part of ISU's Homecoming extravaganza. ISU's letter stated that acceptance "must be by certified mail and must be received by ISU before noon on September 6." A delighted Ditty sent a telegram of acceptance immediately after reading ISU's letter. The telegram was delivered on September 4 to the same ISU official who had signed the earlier letter received by Ditty. When Ditty contacted the ISU official on September 9 to discuss concert-related details, she informed Ditty that another internationally known star would be performing the concert instead. Ditty later sued ISU for breach of contract. The court should rule:
    a. in Ditty's favor because a contract was formed when he dispatched his telegram.
    b. in Ditty's favor because a contract was formed when the ISU official received Ditty's telegram.
    c. in ISU's favor because there was no valid acceptance by Ditty.
    d. in ISU's favor because Ditty, despite having validly accepted ISU's offer, had not yet performed the concert as of the time ISU effectively revoked its offer.

18. Specific General Hospital (SGH) issued a purchase order to Dopex Pharmaceuticals Co. for the prompt or current shipment of 100 units of morphine. Dopex promptly shipped SGH 100 units of a narcotic other than morphine. SGH sued Dopex for breach of contract. Who should win, and why?
    a. Dopex, because it made no promise that would constitute an acceptance of SGH's offer to purchase.
    b. SGH, because Dopex's shipment of non-conforming goods was both an acceptance of SGH's offer to purchase and a breach of the parties' contract.
    c. Dopex, because its shipment of non-conforming goods was an accommodation and therefore not an acceptance.
    d. SGH, because Dopex's shipment of a different narcotic than the one ordered was a counteroffer that reflected a lack of good faith.

19. Frank sent Nancy a letter offering to sell her a certain antique brass bed for $10,000. After Nancy received the letter, she promptly sent Frank a letter of acceptance. Frank never received Nancy's letter. Which is a true statement?
    a. There is a contract between Frank and Nancy even though Frank never received Nancy's acceptance.
    b. There is no contract between Frank and Nancy because Frank never received Nancy's acceptance.
    c. There is no contract between Frank and Nancy because Frank's letter was not a legally sufficient offer.
    d. There is a contract between Frank and Nancy only if Nancy has relied to her detriment on Frank's offer.

20. Looking for every possible opportunity to improve his team's sagging fortunes, New England Patsies owner Richter Sliam sent former All-Pro offensive guard Dwight "Downright" Brutal (who last played pro football in 1978) a letter offering him a no-cut $1 million contract if he would come out of retirement and agree to play for the Patsies. The letter, dated Aug. 12, 1991, stated that "you can have until Aug. 26, 1991 to decide," and that "your acceptance may be by mail." Brutal mailed Sliam a counteroffer (requesting $1.25 million) on Aug. 14, 1991, but then reconsidered. Not wanting to appear greedy, Brutal mailed Sliam another letter on Aug. 16, 1991. In that letter, he stated that he wished to accept the Patsies' offer, and that Sliam "should ignore any communication to the contrary from me." Sliam received Brutal's counteroffer on Aug. 16, 1991 and his letter of acceptance the following day. On Aug. 19, 1991, Sliam sent Brutal this telegram: "Don't report to training camp. We have enough over-the-hill players as it is." Brutal believes that he and the Patsies have a contract? Do they?

    a. No, because the counteroffer arrived before the letter of acceptance did.

    b. No, because Brutal's counteroffer was effective on dispatch and thus operated to terminate the Patsies' offer.

    c. Yes, because the acceptance letter, which was effective on dispatch, was mailed before the counteroffer arrived.

    d. Yes, because Brutal's making of a counteroffer did not terminate his ability to accept the original offer within the time period specified by Sliam.

Short Essay

21. Jacqueline Flash sent Reuben Tuesday a letter containing an offer which stated that "your acceptance will be effective when I receive it." Tuesday mailed Flash a letter of acceptance promptly after receiving the offer. He then received a telephone call from Flash, who stated that her offer was revoked. Tuesday protested, stating that he had already mailed Flash a letter of acceptance. "So what?" was Flash's response. The day after this conversation, Flash received Tuesday's letter. On these facts, do Tuesday and Flash have a contract? Why or why not?

22. Bored Motor Co., a manufacturer of vans and various other motorized vehicles, decided that it would prefer to purchase vans from another manufacturer and, with that manufacturer's permission, sell the vans under the Bored name. Bored therefore made Shyster Corp., a manufacturer of vans, a detailed written offer for such an arrangement between the two firms. The offer was made on Bored's standard offer form, with certain specialized terms having been typed in. Shyster responded on its standard acknowledgement form with what it intended (and what generally appeared to be) an acceptance. On the back of Shyster's form was a provision stating that Shyster disclaimed any legal responsibility it would otherwise have to Bored for any supplied vans that proved to be defective. Bored's offer made no mention of remedies in the event that defective vans were supplied. Do the parties have a contract? Why or why not? If they have a contract, is Shyster's disclaimer part of it? Why or why not?

23. What advantages are there for the offeror in requiring in his offer that he must actually receive the acceptance in order for it to be effective?

24. In what way has the application of the common law's mirror image rule arguably been altered by courts in recent years?   How does Article 2 of the UCC approach the "mirror image" issue?

CHAPTER 12

CONSIDERATION

True-False - Circle T for True and F for False.

T F 1. A's promise to perform a preexisting duty will constitute consideration for B's promise if such a promise by A was what B requested.

T F 2. When the debt owed by the debtor is both due and liquidated, the creditor's promise to accept partial payment in full satisfaction of the debt is not binding on the creditor.

T F 3. A promise may be sufficient consideration for someone else's promise.

T F 4. Under the UCC, a modification of a contract for the sale of goods is not enforceable unless there is new consideration.

T F 5. The presence of a cancellation clause in a "contract" renders illusory the promises of the party with the cancellation right.

T F 6. Forbearance by the promisee may be enough by itself to constitute consideration for the promisor's promise.

T F 7. An act or promise must have monetary value if it is to constitute consideration to support a return promise.

T F 8. Promises in requirements contracts are not illusory even though such contracts do not specify an exact quantity of goods to be purchased.

T F 9. If the promisee's act or promise satisfies the legal value test, courts generally do not ask whether that act or promise was worth what the promisor gave in return for it.

T F 10. Even if the employment-at-will rule would otherwise render a promise of employment illusory, the doctrine of promissory estoppel may protect rhe party to whom the promise of employment was made.

Multiple Choice - Circle the best answer.

11. Al Truistic, the sole proprietor of a retail business, entered into a written contract with Expo Co. for the purchase of 1,000 Pee Wee Vermin posters. According to the contract, Expo was to deliver the posters to Truistic's place of business on October 1, and Truistic was to pay the full purchase price of $9,999 on October 12. Expo performed its obligation. Truistic did not pay the purchase price on October 12, but on October 15 he sent Expo a check in the amount of $7,777. The following handwritten notation appeared prominently on the front and back sides of the check: "This check constitutes payment in full of all sums due from Al Truistic pursuant to contract for Pee Wee Vermin posters." Upon Expo's receipt of the check, the firm's manager of accounts receivable read the notations and then deposited the check in an Expo account. Expo later demanded payment of $2,222 from Truistic, and when he refused to pay, Expo sued him for that amount. Should Expo win the suit?

    a. Yes, because the debt owed by Trustic was unliquidated.

    b. No, because the parties had reached a binding accord and satisfaction.

    c. Yes, because under the circumstances, the notations on the check had no effect on Expo's rights.

    d. No, because Trustic created a dispute over the amount of the debt by placing the notations on the check.

12. Jim and Jessica entered into a written contract under which Jim was to pay Jessica $265,000 in return for the obligation Jessica was to perform. Before the arrival of the date on which the parties were to perform their respective contractual duties, Jessica persuaded Jim to agree to modify the payment term so that Jim would pay her $290,000 instead of $265,000. Besides agreeing to this change, Jim agreed that in return for the $290,000, Jessica would perform the obligation called for under the original version of the contract. When the agreed date of performance arrived, Jessica performed her obligation, but Jim refused to pay anything more than $265,000. Jessica has sued Jim on the theory that he breached the modified version of their contract. Jessica should:

a. win the suit only if the parties' contract was for the sale of goods.

b. win the suit only if the parties' contract was for something other than the sale of goods.

c. win the suit regardless of whether the parties' contract was for the sale of goods.

d. lose the suit regardless of whether the parties' contract was for the sale of goods.

13. For 33 years, 65-year-old Eleanor Rigby had been a dedicated employee of Lady Madonna Church. On the day before her official retirement, Rigby was picking up rice from the steps of the church, where a wedding had just taken place. She was observed while doing this by Father McKenzie, the church's priest and chief administrative officer, who had authority to make all decisions regarding use of the church's funds. Touched by what he had observed and mindful of Rigby's loyalty and service to the church over the years, Father McKenzie verbally promised Rigby that in recognition of all she had done for the church, the church would pay her the sum of $10,000 at the expiration of one week following her retirement. Rigby retired as planned, and a week went by. Father McKenzie declined to pay the $10,000, however, explaining that even though he would like to pay her the money, doing so would be an improper use of church funds. Rigby then sued the church for the $10,000. She should:

a. win the suit because Father McKenzie's promise was clear and explicit.

b. win the suit because the years of service she gave the church constituted consideration for Father McKenzie's promise.

c. lose the suit because Father McKenzie's promise was not in writing.

d. lose the suit because there was no consideration for Father McKenzie's promise.

14. After Bill and Ted returned from a lengthy trip, their elderly friend, Joan Ofarc, promised the teenage lads that she would pay each of them $2,500 if they would refrain from any further traveling until their respective 21st birthdays. Both Bill and Ted so refrained until after their 21st birthdays. Ofarc then told them that she had changed her mind and would not be paying them the money after all. Which of the following is true?

a. Ofarc must pay Bill and Ted because she received consideration in exchange for her promise to pay.

b. Ofarc does not have to pay Bill and Ted because she properly revoked her offer.

c. Ofarc need not pay Bill and Ted because her promise to them was gratuitous.

d. Ofarc need not pay Bill and Ted because their failure to promise her anything meant that she received no consideration in exchange for her promise to pay.

15. Able, a manufacturer, and Baker, a retailer, entered into a contract for the sale of a designated quantity of widgets. According to the contract, Able was to deliver the widgets to Baker not later than April 1. In mid-March, Able realized that because of a large number of orders from widget retailers throughout the country, Able would not be able to deliver the widgets to Baker until May 1. Able therefore contacted Baker in mid-March, explained the circumstances, and asked Baker to agree to May 1 as a revised delivery deadline. Baker agreed. Able delivered the widgets to Baker on April 30. Baker later sued Able for breach of contract, alleging that Able's failure to deliver the widgets on April 1 caused Baker to lose sales that he could have made to his retail customers during the April 1-30 time period if he had had the Able widgets. Assuming that Baker did in fact lose sales that he could have made if he had had the widgets before April 30, does Baker have a valid breach of contract claim?

a. Yes, because the lack of consideration to support the supposed modification of the contract made the modification unenforceable.

b. No, because Able complied with its obligation, as set in the modified version of the contract.

c. Yes, because Baker's loss of sales was directly traceable to Able's failure to deliver on April 1.

d. No, because both parties are merchants.

16. On September 1, E.Z. Pickens promised that on the following November 1, he would give $100,000 to the Tim and Pammy Takker Foundation for the Enrichment of Tim and Pammy Takker (referred to hereinafter as "the foundation"), a noncharitable, for-profit organization. After Pickens made this promise, the Takkers sent him a lengthy thank-you note. As further gestures of appreciation, they sent Pickens a complimentary jar of Pammy's industrial strength facial makeup and several autographed 8x10 glossy photographs of Tim. In addition, even though Pickens had not requested such a promise, the Takkers informed Pickens that they would mention his name on one of their television programs. November 1 came and went without payment of the $100,000 by Pickens. When it become apparent that Pickens would not be paying the $100,000 voluntarily, the Takkers and the foundation sued him in an effort to collect the money. Should the plaintiffs win?

a. No, because the consideration provided by them was inadequate to support a promise to pay $100,000.

b. Yes, because the items they sent to Pickens and the promise they made to him constituted consideration, and because courts very seldom inquire into the adequacy of consideration.

c. Yes, because promises to foundations are enforceable regardless of whether consideration existed.

d. No, because Pickens's promise was unsupported by consideration.

17. Of the following statements about supposed differences between an accord and satisfaction and a composition agreement, which is/are accurate?

a. Whereas an accord and satisfaction is usually voidable, a composition agreement is usually void.

b. Whereas an accord and satisfaction involves an unliquidated debt, a composition agreement is likely to involve liquidated debts.

c. Whereas an accord and satisfaction involves one debtor and one creditor, a composition agreement always involves a debtor and more than one creditor.

d. Both b and c.

18. Which of the following is a true statement about consideration?

a. In disputes over consideration, the court will routinely inspect the parties' contracts to ensure that the consideration exchanged was adequate.

b. Promises cannot serve as consideration because they are intangible and have no legal value.

c. Consideration may consist of one's agreeing not to do something she otherwise had a legal right to do.

d. To have legal value, the thing claimed as consideration must also have economic value.

19. Which of the following will be legally binding on all parties even in the absence of consideration?

a. A promise to donate money to a charity, which incurs expenditures in reliance on the promise.

b. An oral promise by a merchant to keep his offer to sell widgets open for 30 days.

c. A written modification of a contract to purchase real estate, if the modification is made in good faith and signed by both parties.

d. A written promise by a person who has offered to buy real estate to give the owner of the property 30 days to consider her offer.

e. Each of the above.

20. Ex-deputy sheriff Barney Fife owns the "Nip It in the Bud" flower shop. Fife recently promised to pay all tuition for his friend and trusted employee, Howard Sprague, to attend Mount Pilot Technical Institute (MPTI) if Sprague would promise to complete MPTI's two-year program in cosmetology. Fife made his promise knowing that Sprague would be happier working as a cosmetologist than as a flower shop employee. Sprague promised to complete the cosmetology training program. Is there consideration for Fife's promise?

    a. No, because Fife really was making a gratuitous promise that would benefit Sprague without Fife's receiving anything of value in return.

    b. No, not until Sprague actually completes the cosmetology training program.

    c. Yes, even though Fife would not personally be benefiting from Sprague's promise.

    d. Yes, because Sprague had provided valuable services through the years as Fife's employee.

21. Shoddy Construction Co. and the Church of What's Happening Now (CWHN) agreed that Shoddy would construct a new church building in Cactus Junction for the sum of $1 million. The average annual rainfall in Cactus Junction over the preceding 50 years had been two inches. Shoddy had partially completed the church building when Cactus Junction was deluged with heavy and prolonged rains. As a result, the first flood in the long history of Cactus Junction occurred. Shoddy promised to finish the church building only if CWHN agreed to pay Shoddy an additional $200,000 to cover extra expenses caused by the flood. CWHN promised to pay the extra money. Is this promise enforceable against CWHN?

    a. No, because CWHN received no new consideration in return for it.

    b. Yes, because of the unforeseen circumstances exception to the general rule on modifications of contracts.

    c. No, because CWHN would be classified as a charitable organization.

    d. Yes, because this case would be governed by the Uniform Commercial Code.

Short Essay

22. Jagger Corp. produces various prosthetic devices, including prostheses for persons who believe their lips are insufficiently prominent. Jack Flash operates a wholesale medical supply business in which he sells lip prostheses and numerous other items. Jagger and Flash entered into a written contract under which Jagger was to provide Flash three installment deliveries of lip prostheses at two-month intervals. Each of these installment deliveries was to be of 100 lip prostheses. The contract called for Flash to pay $100 per prosthesis, with payment for an installment being due upon delivery of that installment. Jagger delivered the first two installments and Flash made the required payments. Two weeks before delivery of the final installment was to occur, Flash wrote to Jagger. Flash explained that his business was not exactly "jumpin'" and that he was experiencing a serious cash flow problem. Flash therefore requested that the contract be modified so that the final installment delivery would be of only 50 lip prostheses and that his payment obligation would be reduced to $80 per prosthesis. An appropriate Jagger official agreed in writing to Flash's request. Later, claiming that rules regarding what is and is not consideration made the supposed modification of the contract unenforceable, Jagger shipped Flash 100 lip prostheses and demanded payment of $100 per item. Is Flash obligated to accept all 100 lip prostheses and to pay $100 per item? Why or why not?

23. As a surprise for his wife, Lisa (who was away on a lengthy trip), Oliver Douglas wished to have an addition built on to their bedroom. Douglas therefore retained the Monroe Brothers to do the work. The parties' contract called for Douglas to pay the Monroe Brothers $12,000 upon completion of the addition. They completed the job during a week of favorable, non-windy weather. but before they had time to collect from Douglas, the walls of the addition collapsed. Douglas called upon them to remedy the situation, but they refused to do so unless Douglas agreed to their proposal that he would pay them an additional $2,500 (over and above the contract amount) to compensate them for the work involved in putting the walls up again. Because Lisa was coming home soon and he wanted to surprise her, Douglas promised to pay the additional $2,500. After the Monroe Brothers put up the walls again, Douglas paid them $12,000 but refused to pay anything more. The Monroe Brothers have sued him for the additional $2,500. Should they win their suit? Why or why not?

24. For purposes of a decision about whether a promise to accept less than the full amount of a debt is enforceable, what is the significance of the liquidated-unliquidated distinction?

CHAPTER 13

REALITY OF CONSENT

True-False - Circle T for True and F for False.

T F 1. If B's decision to enter into a contract with A was strongly influenced by A's misrepresentation, B will have a valid claim for damages against A.

T F 2. Most contracts made by persons whose consent was not real are voidable rather than void.

T F 3. Modern courts are more likely to allow a party to avoid his contractual obligation on the ground of duress than were courts during the period of classical contract law.

T F 4. If a person making a misrepresentation believes in good faith that what she says is true, the contract that results cannot be avoided on the basis of misrepresentation or fraud.

T F 5. Although courts will allow a party to be relieved from his contractual obligation when he was unilaterally mistaken about an important matter, courts normally will not allow either party to get out of the contract in cases of mutual mistake.

T F 6. A threat is coercive if it leaves the victimized party with no reasonable alternative to entering into the contract.

T F 7. One contracting party's statement of opinion cannot later serve as a basis for the other party to be relieved from her contractual obligation on misrepresentation or fraud grounds.

T F 8. The only remedy available for undue influence is rescission.

T F 9. Although concealment may constitute fraud, mere nondisclosure cannot do so.

T F 10. An important difference between mistake and misrepresentation is that with mistake, the erroneous belief is not the result of the other party's untrue statements.

Multiple Choice - Circle the best answer.

11. Orville and Maxine Portly live in Gnaw Bone, Indiana. Their son, Junior, is a sophomore at Quicksand Tech, a college located in Snakebite, New Mexico. Junior needed a car for basic transportation in and around Snakebite. Orville concluded that in view of the distance between Gnaw Bone and Snakebite, it would make sense to locate a reputable used car dealer in Snakebite and work out a deal by phone and through the mail. A fellow Gnaw Bonian knew Dub Ulknit, a used car dealer in Snakebite, and recommended Ulknit to Orville. Orville telephoned Ulknit, explained Junior's needs, and stated that he (Orville) wanted to buy a car for Junior. Orville also explained that he did not want to spend more than $750. Ulknit said he had a car that was "just the ticket, Orv, a real creampuff." Ulknit then proceeded to describe the car. Orville stated that the description sounded good, and that he would immediately forward a check for $749.99 (the agreed purchase price). One fact Ulknit did not mention to Orville was that the tires on the car were completely bald, and that for safety reasons, better tires were a necessity. Ulknit received Orville's check a few days later. When Junior arrived, as agreed, to pick up the car, he noticed the baldness of the tires. He immediately telephoned his father. An angry Orville then demanded that Ulknit refund his money, because neither he nor Junior wanted a car with bald tires. Ulknit refused to refund the purchase price. Which of the following is an accurate statement about Orville's demand for relief?

    a. He is seeking rescission, an extreme form of relief to which he would be entitled only if he proves that Ulknit committed fraud.

    b. He cannot obtain the relief he seeks, because nothing in the facts indicates that he ever asked Ulknit about the condition of the tires.

    c. He is entitled to the relief he seeks if he proves that Ulknit's failure to disclose the condition of the tires was at least misrepresentation.

d. He cannot obtain the relief he seeks because he could not reasonably have expected a $749.99 car to be in perfect condition, and because Ulknit's calling the car "just the ticket" and "a real creampuff" were statements of opinion.

12. Eleanor Rigby owned the Norwegian Wood property, which lacked direct access to an important public highway, Abbey Road. Two other parcels of property, Strawberry Fields (owned by Penny Lane) and Junior's Farm (owned by Loretta Martin) sat side-by-side between Rigby's property and Abbey Road. Access across either Strawberry Fields or Junior's Farm would have given Rigby a direct link from Norwegian Wood to Abbey Road. Rigby decided to expand her property holdings and acquire the necessary access at the same time by purchasing either Strawberry Fields or Junior's Farm. During the negotiations over a possible sale, Lane represented to Rigby that the long and winding road running through the center of Strawberry Fields had been paved in March 1990 and that the paving company whose services were used had unconditionally guaranteed the paving job against all defects of whatever nature for a period of two years from March 1, 1990. (This road was a privately owned part of Strawberry Fields, rather than a public road.) Lane also represented that the paving company's guarantee was to be enforceable by any owner of Straw-berry Fields during the guarantee's duration. These statements by Lane concerning the guarantee and the time of the paving were among the major reasons Rigby purchased Strawberry Fields rather than Junior's Farm. Rigby paid the full purchase price to Lane on April 1, 1991, and Lane provided Rigby a deed to Strawberry Fields on the same day. In late April 1991, Rigby noticed that numerous cracks and holes had appeared in the surface of the road through Strawberry Fields. After calling upon the paving company in an effort to enforce the guarantee, Rigby learned that the paving work had been done in March 1989 (rather than in March 1990) and that the two-year guarantee had expired in March 1991. Rather than simply let it be (or live and let die), Rigby has sued Lane. Which of the following is an accurate statement about the suit?

a. Even if Lane intended to deceive Rigby by means of statements about dates that Lane knew were false, punitive damages cannot be assessed against Lane in this suit because such dam-ages are not allowed in breach of contract cases.

b. Rigby will not obtain relief in her suit because the false statements by Lane clearly were not the only reasons for Rigby's decision to purchase Strawberry Fields.

c. Rigby will not obtain relief in her suit because Lane's statement about the guarantee's suppos-edly being enforceable by later owners of Strawberry Fields would be classified as a state-ment of pure opinion.

d. Even if Lane's misstatements about dates resulted from a faulty memory and not from any de-liberate attempt to mislead Rigby, Rigby would be entitled to rescission.

13. Which of the following is an accurate statement about mistake?

a. Mistakes resulting from poor judgment or inexperience may not enable one to avoid contrac-tual liability.

b. Mutual mistake makes a contract void, whereas unilateral mistake makes a contract voidable.

c. Mistake includes situations in which both parties erroneously believe that some future event will occur and contract on that basis.

d. Under modern principles, mistake of law cannot be a basis for avoiding contractual liability.

14. X bought a tract of land from Y. Before the sale, Y told X that a two-lane highway ran near the land, when in fact the nearest road was 10 miles away. X, however, paid no attention to this state-ment because his only reason for buying the land was the fact that country western legend Tammy Hairnet once owned it. Which of the following is a true statement?

a. X was under a duty to inspect the land to ascertain the location of the nearest road.

b. X may rescind the sale on these facts.

c. X cannot rescind the sale because he did not rely on Y's misstatement.

d. X may rescind the sale and also obtain punitive damages from Y.

15. Austin Tatious was thinking about purchasing a 1988 Cadillac from Glen Plaid, a used car dealer. Tatious asked Plaid whether the 49,700 mileage figure showing on the Cadillac's odometer was accurate. He asked this question because it was important to him to acquire a car with no more than 60,000 miles on it, not because he had any reason to suspect that the 49,700 figure was inaccurate. Plaid responded by saying that the 49,700 figure was "right as rain" and "the real McCoy." Plaid added that "it'd be a sweet-smelling day in Terre Haute before I'd hoodwink a customer," and that the Cadillac "ain't one of them rollbacks an unethical dealer might try to unload on you." After the conclusion of his conversation with Plaid, Tatious purchased the Cadillac. Two weeks later, Tatious began to notice that the Cadillac was not performing satisfactorily and to suspect that it had traveled more than 49,700 miles before he purchased it. After checking motor vehicle records at the local Bureau of Motor Vehicles office, and after obtaining copies of pertinent records from another state, Tatious correctly concluded that a previous owner of the Cadillac (prior to Plaid) must have "rolled back" the odometer so that it would register a mileage figure lower than the actual number of miles traveled. Tatious also accurately concluded that the car had nearly 100,000 miles on it at the time he purchased it from Plaid. Claiming that genuine consent was lacking when he agreed to purchase the Cadillac, Tatious sued Plaid. Which of the following statements is accurate?

    a. Because Tatious could have checked the records referred to above before he purchased the Cadillac, his failure to do so until after he had purchased the car will bar him from obtaining relief on the basis of Plaid's false statement.

    b. If Plaid had reason to believe, and did believe in good faith, that he was telling Tatious the truth during their conversation about the Cadillac, Tatious will not be allowed to recover damages from Plaid in this suit.

    c. In view of the fact that Tatious later checked appropriate records in order to ascertain the Cadillac's actual mileage, Tatious did not demonstrate the requisite actual reliance on Plaid's false statement; therefore, Tatious will lose the suit.

    d. Because sellers and purchasers of automobiles are regarded by the law as having a "special" relationship, Plaid's false statement about the car's mileage entitles Tatious to punitive damages even if Plaid honestly believed he was telling Tatious the truth.

16. A, an antique dealer who should know better, thinks that a chair he has for sale is worth $100, when in fact it is a valuable antique worth $10,000. B, who knows the chair's true value and that A is mistaken about it, buys the chair from A for $100. Later, A discovers the chair's true value and wants to rescind on the basis of mistake. What should be the result?

    a. A may rescind even though only A was mistaken.

    b. A cannot rescind because B would experience substantial financial harm.

    c. A cannot rescind because the mistake was unilateral, not mutual.

    d. A cannot rescind because he was negligent.

17. Appliance dealer Frosty Burns was attempting to convince Norma Nimrod to purchase a used freezer. He therefore told her that the freezer she was admiring was only six months old and had "worked like a dream, with no problems whatsoever" for the previous owner. Burns also represented that the previous owner had "traded this unit in solely because she wanted a larger model." Nimrod purchased the freezer. The next day, her cousin Irene came to visit. Irene immediately recognized the freezer when Nimrod showed it to her. Irene informed a shocked Nimrod that the freezer Nimrod had bought had been Irene's, that she (Irene) had had persistent serious problems with the freezer's compressor during the five years she had owned it, and that, in exasperation, she had traded it in a few days earlier to Burns so that she could purchase a different brand of freezer. That same day, the freezer's compressor ceased working. Nimrod wishes to rescind her purchase of the freezer. Which of the following is/are accurate?

    a. Nimrod will not be able to rescind unless she proves that her reliance on Burns's statement was reasonable.

    b. If Nimrod proves that her reliance was reasonable, the contract is voidable and she may rescind.

    c. If Nimrod proves that her reliance was reasonable, she may be able to obtain tort damages from Burns.

    d. All of the above.

71

18. The following statements pertain to the contract law notion of reality of consent. Which statement is accurate?

    a. If X entered into a contract as the result of Y's exercise of economic duress upon X, the flagrant nature of Y's conduct would make an award of money damages the proper remedy for X.

    b. As a general rule, a party who entered into a contract because he was mistaken about a matter important to the transaction cannot avoid his contractual obligation on the basis of the mistake unless the other party was also mistaken about the same matter.

    c. When a court orders rescission because of one contracting party's misrepresentation, the court's objective is to place the victimized party in the place she would have occupied if the misrepresented "facts" had been true.

    d. Fraud, misrepresentation, duress, and mistake are common law doctrines that do not apply in cases involving contracts for the sale of goods, because the UCC has no sections dealing with those doctrines.

19. The following statements pertain to duress or to undue influence. Which statement is INACCU-RATE?

    a. A threat to sue someone if he does not enter into an agreement with the party making the threat will not necessarily make the agreement voidable on the ground of duress.

    b. Although classical contract law did not recognize economic duress as a basis for avoiding one's contractual obligation, modern contract law allows for its possible use in that way.

    c. If one party induces another party to enter into a contract by using persuasion, the contract is voidable on the ground of undue influence.

    d. The party who proves that undue influence caused him to enter into a contract is not entitled to recover damamges from the party who exercised the undue influence.

20. Charlie Krueger was a lineman for the San Francisco 49ers from 1958 to 1973. He sued the team in 1980 after he became crippled by a degenerative arthritic condition in his left knee. Krueger proved at trial that team doctors knew in the 1960s that continuing to play on his bad knew would cause him to become permanently disabled, and that they failed to disclose this fact to him for nearly a decade while masking his pain with steroids and narcotic drugs. What is the strongest basis on which Krueger could challenge the contracts he signed in the 1970s?

    a. Mistake
    b. Fraud
    c. Duress
    d. Undue influence

Short Essay

21. Coward Hosell, owner of the hairstyling salon known as Hosell's Hair Hut, was negotiating with Pete Woes for the possible sale of the salon to Woes. One of the major reasons Woes was interested in buying the salon was that Hugh Lenson, chief hairstylist at Hosell's Hair Hut and originator of the trendsetting Hugh-Do, had acquired a nationwide reputation for hairstyling innovation. Woes accurately concluded that Lenson had tremendous customer-drawing ability. On April 1, Woes asked Hosell whether Lenson still worked at Hosell's Hair Hut and whether Lenson planned to continue working at the salon if he (Woes) decided to buy it. Hosell had discussed such matters earlier that day with Lenson and had been told by Lenson that he planned to work at the salon "for a long time, probably until the University of Illinois wins an outright Big Ten championship in basketball or the Indianapolis Colts win the Super Bowl, whichever happens second." Hosell therefore truthfully responded "yes" to both of Woes's questions about Lenson. On April 2, Lenson informed Hosell that he was quitting his job, effective immediately, and that he was beginning work that same day as full-time hairstylist for singer Barry Manornot. Rose decided on April 3 that purchasing Hosell's Hair Hut was a safe bet. Therefore, he and Hosell entered into a contract of sale on April 3 and completed all aspects of the purchase the same day. Shortly after Woes arrived at the salon on April 4, he learned that Lenson no longer worked there. Woes then complained to Hosell, who responded this way:

72

"That, as some are wont to say, is life in the Big Ten, Peter. I uttered the truth during our April 1 meeting. Hugh Lenson, however, was an employee-at-will, meaning that either he or I could end the master-servant relationship at any time. You should not have gambled on the idea that the talented but volatile Lenson would remain in my or your employ. Freedom of contract includes the freedom to make what in retrospect are less than optimal deals. As our mutual friend, the indefatigable Mr. Jagger, melodiously—and aptly—intoned years ago, 'you can't always get what you wa-ant.'"

Woes wishes to sue Hosell on the basis of the above facts. What legal theory or theories should Woes use, and why? Is Woes likely to prevail? Why or why not?

22. Sincere Corp. and Andre Preneur were parties to a contract under which Preneur sold Sincere the business he had operated for several years as a sole proprietorship. After both parties had performed their respective contractual obligations, Sincere officials realized that Preneur made certain false statements about important matters during pre-contract negotiations. When the statements were made, they reasonably appeared (to Sincere's negotiators) to be true. Claiming that it would not have entered into the contract if it had known that Preneur's statements were false, Sincere has sued Preneur. Assume that Sincere can prove what it alleges about Preneur's statements and the effect they had on Sincere's decision to contract with him. Also assume that Preneur had a reasonable basis for believing (and did believe in good faith) that his statements during the negotiations were true. *Sincere argues* that it is entitled to collect money damages from Preneur because of his false statements. *Preneur argues* that in view of his good-faith and reasonably-based belief in the truth of his statements, plus the further fact that the contract has been fully performed by both parties, Sincere cannot obtain legal relief in this suit. Is Sincere's argument correct? Why or why not? Is Preneur's argument correct? Why or why not?

23. In what sense is the doctrine of mistake different from the doctrines of misrepresentation, fraud, duress, and undue influence?

CHAPTER 14

CAPACITY TO CONTRACT

True-False - Circle T for True and F for False.

T F 1. If a person who entered into a contract while lacking mental capacity later regains capacity and fails to disaffirm the contract within a reasonable time thereafter, he may be deemed to have ratified the contract.

T F 2. An adult contracting with a minor has no power to disaffirm the contract, and is bound unless the minor disaffirms.

T F 3. An emancipated minor is assumed to have capacity to contract.

T F 4. A person who lacked capacity to contract may nonetheless be compelled to pay the reasonable value of necessaries furnished to her by another party.

T F 5. In general, a minor may disaffirm even if he is unable to return the consideration he received from the adult.

T F 6. One who entered into a contract while intoxicated need not later disaffirm the contract in order to avoid being bound by it, because such a contract is void.

T F 7. A person who entered into a contract while a minor cannot disaffirm it after he reaches adulthood.

T F 8. As a general rule, an adult's contract with a minor is voidable at the option of either party.

T F 9. Contracts made by a person who has previously been adjudicated to be incompetent are void, not voidable.

T F 10. Ratification is effective only if done after the minor reaches majority.

Multiple Choice - Circle the best answer.

11. Wheeler Dealer, age 17, entered into a written contract to purchase an apartment building from Ariel Slumlord. Which of the following is an accurate statement about Dealer's rights?
   a. If he wishes to ratify the contract, he must do so before he reaches the age of majority.
   b. Because owning real estate is not a necessary, Dealer will not be permitted to ratify the contract once he reaches the age of majority.
   c. If he wishes to disaffirm the contract, he must do so before he reaches the age of majority in order to avoid a conclusion that he has ratified the contract.
   d. If he wishes to disaffirm the contract, he cannot do so until he reaches the age of majority.

12. When an adult enters into a contract with a minor,
   a. the minor cannot effectively ratify the contract until she reaches the age of majority.
   b. the contract is void.
   c. the minor normally cannot effectively disaffirm the contract until she reaches the age of majority.
   d. the contract may be cancelled if the adult so chooses.

13. In cases involving contractual incapacity caused by mental impairment,
   a. the contract is usually void.
   b. the rules regarding necessaries are the same as in cases involving incapacity caused by minority.
   c. a party may ratify his contract at any time before he regains capacity.
   d. the contract is always void.

14. Otis Boozer placed the following classified ad in the local newspaper: "4 Sale. 1977 Chevy Impaler. Runs super. Ain't taking nothing less than $1250 for this creampuff. Call Otis at 123-4567, or stop by Lot #17 at Trixie's Trailer Park to see car." Larry Laggard, who did not know Boozer, responded to the ad by stopping by the trailer park to see the car. After examining the car, Laggard offered Boozer $700 for it. Boozer, who was intoxicated at the time, accepted the offer. Laggard immediately made full payment and Boozer signed over the title to the car. When Boozer sobered up, he learned what he had done. He promptly notified Laggard that he was disaffirming the contract. Laggard, however, refused to return the car and would not accept Boozer's offer to refund the purchase price. Assume that the car in fact had a reasonable value of $1300. Is Boozer entitled to disaffirm?

    a. Yes, regardless of whether Laggard knew that Boozer was intoxicated.
    b. Yes, if Boozer can show that he is an alcoholic.
    c. No, if Laggard neither knew nor had reason to know of Boozer's intoxication.
    d. No, even if Laggard knew that Boozer was intoxicated and that Boozer therefore could not understand what he was obligating himself to do.

15. Marvin "Moose" Lodge, a minor who lives at home, works at Benny's Restaurant. Moose's parents do not provide his meals, so he contracted with Benny's for 21 meals per week. Which of the following is an accurate analysis of the parties' rights and obligations if Moose decides to disaffirm the meals contract?

    a. The meal "contract" was void from its inception, so Moose may disaffirm and is not obligated to pay Benny's for the meals he has eaten.
    b. If Moose is emancipated, he is bound on his meal contract just as an adult would be, meaning that he cannot disaffirm and Benny's can recover the full contract price from him.
    c. Moose may disaffirm but Benny's is entitled to recover, on a quasi-contract theory, the reasonable value of the meals Moose ate.
    d. Moose cannot disaffirm yet, but he does not have to pay Benny's for the meals he has eaten until he reaches majority and becomes entitled to disaffirm.

16. Al Scruem, age 16, used a false driver's license that said that he was 18 years old to convince Grudget Rentals to lease him a car. After reaching his destination 400 miles away, Al returned the car to the nearest Grudget agency. He refused to pay the contract price for the car rental, however, on the ground that he wished to disaffirm the contract. Which of the following is a true statement?

    a. In some states, Al could be liable to Grudget for the tort of deceit but would still be permitted to rescind.
    b. Because he misrepresented his age, Al may disaffirm the contract only if it is considered to be a contract for necessaries.
    c. Because he misrepresented his age, Al would be prevented by the law of all states from disaffirming the contract.
    d. In all states, Al's misrepresentation of his age would be irrelevant because the law seeks to protect the minor from his own foolish misconduct.

17. Of the following statements regarding mental incapacity and entry into contracts, which is/are accurate?

    a. One who has periodic psychotic tendencies may, during a lucid interval, enter into a contract that is binding on him.
    b. When the mental capacity of a contracting party is at issue, courts ordinarily will apply the test of whether that person had sufficient mental capacity to understand the nature and effect of the contract.
    c. If one entered into a contract at a time when she did not have sufficient mental capacity, she cannot effectively ratify the contract even if she later regains mental capacity.
    d. Both a and b.
    e. Both b and c.

18. Polly Graf is 17 years old and is employed full-time. She fully supports herself. Graf entered into a six-month lease on an apartment, but moved out after living there for three months. Graf paid the landlord only one month's rent. The landlord has sued her in an effort to enforce the lease and collect the unpaid rent. Which of the following is an accurate analysis of the case?

    a. Graf's lease for six months is enforceable against her and cannot be disaffirmed by her. Therefore, the landlord is entitled to five more months' rent.

    b. Graf's lease for six months is unenforceable due to her minority; therefore, she can disaffirm the lease, meaning that the landlord is entitled to no more money.

    c. Graf's lease for six months is unenforceable due to her minority. She therefore may disaffirm the lease. The landlord, however, is entitled to payment of two more months' worth of reasonable rental value on the apartment.

    d. Graf is liable for rent for two more months only if she misrepresented her age to the landlord.

19. What if Graf (see question #18) had done terrible damage to the inside of the apartment and then tried to disaffirm her lease?

    a. She would be prohibited from disaffirming the lease.

    b. She would be permitted to disaffirm, and in most states would not be obligated to pay the landlord for the damage to the apartment.

    c. She would be permitted to disaffirm, but in most states would be required to put the landlord in *status quo*.

    d. She would be permitted to disaffirm in all states without paying the landlord for the damage to the apartment.

20. Of the following statements about contracts entered into by minors, which is INACCURATE?

    a. If a minor enters into a contract, he may ratify it at any time between his entry into the contract and the expiration of a reasonable time after he reaches the age of majority.

    b. In most states, the age of majority is 18.

    c. Even though minors lack legal capacity to contract, they may be compelled to pay the reasonable value of necessaries furnished to them.

    d. A minor's contract is voidable at her option but not at the option of the adult with whom she contracted.

Short Essay

21. For over 30 years, Ingrid Cognito had been affected by intermittent mental problems. She had never been adjudicated incompetent, however. During an interlude when her mental problems rendered her unable to understand the nature and effect of such a contract, Cognito entered into a written agreement to lease 1000 acres of her farmland to Milo Wheat. Under the terms of the lease, Wheat was to have possession of the leased acres beginning 30 days after the date of the lease. Two days after she entered into the lease, Cognito regained her full mental faculties and was able to function normally. A family member promptly showed her the lease she had signed. Cognito indicated that she understood its terms. Wheat telephoned her a week later to discuss a few matters concerning the leased acres. Cognito gave no indication that she did not wish to proceed according to the terms of the lease. Two weeks after Wheat took possession of the property in accordance with the lease, Cognito sought to evict him because she had decided to disaffirm the lease on the ground of mental incapacity. When Wheat refused to abandon the property, Cognito sued him in an attempt to have the court rule that she is entitled to disaffirm. How is the court likely to rule? Explain your reasoning.

22. Ned Nerdley, age 17, purchased a 1978 Ford Fallacy 400 automobile from used car dealer Eddie Eager. Nerdley paid $800 for the car. One day later, Nerdley wrecked the car in a collision caused by his own negligence. Nerdley then decided to disaffirm the contract of sale and recover the $800 he paid Eager. May Nerdley disaffirm even though he cannot return the car to Eager in a condition comparable to the car's condition at the time of purchase? In order to be able to disaffirm, will Nerdley be obligated to compensate Eager for the damage to the car? Explain.

23. In what ways have courts, attempting to protect adults who deal in good faith with minors, modified the general rule that minors may disaffirm at will?

CHAPTER 15

ILLEGALITY

True-False - Circle T for True and F for False.

T F 1. A's knowledge that B has an illegal purpose for the goods purchased under a contract between A and B means that a later attempt by A to enforce the contract will be barred on the ground of illegality.

T F 2. All exculpatory clauses seeking to relieve a person from tort liability are unlawful.

T F 3. Any transaction in which a person will profit from the happening of an uncertain future event is an illegal wagering transaction.

T F 4. As a general rule, courts do not give any remedy to the parties to an illegal agreement.

T F 5. Procedural unconscionability exists when a term in a contract is extremely harsh or grossly one-sided in effect.

T F 6. A contract for insurance on property in which a person has an economic interest is legal, as it merely shifts an existing risk.

T F 7. If a court finds one term in a contract to be unconscionable, it can refuse to enforce the entire contract.

T F 8. A contract made by a person who has not obtained the license required by a revenue-raising licensing statute is generally illegal.

T F 9. Courts allow a person who rescinds an illegal contract before any illegal act has been performed to recover any consideration that he has given.

T F 10. An agreement whose sole purpose is to restrain competition is not necessarily illegal.

Multiple Choice - Circle the best answer.

11. Norm Hefty was a door-to-door salesman for Toothrot Candy Co. His duties were to call on customers and make sales in Bedford, Indiana, which is located in the southern part of the state. Toothrot's business territory covers the entire state of Indiana. Hefty and Toothrot had entered into a written employment contract at the time he joined the firm. One of the clauses in the contract stated that if Hefty ceased working for Toothrot, he could not work as a salesman for a competing company anywhere in Indiana for a period of a year. Hefty left his employment with Toothrot and promptly went to work as a salesman for a candy company that competed with Toothrot. His duties with the new employer were confined to the town of Elkhart, which is located in northern Indiana. Toothrot has sued Hefty in an effort to obtain an injunction against further violation of the non-competition clause in the parties' employment contract. On these facts, the court is likely to rule in favor of:

    a. Hefty, because a non-competition clause in an employment contract is unenforceable regardless of whether the employer has a legitimate business purpose for it.

    b. Toothrot, because the clause's geographic scope was restricted to the state in which Toothrot does business.

    c. Toothrot, because Hefty is not a member of a profession and the clause would merely restrict him from engaging in a common calling for a reasonable period of time.

    d. Hefty, because when the non-competition clause is examined in light of the employment actually obtained by Hefty, its geographic scope appears excessive.

12. Which of the following is most likely to be judicially enforced?

    a. A contract for the purchase of "bootleg" tapes (tapes unauthorized by the relevant copyright owner) of a recording session at which the heavy metal group Rancid Meat made a copyrighted recording.

b. A contract in violation of a revenue-raising licensing statute.

c. A contract whose only provision is a clause in which two competitors agree to stop competing with each other.

d. An exculpatory clause that attempts to relieve a party from liability for fraud.

13. Which of the following is an INACCURATE statement about unconscionability?

a. Proof of either procedural or substantive unconscionability in connection with a clause in an contract will normally cause a court to conclude that the clause is unconscionable.

b. If a court concludes that a term in a contract is unconscionable, it need not rule that the entire contract is unenforceable.

c. The term "unconscionability" is clearly defined in a section of the Uniform Commercial Code.

d. When two contracting parties possessed unequal bargaining power, their contract is not necessarily unconscionable.

14. In March 1985, while he was a junior running back at the University of Iowa, Ronnie Harmon signed a contract with agent Norby Walters. Pursuant to this contract, Harmon received cash, airline tickets, and a car from Walters. These items totaled $54,924.42 in value. Assume that the contract violated NCAA regulations and applicable law, and that Harmon and Walters knew this. Harmon, the top draft pick of the Buffalo Bills in 1986, later refused to employ Walters as his agent. Walters sued Harmon to collect the $54,924.42 Harmon had received from him. How should the court rule?

a. That despite the contract's illegality, Harmon must repay Walters.

b. That the contract was legal because it was of a revenue-rasing nature, and that Harmon therefore must repay Walters.

c. That in view of the contract's illegality, neither Walters nor Harmon will receive a remedy.

d. That the contract is enforceable against both Harmon and Walters, that Harmon must repay Walters, and that Walters must act as Harmon's agent.

15. In which of the following situations will a court grant some remedy even though the parties' contract is illegal?

a. When the contract merely creates a risk in which a party will have some financial stake.

b. When the contract is for the commission of a criminal act that was not performed but for which payment was made.

c. When the contract is void rather than voidable.

d. When one of the parties rescinds the contract before any illegal act contemplated by the contract is actually performed.

16. A contract will generally be classified as illegal if it:

a. shifts an existing risk to another party.

b. restricts competition in any way.

c. violates a regulatory licensing statute.

d. does any of the above.

17. Julia Childish recently opened a restaurant. In prominent locations on the restaurant's walls, she placed signs that read as follows: "Management not responsible to customers for *any* loss, injury, or damage occurring on premises." Childish's assistant chef, Henri Scrusuppe, accidentally added Vomet scouring powder to the batch of Surprise Stew he was preparing. Several customers were hospitalized after eating the stew. Which of the following is an accurate statement about the hospitalized customers' rights of action, if any, against Childish?

a. Those who saw the signs cannot recover damages for the mere negligence of Childish's employee, because negligence does not amount to willful harm.

b. Those who saw the signs are entitled to recover damages from Childish, just as those who did not see the signs are.

c. Those who did not see the signs may recover damages from Childish, but those who saw the signs may look only to Scrusuppe for a suitable remedy.

d. Those who did not see the signs are entitled to recover punitive damages from Childish.

18. House painter Eddie Picasso and Ann Oldcodger entered into a contract that called for Picasso to paint Oldcodger's house. Applicable state law requires all house painters to obtain a license from the state. Any house painter who files an application and pays the $75 fee is issued a license. Picasso was unlicensed at the time he entered into the contract with Oldcodger because he had forgotten to send in the necessary fee that year. On these facts, the contract between Picasso and Oldcodger is:
    a. illegal and voidable.
    b. legal and enforceable.
    c. illegal and void.
    d. legal but unenforceable.

19. Gargantuan, Inc. and Fritz Furd entered into a contract, which Gargantuan now claims was breached by Furd. Furd asserts that a critical clause (referred to below as "the clause") in the contract is unconscionable and therefore should not be enforced against him. Which of the following is an accurate statement?
    a. If the contract is for the sale of goods, if Furd is an unsophisticated consumer, and if the court finds that either procedural unconscionability or substantive unconscionability existed, the court will not allow the clause to be enforced against Furd.
    b. If the parties' contract was for something other than the sale of goods, the court cannot hold the clause unconscionable because the unconscionability doctrine does not apply outside the UCC-controlled setting.
    c. Regardless of whether the contract is for the sale of goods, the court could hold that the clause is unconscionable and therefore unenforceable even if Furd is a businessperson with many years of experience.
    d. Courts' treatment of unconscionability cases is a notable example of modern judicial activism in contravention of what state legislatures intended, because courts consistently have disregarded the very narrow statutory definition of unconscionability set forth in the UCC.

20. Of the following statements about exculpatory clauses, which is accurate?
    a. They cannot operate to relieve a party from liability for a willful tort.
    b. They violate public policy and are therefore unenforceable.
    c. They may operate to relieve an employer from laibility for workers' compensation benefits.
    d. They are effective only when the party benefited by them owes a duty to the public.

Short Essay

21. Svelte Corp. manufactures rowing machines and sells them to retailers, who then sell the machines to consumers for use in their homes. As of July 1, 1990, the Svelte rowing machine was the best-selling machine of its type in the United States. On that date, Svelte entered into a written contract with First Class Co., which owns the highly successful nationwide chain of First Class Sporting Goods stores. This contract, which was drafted by First Class's attorney, called for Svelte to sell First Class 1,000 rowing machines at a price of $100 per machine. The contract also provided that if First Class, despite its best efforts, was unable to sell all of the 1,000 rowing machines in its numerous stores by June 30, 1991, it was entitled to return any unsold machines to Svelte, which would then be obligated to remit $100 to First Class for each returned machine. Svelte and First Class had dealt with each other repeatedly over the years. Although Svelte was aware that the parties' previous contracts had always included such a "return" clause, First Class had never invoked the clause because it had always been able to resell all of the rowing machines it had purchased from Svelte. On July 15, 1990, Svelte delivered all 1,000 rowing machines contemplated by the contract, and First Class made payment in full. In September 1990, the Surgeon General of the United States released a highly publicized report in which the Surgeon General harshly criticized rowing machines and expressed the view that the use of a rowing machine is an unsafe way to obtain exercise. After the release of this report, nationwide sales of rowing machines declined drastically. First Class stores had sold 334 of the 1,000 Svelte rowing machines as of the report's release, but sold only 36 more between September 1990 and June 30, 1991.

Therefore, shortly after June 30, 1991, First Class sought to return 630 unsold machines to Svelte and to obtain a refund of $63,000, pursuant to the contractual provision noted above. Svelte neither accepted the machines nor gave the requested refund. Instead, Svelte sued First Class and asked that the court declare the contract's "return" clause unconscionable under the circumstances, and therefore unenforceable. Should Svelte succeed with its unconscionability claim? State the reasons supporting your conclusion.

22. Walt Shoddy, the owner of Shoddy Shoe Repair, was contemplating retirement. He therefore contracted to sell the business to Pauline Parker. Shoddy Shoe Repair was located in Hoosierburg, Indiana, which has a population of 5,233. Besides containing a provision entitling Parker to use the Shoddy Shoe Repair name for the business, the parties' contract included a clause that prohibited Shoddy from opening up a competing shoe repair shop in Hoosierburg for a period of one year from the date of the parties' contract. Two months after the date of the contract (and one and one-half months after the sale of the business to Parker had been completed), Shoddy grew tired of retirement. He realized that he needed something to occupy his time. As shoe repair had been his life's work, he opened up a shoe repair shop (calling it Walt's Shoe Repair) in Hoosierburg. Parker has sued him in an effort to obtain an injunction against his operation of the competing business in supposed violation of the parties' contract. How is the court likely to rule? Explain your reasoning.

23. Why is purchasing stock a legal speculative bargain, but betting on the performance of stock an illegal wager?

CHAPTER 16

WRITING

True-False - Circle T for True and F for False.

T F 1. Although leases are contracts for the transfer of an interest in real estate, not all oral leases are barred by the statute of frauds.

T F 2. A contract in which a guarantor promises to pay the promisee if the original promisor does not must be evidenced by a writing if the guarantor's promise is made primarily to benefit himself.

T F 3. An oral prenuptial agreement is likely to be unenforceable due to the statute of frauds.

T F 4. An executory bilateral contract that is unlikely to be performed within a year after it is made must be evidenced by a writing to be enforceable.

T F 5. The parol evidence rule prohibits the admission of evidence of oral agreements made after the parties have entered into a complete written agreement on the same subject matter.

T F 6. Oral contracts for the sale of more than $500-worth of goods are sometimes enforceable if specially manufactured goods are involved.

T F 7. A party may use parol evidence to show that a contract was entered into as the result of the other party's misrepresentation.

T F 8. Promissory estoppel will sometimes cause a contract falling within the statute of frauds to be enforceable even in the absence of a writing.

T F 9. A memorandum that was not signed by both parties to the supposed contract cannot serve to satisfy the writing requirement of the statute of frauds.

T F 10. When an estate's executor, acting in his representative capacity, orally promises to pay the decendent's debt from funds of the estate, the statute of frauds bars enforcement of the promise.

Multiple Choice - Circle the best answer.

11. Perennial All-Pro linebacker Jake Pitbull (of the Indianapolis Dolts) signed a highly detailed written contract under which he and XYZ Co. agreed that he would appear in television commercials for XYZ's "X&O" brand athletic supporters. One of the terms in the contract stated that Pitbull was to receive a lump sum payment of $100,000, plus $1,000 for each time an X&O commercial featuring Pitbull was aired on national television. Pitbull performed his obligations under the contract, and XYZ paid him according to the payment term just mentioned. No other payment term appeared in the written version of the contract. The parties now disagree over an assertion by Pitbull that the parties' actual agreement nonetheless included a further term: that XYZ would pay Pitbull an extra $1 for every X&O athletic supporter sold during the six-month period when the commercials featuring Pitbull would be on television, if XYZ sold at least 50,000 X&O supporters during that time period. Pitbull alleges that this further payment term was stated verbally to him by Jacques Strapp, XYZ's vice-president for marketing, an hour before the parties signed the written version of the contract. It is undisputed by the parties that during the six-month period when the Pitbull-featured X&O commercials were on TV, XYZ sold 63,397 X&0 supporters. Because XYZ has refused Pitbull's demands for payment of $63,397.00, Pitbull has sued XYZ for breach of contract. Which of the following is an accurate observation about the suit?

   a. If the court concludes that Strapp made the promise referred to above, Pitbull will win the suit because of the "partial payment" exception to the statute of frauds.

   b. Pitbull will lose the suit because the statute of frauds will provide XYZ a defense.

   c. If the court concludes that Strapp made the promise referred to above, Pitbull will win the suit because of the leading object rule.

   d. Pitbull will lose the suit because of the operation of the parol evidence rule.

12. According to Rae Spondeat, Superior Corp. CEO Rex Regis verbally offered Spondeat a position as Superior's vice-president in charge of risk management, at a salary of $120,000 per year. Spondeat claims that in this offer, Regis promised her that the position would be hers for a minimum of two years if she agreed to remain with Superior for at least two years. In addition, Spondeat asserts the following: that she notified Regis of her acceptance in a timely fashion during a telephone conversation between the two of them; that she then quit her job as a mid-level executive for Marginal Co.; that she sold her house in Peoria, Illinois (where Marginal Co.'s offices are located); that she purchased a house in Toledo, Ohio (where Superior Corp.'s offices are located); and that she incurred expenses in moving from Peoria to Toledo. Finally, Spondeat alleges that before she was to begin work for Superior, Regis notified her that her services would not be needed. Assume that Spondeat has made these allegations in a breach of contract suit filed against Superior. Which of the following is an accurate statement about the suit?

    a. Because the contract could have been fully performed by the parties within a year from the date of its formation, the oral nature of the contract will not prevent Spondeat from enforcing it by way of this suit.

    b. The court is likely to apply the doctrine of promissory estoppel as a means of preventing Superior from asserting what otherwise would be Superior's best defense to enforcement of this supposed contract.

    c. The court is likely to conclude that the oral nature of the contract will prevent Spondeat from enforcing it, unless Spondeat introduces into evidence a memorandum signed by her.

    d. Because nothing in the facts indicates that applicable state law does not adhere to the employment-at-will rule, Regis was free to "fire" Spondeat before she began working for Superior.

13. Conrad went to First Bank to borrow money. First Bank did not want to loan her anything because of her bad credit history. Conrad's friend, Willis, orally promised First Bank that if Conrad failed to repay the money, he (Willis) would repay it. First Bank loaned the money to Conrad, who failed to repay it. First Bank sued Willis. Willis's best defense to having to repay the loan is:

    a. the main purpose/leading object rule.

    b. the parol evidence rule.

    c. the statute of frauds.

    d. promissory estoppel.

14. Gerry Manderer, professor of political science at Obscure State University, telephoned Sight & Sound, Inc. (S&S), a retailer of televisions and stereo equipment, and ordered two standard $1,200 big-screen televisions for use at his home. The manager of S&S agreed that S&S, which had the requested TV's in stock, would ship them to Manderer on Dec. 1 and would bill him for the $2,400 purchase price at that time. As a precautionary measure, S&S (within minutes after the conclusion of the conversation) sent Manderer a letter confirming S&S's understanding of the terms of the parties' oral agreement. Manderer received the letter on Nov. 10, but made no response until Nov. 24, when he telephoned S&S and stated that S&S's letter was inaccurate. He also informed S&S that he did not intend to purchase the TV's. S&S was finally able to sell the two TV's to someone else, but only after it lowered the price to $1,000 apiece. S&S then sued Manderer in small claims court for breach of contract. Manderer properly raised all potentially available defenses. On these facts,

    a. S&S's letter to Manderer was a memorandum sufficient to satisfy the statute of frauds' writing requirement.

    b. S&S's letter and Manderer's failure to object until Nov. 24 enable S&S to rely on the confirmatory memorandum method of satisfying the statute of frauds' writing requirement.

    c. S&S will lose the suit because the contract was subject to the statute of frauds and there was no compliance with its writing requirement.

    d. the difficulty S&S had in selling the TV's to someone else means that the goods were not suitable for resale in the usual course of business and that under the specially manufactured goods rule, the contract with Manderer was enforceable.

15. Elvis Greasely and Zsa Zsa Saboar entered into an oral contract under which Greasely was to sell his famous Disgraceland mansion and surrounding grounds to Saboar for a price of $1.1 million. Saboar paid Greaseley $700,000 of the purchase price at the time the parties reached their agreement, which called for a closing date two weeks later (at which time Saboar was to pay the remainder of the purchase price and Greasely was to transfer title to the property). A week before the agreed closing date, Greasely informed Saboar that he no longer wished to sell the property. He tendered Saboar a return of her $700,000, but she said, "no dices, dahling, deals is deals. I belong at Disgraceland." When Greasely refused to sell her the property on the agreed terms, Saboar sued him for breach of contract and asked the court for an order of specific performance. How should the court rule?

    a. In favor of Greasely because specific performance orders are inappropriate in cases involving contracts for the sale of real estate.

    b. In favor of Saboar because of the "part performance" exception to the statute of frauds.

    c. In favor of Saboar because Greasely acted in bad faith by not honoring his oral agreement with her.

    d. In favor of Greasely because the contract is unenforceable (though Saboar is of course entitled to a return of her $700,000).

16. A, a retailer of clothing, and B, a wholesaler of clothing, agreed during an April 1 telephone conversation that A would buy 1,000 shirts from B for $5,000, with delivery of the shirts to occur no later than May 1. Shortly after the conversation concluded, A wrote the following note to B: "This is to confirm our deal regarding the 1,000 t-shirts for $5,000. I look forward to delivery." A signed the note and sent it to B, who read it the same day it was delivered (April 2). B never responded and never delivered the shirts. On May 2, A sued B for breach of contract. Which of the following is an accurate statement?

    a. The oral agreement is unenforceable against B because the writing was not signed by B.

    b. The note is a writing sufficient to satisfy the statute of frauds.

    c. If A prepaid any portion of the purchase price, the unenforceable nature of the contract means that B must refund that money to A.

    d. The oral agreement is enforceable only if B had already begun manufacturing the t-shirts before he received A's note.

17. On May 1, 1991, New and Olds signed a written agreement in which New agreed to work for Olds from June 1, 1991 to June 30, 1992, at a salary of $36,000. At the time the writing was signed, the parties orally agreed that if New did not receive his B.S. degree in business later in May 1991, Olds's contractual obligation to employ him would not be triggered. New did not receive his degree in May 1991 and Olds refused to employ him. New sued Olds for breach of contract. Which of the following statements is/are accurate?

    a. Olds may introduce of the parties' oral agreement regarding the need for New to obtain his degree in May 1991.

    b. The statute of frauds will bar Olds from introducing the evidence referred to in answer a.

    c. The parol evidence rule will bar Old from introducing the evidence referred to in answer a.

    d. Both b and c.

18. Each of items a through c, below, sets forth the facts underlying a breach of contract suit. Under applicable law, in which of a through c would the lack of a writing be a reason for the plaintiff to lose the suit?

    a. According to plaintiff Sue Perfluous, she and defendant Al Bilkem entered into an oral contract under which Perfluous was to purchase a certain office building from Bilkem. Perfluous also alleges in her suit that Bilkem has wrongfully refused to sell her the property on the agreed terms. Bilkem says that there was no agreement between the parties and asserts, as a defense, that even if there was a contract—a fact he denies—it would be unenforceable because there was no writing.

b. Boleyn still owed Guillotine Finance Co. $20,000 on an original debt of $80,000. Guillotine asserts that it orally agreed with Boleyn and Henry as follows: that Guillotine would release Boleyn from any further liability on the debt; that Henry would take over Boleyn's debt and be substituted for her on it; and that Guillotine would look only to Henry for payment of the remaining $20,000 owed on the debt. When Henry later failed to pay the $20,000 on its alleged due date, Guillotine sued Henry in an effort to collect that sum. Henry claims that he is not liable because his alleged promise to take over the debt was oral.

c. Computer whiz Del Dull and Acme Corp. entered into an oral contract under which Dull was to provide certain consulting services for Acme. At the time they entered into the contract, both parties assumed that the numerous services called for in the agreement would probably take Dull more than a year to perform. Two months after the contract was agreed to, Acme replaced Dull with another consultant and refused to allow Dull to complete the services called for in the agreement. In addition, Acme refused to pay Dull all of what he was to receive under the agreement. Dull has sued Acme for breach of contract. Acme asserts the lack of a writing as a defense.

d. None of the above.

e. Each of a, b, and c.

19. Jim's Haberdashery, Inc. issued a purchase order to Broadhurst Neckware Manufacturing Co. for 300 neckties at $8 per tie. Broadhurst acknowledged this on its own form as an order for "300 neckties at $8 each." Broadhurst shipped the merchandise, and upon delivery Jim's tendered a check for $1800 (rather than $2400) as payment in full. Jim's asserted that after the parties' exchange of purchase order and acknowledgement forms, Broadhurst agreed in writing to reduce the purchase price to $6 per tie. Claiming that Jim's still owes $600, Broadhurst has filed suit for that amount. Jim's seeks to introduce evidence of Broadhurst's supposed promise to reduce the purchase price. Will Jim's be allowed to do so?

a. No, because such evidence would tend to alter, vary, or contradict a written contract.

b. Yes, because the parol evidence rule has no application to the evidence Jim's seeks to introduce.

c. Yes, because the evidence would merely fill gaps in an incomplete written contract.

d. No, because the forms exchanged by the parties provide the best evidence of their real agreement.

20. XYZ, Inc. made an oral contract with PDQ Manufacturing Co. for the purchase of 1,000 t-shirts at a price of $3 per shirt. XYZ made an initial payment of $1,000. PDQ deposited the check in a PDQ account but failed to deliver any shirts to XYZ. XYZ sued PDQ, which asserted that the absence of a sufficient writing made any supposed contract between the parties unenforceable. What is the proper result?

a. The contract is unenforceable because it was not evidenced by a writing.

b. The entire contract is enforceable against PDQ because PDQ accepted money from XYZ.

c. The contract is enforceable against PDQ up to the quantity for which XYZ has already paid.

d. The entire contract is void.

Short Essay

21. Natalie Attired owns Polyfashions, a retail store at which she sells a wide variety of 100% polyester clothing items. According to used car dealer Dewey Cheatem, he and Attired orally agreed on March 1, 1991 that he was to purchase Attired's 1989 Wonda Quaalude automobile for the sum of $4100. Under the terms of this supposed oral contract, March 15, 1991 was the date on which Cheatem was to pay the purchase price and Attired was to transfer title to the automobile to him. Cheatem also alleges that on March 2, 1991, he wrote, signed, and sent to Attired a letter in which he referred specifically to the March 1 oral agreement and stated his understanding of its terms. Included in this statement of terms were references to Attired's Wonda Quaalude and the $4100 purchase price. Attired received Cheatem's letter but never responded to it. When March 15 arrived, Attired refused to sell the car to Cheatem. Cheatem filed a breach of contract suit against Attired on April 1, 1991. In the answer she has filed with the court, Attired denies

the existence of a contract. As a defense, she asserts that if there was a contract—which she denies—any such contract would be unenforceable because of the lack of a suitable writing. Should Attired succeed with this defense? Why or why not?

22. Cosby, Sills, Ashe & Chung (CSAC) is a musical group and partnership made up of an actor-comedian, an opera star, a tennis great, and a newscaster. CSAC and Shorty Hefty entered into a written contract that contained an entire agreement clause. The contract, which was signed by all parties on July 1, 1990, called for Hefty to serve as the group's agent from that date through June 30, 1991 and stated that Hefty was to receive a salary of $175,000 for the period of the contract. Within a month after the contract was signed, Hefty claimed that two days before the signing, CSAC had verbally promised him that in addition to his regular salary, CSAC would pay him 4% of the profits realized by the group on any concerts booked by Hefty. Although the written contract did not contain the alleged promise concerning the 4% of profits, Hefty claimed that the promise was made in exchange for his promise to serve as CASC's agent. By the time June 30, 1991 arrived, CSAC had paid Hefty his $175,000 salary but had not paid him any portion of the group's profits on the various concerts he had booked. Hefty sued CSAC in an effort to collect the 4% allegedly promised to him. What is the strongest legal argument (i.e., other than merely denying that the promise was made) for CSAC to make in order to avoid being held liable here? Why is that argument appropriate?

23. Wally Whipple and Polly Dudley entered into an agreement under which Whipple was to sell his house to Dudley. Dudley later refused to perform the agreement, which had not been placed in writing. Claiming breach of contract, Whipple has sued Dudley for damages. Whipple has an envelope, on the back side of which are Whipple's handwritten notations that clearly describe the property to be sold under the supposed contract, mention the names of both parties, and set forth the price and the other essential terms of the supposed contract. Is the envelope sufficient to satisfy the writing requirement of the statute of frauds? Explain your reasoning.

CHAPTER 17

RIGHTS OF THIRD PARTIES

True-False - Circle T for True and F for False.

T F 1. Assignments that are unsupported by consideration may be enforceable.

T F 2. Even if a contract contains a provision that expressly forbids assignments, an assignment of rights under the contract may be valid.

T F 3. An obligor who renders performance to the assignor without notice that the contract has been assigned is also obligated to render performance to the assignee.

T F 4. If the assignee is unable to collect from the obligor because the obligor is bankrupt, the assignee has a valid claim against the assignor for breach of the assignor's implied warranty that the obligor is solvent.

T F 5. The effects of an assignment are to extinguish the assignor's right to receive performance and to transfer that right to the assignee.

T F 6. In states that follow the "American rule" on successive assignments, the first assignee does not necessarily have rights superior to those of the second assignee.

T F 7. An assignment may be valid even if it was not made in writing.

T F 8. As a general rule, the assignee is not subject to claims or defenses that the obligor could have asserted against the assignor.

T F 9. A right to receive money or goods is generally assignable.

T F 10. Absent clear indications of the parties' contrary intent, an assignment is not generally interpreted as having included a delegation of the assignor's duties.

Multiple Choice - Circle the best answer.

11. Tara Co. and Maggie, Inc. entered into a contract under which Tara is to supply all of Maggie's dog food requirements for a period of two years. Maggie assigned the contract to Butch Corp. Which of the following is an accurate statement?

    a. If Butch's dog food requirements are significantly greater than Maggie's, this assignment by Maggie is probably ineffective.

    b. Maggie's assignment to Butch is not valid because it violates public policy, regardless of the extent of Butch's dog food requirements.

    c. Even if Butch's dog food requirements are significantly greater than Maggie's, this assignment will be considered valid unless Tara had the foresight to place a "no assignments" clause in her contract with Maggie.

    d. None of the above.

12. Kyle and Bill entered into a contract under which Bill agreed to perform a service for Kyle. Bill is contemplating delegating his duty to Ted. Under which of the following alternative versions of the facts would Bill's duty be least likely to be delegable?

    a. If Bill's duty is to rake the leaves in Kyle's yard.

    b. If Bill's duty is to drive Kyle to San Dimas, California.

    c. If Bill's duty is to give a thorough cleaning to each room in Kyle's house.

    d. If Bill's duty is to sculpt a bust of Kyle.

13. Real estate developer Donna Dunn-Deal contracted with the City of Elvisville to build a convention center for the city. Ernie Dorfman owns a nightclub that is located within a block of the site chosen for the convention center. Dorfman's business stood to benefit financially once the convention center was built and in operation. Dunn-Deal repudiated her contract with Elvisville and

did not build the convention center. Dorfman therefore did not realize the expected benefit to his business. He therefore wishes to sue Dunn-Deal because she did not fulfill her contractual obligation. Which of the following accurately states Dorfman's status and rights, if any, against Dunn-Deal?

a. Dorfman is an intended beneficiary and is not entitled to recover from Dunn-Deal for breach of contract.

b. Dorfman is an incidental beneficiary and is not entitled to recover against Dunn-Deal for breach of contract.

c. Dorfman is a creditor beneficiary and is entitled to recover from Dunn-Deal for breach of contract.

d. Dorfman is a donee beneficiary and is entitled to recover from Dunn-Deal for breach of contract.

14. Marlin sold his bait shop business to Chad, who assumed all of Marlin's outstanding business debts as part of the transaction. These debts included Marlin's obligation to Shark Loan Co. Chad defaulted on the payment of the Shark debt. Which of the following is an accurate statement?

a. Marlin is no longer liable to Shark on the debt because he delegated the duty to pay to Chad.

b. Shark would not be classified as a creditor beneficiary of the contract between Marline and Chad.

c. Unless there has been a novation, Shark remains entitled to look to Marlin for payment of the debt.

d. Marlin is obligated to pay Shark regardless of whether there was a novation.

15. Of the following statements about delegation of duties, which is INACCURATE?

a. Once the delegation occurs, the delegator is discharged from liability to the obligee and the delegatee becomes the sole party with a duty to the obligee.

b. A delegation of duties need not be expressly stated in the assignment contract to be valid.

c. If no notice of the delegation is given to the obligee, the delegation is nonetheless valid.

d. The delegation will be invalid if the duty delegated is dependent on the personal skill, character, or judgment of the delegator.

16. Which of the following contracts is least likely to be assignable?

a. The right to receive goods.

b. The right to receive future payments of wages.

c. The right to receive real estate.

d. The right to receive money.

17. A has assigned his contract with B to C. A will be relieved from further responsibility to B:

a. once B is notified of the assignment.

b. if the assignment was written and expressly stated that C assumed any liability of A to B.

c. if C assigns the contract to D.

d. only if a novation takes place.

18. Archibald and Roy were parties to a contract. Roy assigned the contract to Priscilla. Neither Roy nor Priscilla notified Archibald of the assignment. Archibald rendered performance to Roy, as the contract originally provided. Which of the following is an accurate statement?

a. Priscilla is entitled to recover the value of Archibald's performance from Roy.

b. Because Roy did not notify Archibald of the assignment, Roy must compensate Archibald for the performance Archibald rendered.

c. Priscilla is entitled to performance from Archibald, who must then pursue a claim against Roy because he (Archibald) ended up having to perform twice.

d. Because Priscilla did not notify Archibald of the assignment, she has no remedy against Archibald and no remedy against Roy.

19. Under the "American rule" on assignments,
    a. the assignor impliedly warrants to the assignee that the obligor is solvent.
    b. the first assignee who gives notice of the assignment will have priority if the assignor makes two assignments of the same contract.
    c. the first assignee in time will have priority if the assignor makes two assignments of the same contract.
    d. the obligor who is not given prompt notice of an assignment has no liability to the assignor or the assignee.

20. Opal Convoy borrowed money from Dicey Savings & Loan in order to purchase a new semi-truck and trailer. She contracted with Dicey to repay the loan in monthly installments of $550. Opal later sold the semi-truck and trailer to Biff "Big" Rigg and delegated, to Rigg, the duty to pay Dicey. Rigg agreed to take over the loan payments, but ceased paying Dicey after only two months. There are numerous payments left on the loan. Which of the following is an accurate statement?
    a. Dicey must pursue Convoy, rather than Rigg, for payment because Dicey was not a party to the agreement between Convoy and Rigg.
    b. Dicey is not entitled to seek payment from Convoy because Rigg is now the respnsible party on the debt.
    c. Dicey cannot pursue Convoy for payment unless its loan agreement with Convoy expressly forbade her from delegating her duty to Rigg.
    d. Dicey is entitled to pursue both Convoy and Rigg, or either of them, for payment.

Short Essay

21. Hank and Hannah Hapless purchased a one-acre lot and retained Shoddy Construction Co. to build a 3000 square-foot home on the property. If Shoddy had constructed the home with a reasonable degree of skill (as called for by the parties' contract), the home would have been quite attractive. Its presence would have enhanced the value of the adjacent parcels of property. Shoddy did low-quality work, however. The resulting house was distinctly unattractive amd appeared to be poorly constructed. The Haplesses have sued Shoddy for breach of contract. Dick and Dixie Distraught own the house next door to the Hapless property. The Distraughts have also sued Shoddy on the theory that Shoddy's failure to perform its contractual duties caused them not to realize the enhanced property value they otherwise would have realized. Are the Distraughts entitled to relief for Shoddy's breach of contract? Why or why not?

22. Under Retailer's contract with Manufacturer, Retailer was to pay $50,000 to Manufacturer within two weeks after Manufacturer's delivery of certain goods. Manufacturer delivered the goods and then assigned its right to be paid by Retailer to Bank. Bank notified Retailer of the assignment and sought payment of the $50,000. Retailer refused to pay the full sum, asserting that some of the goods delivered by Manufacturer were seriously defective and therefore not suitable for resale in the usual course of Retailer's business. Bank responded this way: "Gee, that's too bad, but it's not our problem. Take your complaint up with Manufacturer." When Retailer still refused to pay Bank the full $50,000, Bank sued Retailer in an effort to collect that amount. Is Retailer entitled to raise the allegedly defective nature of some of the goods as a partial defense to Bank's claim for payment? Why or why not?

23. Mavis owed Shady Finance Co. a $3500 debt. Shady assigned the debt to Greedco, Inc. Neither Shady nor Greedco notified Mavis of the assignment. Mavis later paid the $3500 to Shady. What are Greedco's rights under the circumstances?

CHAPTER 18

PERFORMANCE AND REMEDIES

True-False - Circle T for True and F for False.

T F 1. A condition may be part of the parties' contract even if it was not expressly stated in the contract.

T F 2. Courts normally enforce liquidated damages clauses that impose a penalty on a party for late performance of his contractual obligation.

T F 3. Anticipatory repudiation is a form of material breach of contract.

T F 4. If a condition in a contract would benefit a contracting party, the conduct of that party may amount to a waiver of the condition.

T F 5. A and B enter into a written employment contract under which B hires A as an attorney for one year at a salary of $60,000. B then decides to use an outside law firm for all of his legal work. B offers A substitute employment as a janitor for $60,000. A must accept this substitute employment or he will be unable to collect damages in his suit for B's breach of contract.

T F 6. A party who performed without fulfilling every contractual duty has not necessarily committed a material breach of contract.

T F 7. An offer to purchase a house "if I can obtain suitable financing" states a condition precedent.

T F 8. Sometimes a person who has promised to perform to another's personal satisfaction is entitled to be paid even if the other party is dissatisfied.

T F 9. A's material breach of her contract with B would not entitle B to withhold his performance.

T F 10. A promisor who has promised to perform a duty for which he is not skilled will be excused from performing on the ground of impossibility.

Multiple Choice - Circle the best answer.

11. Sal Monella has successfully operated a restaurant for several years. Monella contracted with Shoddy Construction Co. to have certain remodeling and repair work done at the restaurant. The work was necessary because of a recent furnace explosion there. Under the terms of the parties' detailed written contract, all of the work was to be done between Dec. 20, 1990 and Jan. 2, 1991, while Monella would be out of town on vacation. The contract also specified that Monella would be able to re-open the restaurant on Jan. 3, 1991, and that Monella was to pay Shoddy $19,500 upon completion of the work. Monella left town on Dec. 19 and returned late in the evening of Jan. 2, only to discover that none of the necessary work had been done. He later learned that Shoddy had not performed its contract because it had been tied up on other jobs. Despite his best efforts, Monella could not get anyone else to begin the necessary work until Jan. 10. The work was not completed by the other remodeling firm (PDQ Co.) until Jan. 23, so the restaurant remained closed until Jan. 24. Monella paid PDQ the lowest price he could negotiate: $22,000. Monella then sued Shoddy for breach of contract. At trial, Monella proved the above facts and established that he lost $3,300 in profits as a result of being unable to operate the restaurant from Jan. 3-23. What amount of damages should the court award Monella?

    a. $2,500

    b. $19,500

    c. $5,800

    d. $25,300

    e. Zero, because Shoddy's having been tied up on other jobs would give rise to a valid frustration of purpose defense.

12. The doctrine of commercial impracticability:
    a. amounts to a relaxation of the traditional impossibility doctrine.
    b. may sometimes be applied when unforeseen developments, occurring after the formation of a contract, would make a party's performance of his duty highly impracticable or unreasonably expensive, and/or would make the contract essentially valueless to him.
    c. is rarely a successful defense when relied upon by a defendant.
    d. is accurately described in each of the above answers.
    e. is accurately described in answers a and b.

13. Tony Sinister hired Mobco Construction, Inc. to build his new restaurant. When the project was completed, Sinister discovered that the rear wall of the restaurant was located two feet short of the location specified by the blueprint. As a result, seating capacity in the restaurant was reduced. The contract price was $900,000. Mobco incurred $700,000 in labor and materials costs in performing the contract. The reduced seating meant that the value of the restaurant building was less than the value it would have had if the building specifications had been met. Sinister therefore held back part of the final payment he was to make to Mobco. He has opened the restaurant but has sued Mobco for breach of contract. Mobco has counterclaimed for payment of what it claims is due and owing. Which of the following is an accurate statement?
    a. The court is likely to order Mobco to relocate the wall so that it complies with the blueprint.
    b. If the court concludes that Mobco materially breached the contract, Sinister will be obligated to pay the reasonable value of the restaurant on a quasi-contract basis.
    c. If the court concludes that Mobco's performance was substantial, Sinister will be obligated to pay Mobco $700,000.
    d. If the court concludes that Mobco's performance was substantial, Sinister will be obligated to pay Mobco the full contract price.

14. Which of the following is an accurate statement about remedies available to successful plaintiffs in breach of contract suits?
    a. If the defendant's breach of contract was proved to have been deliberate, the plaintiff will usually be allowed to collect punitive damages from the defendant.
    b. In most breach of contract suits, the successful plaintiff will be entitled to an order of specific performance if the plaintiff prefers that remedy to money damages.
    c. The premise underlying the damages remedy in breach of contract cases is that the nonbreaching party should be placed in the same position he, she, or it was in before the contract was formed.
    d. None of the above.

15. In which of the following situations would late performance be substantial performance and not material breach?
    a. When the contract states that time is of the essence and performance is one day late.
    b. When there is a definite time for performance stated in the contract and performance is late but occurs within a reasonable time.
    c. When there is no time for performance stated in the contract and performance is delayed for an unreasonable time.
    d. When there is a definite time for performance stated in the contract and performance is delayed for an unreasonable time.

16. Which of the following will not discharge or excuse the obligation to perform one's contract duties?
    a. Incapacitating illness or death of the promisor on a personal service contract.
    b. Commercial impracticability in a contract for the sale of goods.
    c. The happening of a condition precedent.
    d. Supervening or intervening illegality.

17. Austin Healy and Pierce Arrow entered into a valid wrriten contract under which Healy was to sell Arrow his 1957 Edsel automobile for $23,000. Healy had purchased the Edsel one month earlier for only $17,000. Therefore, he expected to make a profit of $6,000 in selling it to Healy. The contract established November 15, 1991 as the date of performance (*i.e.*, on that date, Arrow was to pay the purchase price and Healy was to transfer possession and ownership of the Edsel). It also included this provision: "A term and condition of this contract is that Healy shall at his own expense have the 1957 Edsel, which is currently red in color, repainted so that it is black. If the Edsel has not been painted black by November 15, 1991, Arrow shall have no obligation whatsoever to purchase the Edsel from Healy." After Healy entered into his contract with Arrow, Healy contracted with car painter Roland Stones to have the Edsel painted black. The Healy-Stones contract called for Stones to complete the paint job by November 15, 1991, on which date Healy was to pay Stones the agreed amount of $900 for his services. Healy did not tell Stones why he wanted the car painted black or why he needed the job done by November 15. Stones breached the contract by failing to paint the Edsel by November 15 (or at any time, for that matter). Healy of course did not pay Stones anything. Arrow refused to purchase the Edsel from Healy. Healy still wanted the Edsel painted black, so he retained another painter to do the work for $1,350, which was the best price Healy could obtain under the circumstances. Healy has sued Stones for breach of contract. What amount of damages should the court award Healy?

    a. $450.
    b. $6,450.
    c. $6,900
    d. $1,350
    e. $24,350

18. A contracted to supply to supply 10,000 copper widgets to B at a price of $1 each. Between the time the contract was formed and the date on which A was to make delivery and B was to make payment, the cost of copper (used by A in manufacturing the widgets) increased by 25% because of greatly increased demand. As a result of this increased cost, A would make no profit on the contract with B if A were expected to perform the contract according to its original terms. Which of the following is an accurate statement?

    a. A will be excused from performing on the ground of commercial impracticability.
    b. A will not be excused from performing, but B will be legally required to pay a fair price that is greater than the contract price.
    c. A will not be expected to perform because A obviously had not expected the cost of copper to increase as it did.
    d. A is obligated to deliver the 10,000 widgets on the agreed-upon date, at which time B must then pay the contract price.

19. A condition subsequent in a contract means that:

    a. one party's obligation to perform a duty does not arise until the happening of a certain event.
    b. the parties are under an obligation to perform their respective duties at the same time or essentially the same time.
    c. one party has the obligation to perform his duty until the happening of a certain event, after which event the duty ceases to exist.
    d. the parties have added a condition to the contract by amending it at a later time.

20. Jones and Slipshod Construction Co. contracted for Slipshod to build a house on Jones's lot according to specifications provided by Jones. The contract stated that Slipshod would be paid $205,000 upon completion of the house. Slipshod deviated from the specifications in several minor respects, but finished on time. The house was well-built. Jones refused to pay Slipshod the contract price. Slipshod has sued Jones for breach of contract. Jones argues, in defense, that Slipshod deviated from the specifications. Which of the following is an accurate statement about the suit?

    a. Slipshod is entitled to recover the contract price less any damages caused by its failure to perform fully.

b. Slipshod is not entitled to be paid because it materially breached the contract.

c. Jones is entitled to an order of specific performance, meaning the Slipshod must do what is necessary to bring the house in line with the specifications.

d. Slipshod is entitled to the entire contract price because it substantially performed.

Short Essay

21. Earl Redneck owns a truck-trailer tandem and uses this equipment to haul loads for other parties on an independent contractor basis. On January 4, the engine of Redneck's truck "blew out," rendering the truck inoperable. This occurred one day before Redneck's long-planned vacation, which was to last from January 5-17. Before traveling out of state on vacation, Redneck contracted with Gus Stiffem, owner of Stiffem Truck Service, for the performance of the extensive engine repairs necessary to put the truck in proper working order. Stiffem stated a price of $2,800 for the job—an amount to which Redneck readily agreed. According to the parties' contract, Stiffem was to complete the repair work no later than Jan. 17, with Redneck being obligated to pay the $2,800 when the work was done. Redneck informed Stiffem that the Jan. 17 date was critical because he had already contracted with XYZ Co. to pick up an XYZ load on Jan. 18 and haul it to California during a three-day period. He also told Stiffem that he (Redneck) would make a profit of $1,300 on the XYZ job and that if his truck was not ready to go on the 18th, he would lose the XYZ job to another trucker. Stiffem responded by saying, "Don't say no more, pardner. I'll have the dadgum work did by the 17th." Stiffem also was aware that Redneck would stand to lose various hauling jobs to other truckers during periods when his truck was inoperable.

When Redneck returned from vacation on Jan. 17, he went to Stiffem's repair shop to pick up his truck. Redneck learned there that Stiffem had not performed any of the repairs and that "pressing business" would keep him from getting the work done before mid-March. Redneck therefore paid Stiffem nothing and stated that he would find someone else to do the job. A week went by before Redneck (despite his best efforts) was able to retain another mechanic. That person finished the work on February 9 and charged Redneck a fair and reasonable price of $3,450. Redneck has now sued Stiffem for breach of contract. Besides being able to prove all of the above facts, Redneck is able to prove that because he could not perform the XYZ job, he lost the anticipated profit of $1,300. In addition, he is able to prove that between Jan. 22 and Feb. 8, he lost other hauling jobs on which he would have made $3,500 in profits. What amount of damages should the court award Redneck? Explain your reasoning.

22. Because business had really been jumpin' lately, Jacques Flash decided that he needed a larger and more attractive building to house his gas station. Flash therefore retained Satisfaction Construction Co. to construct the building. Satisfaction owned certain heavy equipment, which it intended to use during the construction process. On the day before Satisfaction was to begin work, the garage housing its heavy equipment collapsed. As a result, the equipment was demolished. Satisfaction could have rented substitute equipment locally, but the costs of doing so would have greatly reduced the profit it expected to make on the contract with Flash. Satisfaction therefore informed Flash that it would not be constructing the building for him. After searching for other reputable contractors, Flash retained Honky Tonk, Inc, which constructed the identical building Satisfaction was to have built. Flash had to pay Honky Tonk $4,000 more than the price called for in his contract with Satisfaction, however. Flash has sued Satisfaction for breach of contract. Satisfaction argues that it should be protected from liability by the impossibility defense. Should Satisfaction succeed with this defense? Why or why not?

23. What must be proved before an injunction will be ordered in a breach of contract case? Give an example of a breach of contract case in which an injunction is likely to be appropriate.

CHAPTER 19
FORMATION AND TERMS OF SALES CONTRACTS

True-False - Circle T for True and F for False.

T F 1. When a contract primarily calls for the performance of services but also contains sales of goods aspects, the contract will not be governed by UCC Article 2.

T F 2. The bulk transfer provisions of UCC Article 6 are designed to minimize the chances that creditors of a financially troubled professional seller of goods will be harmed by that seller's secret sale of a major part of his business.

T F 3. Under UCC Article 2, a buyer of goods cannot receive better title to the goods than the seller had.

T F 4. UCC Article 2's approach to risk of loss is to place the risk on the party who had title to the goods at the time of the loss.

T F 5. Although UCC Article 2 contains provisions concerning risk of loss, the parties to a contract for the sale of goods are generally free to specify, in their contract, which party bears the risk of loss.

T F 6. A party who is to buy goods pursuant to a contract may acquire an insurable interest in the goods before she obtains title to them.

T F 7. A CIF term in a contract for the sale of goods means that the costs of shipping and insuring the goods are not included in the price of the goods.

T F 8. If the delivery term in the parties' contract for the sale of goods is FOB the place at which the goods originate, the buyer is responsible for making reasonable arrangements for the goods to be shipped.

T F 9. If the buyer repudiates a contract for the sale of goods after the seller has already set aside the goods, the risk of loss remains with the buyer for a commercially reasonable time after the repudiation.

T F 10. If the goods serving as the subject of a contract for the sale of goods are in the possession of a bailee, the risk of loss does not pass to the buyer until the buyer receives actual possession of the goods from the baile

Multiple Choice - Circle the best answer.

11. On January 14, Kyle Co. and Tara, Inc. entered into a contract under which Kyle (the seller) was to "ship the goods to Tara [the buyer] via suitable carrier." Kyle delivered the goods to Mary's Truck Lines on January 27. On January 31, the Mary's driver arrived with the goods in Tara's city. Tara picked up the goods on February 1. When did title to the goods pass to Tara?
    a. On January 14, the date of the contract.
    b. On January 27, when Kyle made delivery to the carrier.
    c. On January 31, when the goods arrived in Tara's city.
    d. On February 1, when Tara picked up the goods.

12. Butch stole Maggie's diamond tiara and sold it to Candy, who bought the tiara in good faith and without knowledge of how Butch came into possession of it. Candy then sold the tiara to to Jasmine, another good faith purchaser who had no idea that the tiara had been stolen from Maggie. When Maggie learned of the tiara's whereabouts, she sought to recover it from Jasmine, but Jasmine refused Maggie's request. Of the following observations concerning the facts, which is/are accurate?
    a. Jasmine has title to the tiara and is entitled to retain it because she was a good-faith purchaser who had no knowledge of Butch's actions.
    b. Although Butch's theft of the tiara did not give him title to it, Candy's good-faith purchase from Butch gave her a voidable title that she could, and did, pass on to Jasmine.

c. Maggie still has title to the tiara and is entitled to possession of it because Candy, who did not acquire title when she purchased the tiara from Butch, could not pass title to Jasmine.

d. Both a and b.

13. LDD, Inc., the manufacturer of expensive clothing, sold Michael's Clothing Co., a retailer, a huge selection of items from LDD's exclusive Larry, Darryl & Darryl clothing line. The items were sold by LDD to Michael's on credit, with Michael's granting LDD a security interest in the clothing until Michael's had paid the full purchase price. Utley, an ordinary consumer with no knowledge of the security interest granted by Michael's to LDD, purchased from Michael's a $2,000 clothing ensemble consisting of items from the Larry, Darryl & Darryl line. All of the items purchased by Utley were among those in which LDD held a security interest. Michael's later defaulted on the debt it owed to LDD, which now claims that because of its security interest, it is entitled to obtain possession of the clothing items from Utley. Is LDD's claim correct?

a. Yes, because under the rule that a buyer cannot acquire better title than his seller had, any ownership rights acquired by Utley from Michael's were subject to LDD's security interest.

b. Yes, because LDD entrusted the clothing items to Michael's on the understanding that Michael's would pay its debt to LDD.

c. No, because Michael's, which possessed a voidable title to the clothing items, effectively provided Utley with clear title to them.

d. No, because when Utley purchased the clothing items from Michael's, Utley was a purchaser in the ordinary course of business.

14. Seller is a manufacturer in Manhattan, Kansas. Buyer is a retailer in Hastings, Nebraska. The parties' contract calls for shipment "FOB Hastings." Under this contract, at what point would Seller no longer bear the risk of loss?

a. When the carrier delivers the goods in Hastings.

b. When Seller delivers the goods to the carrier.

c. When the carrier departs from Manhattan.

d. When the goods are identified to the contract.

15. On June 15, Winnie Bago entered into a contract to purchase a certain recreational vehicle from Hefty RV Sales, Inc. The Hefty salesperson told Bago that Hefty would need a day to clean and service the RV before she picked it up. During the evening of June 15, a thief stole the RV from the Hefty premises. On these facts,

a. Bago bears the risk of loss, because the RV was identified to the contract before it was stolen.

b. Hefty bears the risk of loss, because the RV would not have been stolen if not for Hefty's negligenc

c. Bago bears the risk of loss, because the risk passed to her when she signed the contract.

d. Hefty bears the risk of loss, because Bago had not yet received the RV.

16. Bea took her snowblower to Ike's Sales & Service in order to have it repaired. Ike's, which customarily sold both new and used snowblowers, mistakenly sold Bea's snowblower to Fritz. When Bea learned what had occurred, she demanded that Fritz turn over the snowblower to her. Fritz, however, told Bea to "buzz off." Is Bea entitled to obtain the snowblower from Fritz?

a. No, because Bea entrusted the snowblower to Ike's and thereby facilitated the erroneous transfer to Fritz.

b. Yes, because Ike's did not have title to the snowblower; therefore, Ike's did not pass title to Fritz.

c. No, because Ike's, which had a voidable title to the snowblower, passed title to Fritz.

d. Yes, because Bea did not want the snowblower to be sold; therefore, when the sale occurred, it was as if the snowblower was stolen from her.

17. Consignor delivered certain goods to Merchant on consignment. Merchant, who does business under a name different from that of Consignor, regularly sells goods of that kind but seldom pursuant to a consignment arrangement. Of the following statements concerning the parties' *sale on consignment* arrangement, which is accurate?

    a. Under UCC Article 2, the arrangement will be treated as a *sale on approval.*

    b. Consignor's and Merchant's mutual intent that Consignor would retain title to the goods automatically gives Consignor rights to the goods that are superior to the rights of Merchant's creditors.

    c. If Consignor wishes to have his interest in the goods remain superior to the rights Merchant's creditors may have to the goods, Consignor must take appropriate notification action, as set forth in the UCC.

    d. Under UCC Article 2, the arrangement will be treated as a *no arrival, no sale* agreement.

18. Mammoth Electric Corp., an electrical utility, entered into a contract with Gigantic Coal Co. Under the contract, Mammoth was to purchase all of its requirements of coal for a five-year period from Gigantic. During the fifth year the contract was in effect, the market price for coal appeared to have permanently increased to a level far beyond the price established in the Mammoth-Gigantic contract. Therefore, Mammoth decided to order several times the amount of coal it had ordered in any of the previous four years, so that it could stockpile coal for use in future years. When Gigantic refused to fill the order completely, Mammoth sued Gigantic for breach of contract. Mammoth should:

    a. win the suit because it will eventually require the amount of coal ordered; thus, the order fits within the requirements term of the contract.

    b. lose the suit because the amount of its order is unreasonably disproportionate to what normally would be expected, based on Mammoth's past requirements.

    c. win the suit because in refusing to fill the order completely, Gigantic violated its UCC-imposed duty to proceed in good faith.

    d. lose the suit because under the UCC's approach to requirements contracts, a party cannot insist upon being provided a quantity of goods in excess of the quantity requested during the preceding year.

19. Steve Schlemiel and Marginal Construction Co. entered into a contract under which Marginal was to construct an office building for Schlemiel. Although the contract's major focus was on the skilled construction services that Marginal was to provide, it also contained sale of goods aspects because Marginal was obligated to supply certain necessary building materials. On these facts,

    a. the common law will control the contract because the presence of any services aspects in a contract makes the entire contract subject to the common law rather than to UCC Article 2.

    b. UCC Article 2 will control the sales of goods aspects of the contract and the common law will control the services aspects of the contract.

    c. UCC Article 2 will control the contract because the presence of any sale of goods aspects in a contract makes the entire contract subject to Article 2 rather than to the common law.

    d. the common law will control the contract because the contract's sale of goods aspects were incidental to its services aspects.

20. Each of the following statements purports to describe the nature, operation, or effect of a *sale on approval* arrangement. Which statement is accurate?

    a. The seller leaves goods with the buyer primarily for the purpose of resale by the buyer.

    b. Title to the pertinent goods remains with the seller, regardless of whether the buyer has made an acceptance of the goods.

    c. The buyer bears the risk of loss concerning the goods once the buyer has made an acceptance of the goods.

    d. The buyer who notifies the seller of his election to return the goods bears the expense and risk associated with the return.

21. Ritzy Jewelry Sales Co., a retailer, normally made sales on a "cash only" basis. By lying about his income and other pertinent financial information, smooth-talking Earl Sleazeman induced Ritzy's store manager, Todd Pockmarkt, to sell him a $5000 brooch on credit. Sleazeman had no intention of making any payment whatsoever to Ritzy, but he promised Pockmarkt that he would pay the full purchase price in one week. Sleazeman took possession of the brooch, did not pay for it when payment came due, and sold it to Paula Pimpleton for $4000. Pimpleton purchased the brooch in good faith and without knowledge of the false pretenses under which Sleazeman had acquired it. When Pockmarkt learned that the brooch was in Pimpleton's possession, he demanded that she turn over possession to Ritzy. Pimpleton refused. Is Ritzy entitled to obtain the brooch from Pimpleton? Why or why not?

22. Quayleco, Inc., a wholesaler, delivered certain goods to Bayhcorp, Ltd., a retailer, so that Bayhcorp could attempt to resell the goods. Quayleco and Bayhcorp agreed that Bayhcorp could return any goods remaining unsold after the expiration of three months. Answer the following questions about the Quayleco-Bayhcorp transaction:
    a. What sort of arrangement is described above? What facts justify that conclusion?
    b. While the goods are in the possession of Bayhcorp, are they subject to the claims of Bayhcorp's creditors? Why or why not?
    c. If the goods are destroyed while they are in the possession of Bayhcorp, must Bayhcorp still pay Quayleco for them? Why or why not?
    d. If Bayhcorp elects to return the unsold goods in accordance with the facts set forth above, who bears the expense and risk associated with the return?

23. Surfco, Inc., a manufacturer in Los Angeles, entered into a contract to sell certain perishable goods to Hoosier Corp., a retailer in Indianapolis. The parties' contract called for shipment "FOB Los Angeles." After making suitable arrangements for a trucking company to transport the goods to Indianapolis in a truck with a proper refrigeration chamber, Surfco delivered the goods to the trucking company's Los Angeles place of business. While the goods were en route to Indianapolis, the truck's refrigeration chamber malfunctioned and the goods were ruined. Hoosier refused to pay for the goods, so Surfco has sued Hoosier in an effort to collect the purchase price. Must Hoosier pay the purchase price? State the reasons for your answer.

CHAPTER 20

PRODUCT LIABILITY

True-False - Circle T for True and F for False.

T F 1. If the plaintiff's damages consist of direct economic loss, the absence of privity will not bar the plaintiff from winning a strict liability claim against the defendant.

T F 2. A nonmerchant seller may make the implied warranty of fitness for particular purpose.

T F 3. Because most of the information pertinent to a negligent manufacture claim is likely to be in the possession of the manufacturer, the res ipsa loquitur doctrine is unlikely to be of assistance to the plaintiff in such a case.

T F 4. The seller of consumer products costing more than $10 per item may avoid having to comply with the Magnuson-Moss Warranty Act by declining to give a written warranty.

T F 5. If A (a merchant) and B enter into a written contract for the sale of new goods from A to B, and if the contract contains a conspicuous clause stating that "no implied warranties whatsoever exist as part of this contract," the implied warranty of merchantability has not been disclaimed.

T F 6. Although the absence of privity between the plaintiff and the defendant is of virtually no significance in breach of warranty cases, it is normally fatal to a plaintiff's negligence or strict liability claim.

T F 7. The effect of a statute of repose may be to bar a product liability claim that was not barred by the applicable statute of limitations.

T F 8. As a general rule, plaintiffs are not entitled to use the breach of warranty theories established by the UCC for the recovery of damages for mere economic loss.

T F 9. Under the industry-wide liability approach, liability is imposed on various manufacturers of a standardized product, regardless of whether the plaintiff is able to prove which manufacturer produced the injury-causing product.

T F 10. The probable effectiveness of a warning, if it had been given, is among the factors considered by courts as they determine whether a seller had a duty to warn about alleged product defects.

T F 11. Although states that adhere to comparative fault principles may disagree concerning the theories of recovery to which those principles apply, the states agree that under a pure comparative fault system, the defendant has a complete defense if the plaintiff's fault was greater than the defendant's.

Multiple Choice - Circle the best answer.
Questions 12 and 13 are based on the following facts:
Trixie Belcher went to Kingly Treasures, a Memphis, Tennessee shop owned and operated by KT Corp. The shop specializes in clothing and souvenirs that would appeal to die-hard fans of the late Elvis Presley. What Belcher wanted was a jumpsuit for her boyfriend, Eddie Studley, a 320-pound insurance salesman and part-time Elvis impersonator. A Kingly Treasures salesclerk, Irv Griese, showed Belcher a size 64 sequined jumpsuit that was made of 100% polyester and was slit approximately to where the wearer's navel would be. Griese told Belcher that "this treasure [the jumpsuit] was worn by Elvis himself during his next-to-last public performance prior to his rumored death." This statement by Griese was the major reason Belcher paid $5,500 for the jumpsuit instead of purchasing one of the many other (and much less expensive) polyester jumpsuits sold at Kingly Treasures. When Griese made the statement about Presley's having worn the jumpsuit, Griese reasonably believed it to be true because Presley's cousin had made such a statement to KT officials when he sold KT the jumpsuit. Unbeknownst to Griese, KT officials, and Belcher, the statement was untrue. Presley had never worn the jumpsuit. Before Belcher learned the awful truth, she gave the jumpsuit to an ecstatic Eddie, who predictably responded with a "thank you very much, pretty mama." Eddie then wore the jumpsuit while performing his Elvis act at a Moose Lodge meeting. After the perfor-

mance, Eddie pronounced the jumpsuit "just the ticket for this sort of shindig. I couldn't ask for a better-looking, better-fitting, or better-quality jumpsuit." Later, however, the falsity of Griese's statement became known to Belcher. She therefore sued KT for damages on two alternative theories: (1) breach of express warranty; and (2) breach of the implied warranty of merchantability.

12. On the breach of express warranty claim, Belcher:
   a. will lose despite the impression created by Griese, because an express warranty can only be created in writing.
   b. will win despite Griese's (and KT's) reasonable belief that the jumpsuit had been worn by Elvis.
   c. will win because Griese (and therefore KT) should have known better than to believe the statement of Presley's cousin.
   d. will lose because she will be unable to prove that Greasy and KT intended to deceive her.

13. On the breach of implied warranty of merchantability claim, Belcher:
   a. will win because both she and Eddie would logically have been disappointed after the truth was learned.
   b. will win because the jumpsuit turned out not to be fit for the special purpose Belcher had in mind.
   c. will lose because Griese said nothing about the jumpsuit's being "merchantable;" hence, that warranty never arose.
   d. will lose because the jumpsuit was suitable for the purposes for which one would normally use a jumpsuit.

14. Through a local retailer (Woody's Boat Sales), April May purchased a new motorboat that had been manufactured by Lemon Seacraft, Inc. In order to keep the prices of its boats relatively low, Lemon made no written warranties. Because of a motor defect that had existed since May's boat left the Lemon factory, the motor did not operate and the boat was therefore unusable. When Lemon ignored May's complaints, she sued Lemon on a strict liability theory under the rule of Section 402A of the *Restatement (Second) of Torts*. Which of the following is an accurate statement about the suit?
   a. May is likely to win this suit even though she did not deal directly with Lemon, because privity is not required in strict liability cases.
   b. Lemon should argue that May's claim fails for two reasons: the nature of the supposed defect about which she complains; and the type of damages she is seeking to recover.
   c. Lemon is a seller engaged in the business of selling boats, and the Lemon boat acquired by May was defective; therefore, May should win this suit.
   d. May's biggest obstacle in her attempt to win this strict liability suit will be the difficulty of proving that Lemon failed to use reasonable care in manufacturing the boat she ultimately purchased.

15. Edith Bouffant decided to retire after many years as a self-employed beauty operator. She placed an advertisement in the local newspaper in an effort to sell her business-related equipment. With regard to a freestanding hairdryer Bouffant desired to sell, the advertisement stated that the hairdryer "has at least three repair-free years of service left in it." Spike Punk, owner of Mr. Spike's Hair Emporium, had neither seen the advertisement nor heard of its content, but he had learned through the hairdressers' grapevine that Bouffant had a hairdryer to sell. After examining the hairdryer and trying it out briefly, Punk purchased it from Bouffant. He made normal use of the hairdryer at his salon for one week, after which time the hairdryer ceased working. It was found to be in need of substantial repair. A friend of Punk's then showed him a copy of the newspaper advertisement referred to above. If Punk brings a breach of express warranty suit against Bouffant on the basis of the statement in the advertisement, Punk will:
   a. win the suit because advertisements may contain express warranties and because the hairdryer did not conform to what the advertisement stated.
   b. lose the suit because Bouffant, who is not in the business of selling equipment such as hairdryers, is not a merchant.
   c. lose the suit because the statement in the advertisement did not become part of the basis of the bargain.
   d. win the suit because the hairdryer was not fit for the ordinary purposes for which hairdryers are used.

16. Of the following statements about negligence-based product liability suits, which is accurate?

a. If the defendant was a defective product's wholesale or retail seller rather than its manufacturer, the defendant cannot be held liable on a negligence theory; instead, the strict liability theory or a warranty theory must be applied against the defendant.

b. A wholesaler or retailer will be held liable on a negligence theory for any failure to inspect a product before selling it, if an inspection would have revealed the presence of the defect that caused the plaintiff's injury.

c. Manufacturers, wholesalers, and retailers may be held to have had a duty to give an appropriate warning when the products they sold posed a reasonably foreseeable risk of harm that was not obvious to users of the products.

d. If a manufacturer's design of a product creates a risk of harm to users of the product, the manufacturer will be held liable to an injured party in a negligent design suit.

17. Floyd Lawson, a retired barber, bought a new television set and decided to sell his old one. Howard Sprague, who had not previously owned a television, informed Lawson that he (Sprague) wanted to buy a television so that he could watch programs of his choice. Lawson then expressed a willingness to sell the television to Sprague, who paid the purchase price established by Lawson and took the television home. The television worked properly for approximately an hour, but then its picture and sound failed simultaneously. When Lawson ignored Sprague's subsequent complaints, Sprague sued Lawson for alleged breaches of the implied warranties of merchantability and fitness for particular purpose. Which of the following sets forth a valid argument for Lawson to use in an effort to avoid being held liable?

a. Lawson's nonmerchant status means that no implied warranty of merchantability arose; no implied warranty of fitness for particular purpose arose because Sprague had in mind only the ordinary purpose for which televisions are used.

b. Because there was no privity between Sprague and Lawson, Sprague cannot credibly assert that there was a breach of either of the warranties on which he is relying.

c. Because implied warranties exist only as to sales of new goods and not as to sales of used goods, neither of the implied warranties being relied on by Sprague even arose.

d. Lawson's nonmerchant status means that no implied warranty of fitness for particular purpose arose; the implied warranty of merchantability was not breached because Lawson made no guarantee concerning how long the television would operate.

18. Delbert Smiley purchased a used tanning bed from real estate broker Ivana Dunn-Deal. The tanning bed had a latent defect at the time Dunn-Deal sold it to Smiley. However, Dunn-Deal neither knew, nor had reason to know, of this defect because the tanning bed had always worked properly when she had used it. When Smiley took his purchase home and put it into operation, the defect caused the tanning bed to "short out." As a result, a fire started. A significant portion of Smiley's home was destroyed before the fire could be extinguished. In an effort to collect damages for the harm to his home (which he owned) and for the minor burns he suffered in the fire, Smiley has sued Dunn-Deal. His suit is brought on a strict liability theory (under the rule in section 402A of the *Restatement (Second) of Torts*). Consider the reason or reasons why Smiley will lose this strict liability suit. Which of the following is such a reason?

a. The fact Smiley is seeking to recover for property damage.

b. The likelihood that Smiley will be unable to prove a lack of reasonable care on Dunn-Deal's part in connection with the sale.

c. The sort of seller Dunn-Deal is.

d. Each of the above.

19. Sam purchased a Sham brand personal computer from Pharaoh Corp. Assume that the implied warranties of merchantability and fitness for particular purpose would apply to the transaction unless they were effectively disclaimed. Immediately before Sam purchased the computer, Pharaoh's ultra-businesslike manager verbally told Sam that "Pharaoh hereby disclaims any and all implied warranties, including, but not limited to, the implied warranty of fitness for the purchaser's purpose." On these facts, what warranty or warranties has Pharaoh validly disclaimed?
    a. The implied warranty of merchantability.
    b. The implied warranty of fitness for particular purpose.
    c. Both the implied warranty of merchantability and the implied warranty of fitness for particular purpose.
    d. Neither the implied warranty of merchantability nor the implied warranty of fitness for particular purpose.

20. Which of the following doctrines are generally available for use as defenses in a product liability suit, regardless of the legal theory on which the suit was brought?
    a. Assumption of risk and product misuse
    b. Product misuse and contributory negligence
    c. Assumption of risk and contributory negligence
    d. Product misuse and res ipsa loquitur

21. Oma Gosch was eating Surprise brand canned tuna (processed and canned by Surprise Tuna Co.) when she choked on a small bone that was in the tuna. Gosch sustained serious injuries and incurred substantial medical expenses as a result. She has filed a breach of implied warranty of merchantability suit against Black & Blue Food Mart, where she purchased the Surprise tuna. Assume that courts of the state whose law governs the case adhere to the "reasonable expectations" test in breach of implied warranty of merchantability cases involving food. Which of the following is an accurate statement about Gosch's suit against Black & Blue?
    a. Gosch will lose the suit because only those substances that are foreign to the food item are not reasonably to be expected by the consumer.
    b. Gosch will lose the suit because there was no way that Black & Blue, which did not can the tuna, could have known about the bone; Gosch's exclusive remedy would instead be a negligence suit against Surprise Tuna Co.
    c. Gosch would have a better chance of winning the suit if applicable state law adhered to the foreign-natural test instead of to the reasonable expectations test.
    d. None of the above.

22. A limitation of remedy:
    a. prevents the plaintiff from using one or more legal theories for imposing liability on the defendant.
    b. prevents the plaintiff from recovering one or more types of damages from the defendant.
    c. is unconscionable and therefore unenforceable, whenever it pertains to damages for personal injury.
    d. is usually designed to restrict the plaintiff's ability to recover damages for direct economic loss.

23. Bart Suave, district sales manager for PDQ Corp. (a pharmaceuticals manufacturer), sold his nearly new BMW automobile to Tark Theshark, a recent graduate of UNLV's JD-MBA program. Although neither Suave nor Theshark was aware of it at the time of the sale, the BMW had a serious defect in its steering mechanism. A few days after the sale took place, Theshark was driving the BMW down a Nevada freeway when the defect in the steering mechanism caused the car to go out of control. There was nothing that Theshark could do to regain control. The BMW crashed into a bridge support as a result. Theshark was injured so severely that he incurred over $80,000 in medical bills and $63,000 in lost income, not to mention the considerable pain and suffering he experienced. He has sued Suave on a strict liability theory (under the rule of *Restatement (Second) of Torts* section 402A) and on the alternative theory of breach of the implied warranty of merchantability. Should Theshark win his suit? Why or why not? Be certain to address each of his two claims.

24. Police detective Joe Friday was considering purchasing a diamond ring for his girlfriend. He became interested in a ring he saw on display at Ruby Tuesday's jewelry store. Wanting information about the ring, Friday asked Tuesday for "just the facts, ma'am." Tuesday responded by stating that "the price I'm asking is a steal of a deal for a two-carat diamond." At the time she made the statement just quoted, Tuesday had good reason to believe, and did in fact believe, that the diamond in the ring was two carats in size. The diamond reasonably appeared to Friday to be that size. Influenced by Tuesday's statement, Friday purchased the ring. He later learned from a jewelry expert that the diamond was actually 1.5 carats in size and that he therefore had paid Tuesday an excessive price. Friday has now brought a breach of express warranty suit against Tuesday. In defense, Tuesday's argues that when she made the statement quoted above, she made no express warranty because she: a) was merely engaged in sales talk; b) did not intend to make a warranty; and c) reasonably believed the diamond was two carats in size and therefore had no intent to deceive Friday. Discuss the strength or weakness of Friday's claim, as well as the strength or weakness of each of Tuesday's arguments.

25. Retailer Dick Slitale regularly sells Boorish brand electric brain vibrators. These appliances are manufactured by ABCCBS Corp. and are furnished to retailers such as Slitale in a prepackaged state. Slitale sold a prepackaged Boorish brain vibrator to Mike Franseptictank. The first time Franseptictank used the brain vibrator, the appliance "shorted out" and caused a fire in which Franseptictank suffered serious burns. It was later determined that the shorting out and the fire had resulted from a frayed electrical cord that was a permanent part of the brain vibrator. Slitale did not remove the brain vibrator from the package to examine it before selling it to Franseptictank. If Slitale had done so, he presumably would have noticed the frayed cord, and his familiarity with the product would have caused him to realize that the frayed cord made the product unsafe for use. Franseptictank has sued Slitale for negligence, claiming that Slitale negligently failed to inspect the brain vibrator. Discuss Franseptictank's chances of winning this negligence suit.

26. Langley purchased a new Groover brand vacuum cleaner from a Groover retail dealer, XYZ Co. One day after the purchase, he loaned the vacuum cleaner to his former sister-in-law, Myrtle, who lived approximately a mile from Langley's house. While Myrtle was using the vacuum cleaner on her living room carpet, a defect in the vacuum cleaner caused the machine to give off sparks. A fire began when the sparks came in contact with the room's drapes. Myrtle's house was destroyed by the fire. Myrtle suffered severe burns. Because the facts would not justify a negligence claim against XYZ and because the state whose law is controlling does not allow nonmanufacturers such as XYZ to be held liable on a strict liability basis, Myrtle has sued XYZ on a breach of implied warranty of merchantability theory. The state whose law applies has enacted Alternative A of Uniform Commercial Code section 2-318. On these facts, should Myrtle win her suit and collect damages for the harm to herself and her property? State the reasons for your answer.

CHAPTER 21

PERFORMANCE OF SALES CONTRACTS

True-False - Circle T for True and F for False.

T F 1. In the event of a conflict between the express terms of a contract and the practices established by the parties' past course of dealing, the express terms prevail.

T F 2. A buyer who properly revokes her acceptance does not acquire the same rights she would have had if she had rejected the goods when delivery was made.

T F 3. If the goods sold by the seller to the buyer are covered by a negotiable warehouse receipt and are in the possession of a third party warehouse operator, the seller satisfies his obligation to tender the goods to the buyer by indorsing the warehouse receipt and giving it to the buyer.

T F 4. Under UCC Article 2, a contract obligation whose performance is not impossible cannot be declared commercially impracticable.

T F 5. Under UCC Article 2, consideration is not necessary to support a modification of a contract for the sale of goods.

T F 6. Usage of trade may supplement, and provide a basis for interpreting, the express terms of a contract for the sale of goods.

T F 7. In any sale of goods transaction in which the buyer has rejected the goods supplied, the seller has a legal right to a written statement of all of the defects on which the rejection decision was based.

T F 8. If the buyer informs the seller, prior to the previously agreed date for delivery of the goods, that the buyer will not be performing his contract obligation, the seller is free to cancel the contract without waiting until the agreed delivery date to do so.

T F 9. Even if the seller insists that the buyer pay cash for ordered goods, the UCC allows the buyer to pay by any method used in the ordinary course of business.

T F 10. If the seller and the buyer have agreed that the goods are to be delivered in more than one lot or installment but have not agreed on when payment is to be made, the seller cannot insist on being paid for any delivered lot or installment until all lots or installments have been delivered.

Multiple Choice - Circle the best answer.

11. Ann Onymous ordered a certain dress from Bland's End Co.'s mail order catalog. When the dress arrived, Onymous noticed that it was not the one she had ordered. Because she was going out to dinner that evening with a friend, she wore the dress anyway. A week later, Onymous sent the dress back to Bland's End with a letter stating that she was rejecting the dress because it was not what she had ordered. On these facts, Onymous:
    a. made a valid rejection of the dress.
    b. exercised her right to cure.
    c. properly revoked her acceptance of the dress.
    d. accepted the dress.

12. In August, automobile dealer Lola Lemon and Easy State University treasurer Emmett Bezzler entered into a contract under which Lemon was to sell a certain $40,000 automobile to Bezzler. Delivery and payment were to take place in November, when Lemon was to obtain the car from its manufacturer. Early in September, Lemon read newspaper stories indicating that Bezzler was under investigation for alleged misappropriation of university funds and was likely to be fired by the university's board of trustees before the end of the semester. A concerned Lemon wrote to Bezzler on September 10 and requested an assurance that he would pay for the car in accordance with the contract terms. Which of the following is an accurate statement?

a. Lemon had no right to request such an assurance from Bezzler, who, accordingly, has no duty to respond to Lemon's letter.

b. If Bezzler fails to respond to Lemon's letter within 30 days after receiving it, he will be regarded as having repudiated the contract.

c. Assuming Bezzler makes no response to Lemon's letter but is ready, willing, and able to pay the purchase price in November, Lemon will be in breach of contract if she fails to deliver the car.

d. Lemon's letter is a repudiation that relieves Bezzler of his responsibility to perform the contract.

13. Block Co. and Shoddy Construction Co. Inc. had a written contract calling for Block to deliver a certain quantity of concrete blocks to Shoddy's place of business on the first day of each month for one year. Block delivered the bricks one week late for each of the first six months, but Shoddy made no objection. When Block delivered the bricks one week late during the seventh month, Shoddy claimed that the late deliveries breached the contract and that it (Shoddy) was therefore cancelling the contract. Was Shoddy within its rights in cancelling the contract?

a. Yes, because there was not a written modification justifying Block's late deliveries.

b. No, because Shoddy waived its right to cancel the contract on the asserted basis.

c. No, because the contract has been modified.

d. Yes, because Block has had ample opportunity to perform in a timely manner but has consistently failed to do so.

14. Which of the following is an accurate statement about the right to cure established by UCC Article 2?

a. It is limited to instances in which the seller provided defective goods before the agreed date of delivery and is still able to supply nondefective goods prior to that date.

b. It exists whenever the seller has shipped nonconforming goods but would be capable of shipping conforming goods if given a reasonable amount of additional time within which to do so.

c. It sometimes applies so as to provide the seller who has shipped nonconforming goods a reasonable time within which to ship conforming goods, even if the original time for delivery has expired.

d. It exists in favor of buyers who wrongfully rejected the goods supplied by the seller but now wish to cure their breach by accepting the goods.

15. Each of the following statements pertains to acceptances and/or rejections of goods delivered by the seller to the buyer. Which statement is accurate?

a. The buyer who accepts nonconforming goods is deemed to have given up the damages claims he otherwise would have had against the seller because of the delivery of nonconforming goods.

b. When the seller delivers defective goods, the buyer cannot reject the goods; instead, the buyer must accept the goods and seek appropriate money damages from the seller.

c. If the buyer fails to give the seller timely notice of rejection of nonconforming goods shipped by the seller, the buyer may be regarded as having accepted the nonconforming goods.

d. None of the above.

16. Assume that the seller has delivered goods that are in part conforming and in part nonconforming. Under these circumstances, the buyer:

a. must reject the entire shipment if he does not wish to pay the full contract price, because the acceptance of any commercial unit in the shipment means that the buyer is deemed to have accepted the entire shipment.

b. must accept the nonconforming goods and pay the agreed contract price, but the buyer will receive an offset equal to the amount of damages stemming from the seller's delivery of nonconforming goods.

c. is free to accept any parts of a commercial unit that are conforming and to reject other parts of the same commercial unit that are nonconforming.

d. may reject nonconforming commercial units and accept conforming commercial units, but if the buyer does so, he must pay at the contract rate for the units accepted.

114

17. Evan Gelist, owner of the Heavenly Waterbeds store, ordered ten waterbeds from Leakco, Inc. When the waterbeds arrived, Gelist inspected them and found them to be defective. Therefore, he refused to accept them. Gelist also provided Leakco a written notice of rejection in which he specifed the defects he had discovered. Which of the following statements accurately sets forth a right or responsibility that Gelist has with regard to the waterbeds?

   a. In the absence of instructions from Leakco regarding disposition of the waterbeds, Gelist has the option of reselling them for Leakco's benefit.

   b. Gelist's sole responsibility is to hold the waterbeds for a reasonable time so that Leakco may remove them.

   c. At his option, Gelist may choose to follow reasonable instructions that Leakco gives regarding disposition of the waterbeds.

   d. If Leakco does not give Gelist instructions for disposition of the waterbeds, Gelist must ship them back to Leakco at Leakco's expense.

18. Which of the following is an accurate statement about the buyer's right to inspect the goods supplied by the seller?

   a. As a general rule, the buyer is entitled to inspect the goods before she accepts or pays for them, regardless of whether the buyer and the seller have expressly agreed to that effect.

   b. In a COD sale, the buyer must inspect the goods before paying for them, or else she loses any remedy she otherwise would have had against the seller for a nonconformity in the goods.

   c. Absent an agreement between the buyer and the seller concerning when, where, and how an inspection of the goods will be conducted, the buyer does not have a right to inspect the goods before accepting or paying for them.

   d. In a COD sale, the buyer cannot reject the goods before paying for them even if the goods possess an obvious defect that can be seen without an actual inspection.

19. Marian purchased a new television on credit from Uncle Lyle's TV Sales. When Marian took the television home and attempted to use it, she discovered that the sound would not work. She immediately took the television back and told Uncle Lyle that she did not want it because of the problem with the sound. Later that day, Marian sent Uncle Lyle a letter reiterating the substance of their conversation. Which of the following statements is accurate?

   a. Marian lost her ability to reject the television because she failed to inspect it before buying it.

   b. Uncle Lyle must be given an opportunity to exercise his UCC-given right to cure.

   c. Because Marian used the television, she lost her ability to reject it.

   d. Marian's actions are consistent with a proper rejection of the television.

20. The contract between Fruitco, Inc. and Bogus Co. called for Fruitco to "ship" Bogus a truckload of perishable fruit. Fruitco arranged for a trucking company to transport the fruit, but did not have the vegetables shipped in a truck with a refrigeration chamber. When the vegetables reached Bogus, the entire truckload's worth had spoiled. Is Bogus entitled to reject the shipment?

   a. No, because Bogus is obligated to try to resell the vegetables to someone else.

   b. Yes, because Fruitco bore the risk of loss until the goods actually were delivered to Bogus.

   c. Yes, because Fruitco failed to make a reasonable contract for shipping the goods.

   d. No, because this was a shipment contract, meaning that the risk of loss passed to Bogus when Fruitco delivered the goods to the carrier.

Short Essay

21. Electorate Co., a retailer of toys, and Running Mate, Inc., a manufacturer of toys, entered into a contract under which Running Mate was to sell Electorate 200 of Running Mate's Veep brand toy robots. The contract called for Electorate to pay the $20,000 purchase price at the time the Veep robots were delivered. Although the Veep robots had no actual thought process and could not speak extemporaneously, they were to be capable (according to Running Mate's sales brochures) of "reading" a few simple words from a prepared text and performing such basis tasks as putting a golf ball. Running Mate delivered the 200 robots, which Electorate accepted by taking possession

115

and paying the agreed purchase price. Several days later, Electorate discovered that although 196 of the robots were as represented in Running Mate's sales brochures, four of them could neither "read" words from a prepared text nor putt a golf ball. Citing the defective robots, Electorate notified Running Mate that it was revoking its acceptance of the 200 robots and that it desired a refund of the $20,000 it had paid. On these facts, is Electorate entitled to revoke its acceptance? Explain your reasoning.

22. Skip Dorfman owns Skip's Fruit Mart, a retail shop at which he sells a wide variety of fruit. Dorfman ordered a large quantity of peaches from a fruit wholesaler. When the peaches arrived, they were more ripe than they should have been in order to be sold in the usual course of Dorfman's business. Dorfman therefore notified the wholesaler that he was rejecting the peaches. What are Dorfman's responsibilities regarding the peaches?

23. Marginal, Inc. and Average Co. entered into a contract under which Marginal was to manufacture certain goods for Average and deliver them to Average by September 1. Shortly after the agreement was reached, Marginal's 300 employees began a lengthy strike without prior warning to Marginal management. Because Marginal was able to hire only a few replacement workers who were willing to cross the picket line, Marginal found it necessary to shut down its plant. When Marginal failed to deliver the goods by September 1, Average sued Marginal for breach of contract. What argument should Marginal make in an attempt to avoid liability? What facts should Marginal stress in making that argument?

CHAPTER 22

REMEDIES FOR BREACH OF SALES CONTRACTS

True-False - Circle T for True and F for False.

T F 1. The objective underlying UCC Article 2's remedy provisions is to place the nonbreaching party in the same position he would have been in if the contract had never been formed.

T F 2. If the buyer's breach justifies the seller in withholding delivery of the goods, the seller may be permitted to retain a portion of the funds already paid by the buyer to the seller, even if the parties' agreement did not contain a liquidated damages clause.

T F 3. When a contract for the sale of goods contains a liquidated damages clause, the enforceability of the clause depends upon its content and effect.

T F 4. If, because of the buyer's breach of contract, the seller intends to resell the goods at a public sale, the seller ordinarily is not required to give the buyer notice of the time and place of the sale.

T F 5. If the buyer breaches the contract and the seller elects to cancel the contract and withhold delivery of the goods, he is not free to seek money damages from the buyer.

T F 6. If the seller discovers that the buyer has received goods on credit from the seller while the buyer was insolvent, the seller may reclaim the goods from the buyer by making a demand to that effect within 10 days after the buyer's receipt of the goods.

T F 7. Under UCC Article 2, a contractual limitation of liability for consequential damages is unconscionable as a matter of law if it purports to exclude liability for commercial losses.

T F 8. Under UCC Article 2, the buyer is entitled to forego purchasing available substitute goods and may instead choose the remedy of specific performance when the seller breaches the contract by failing to provide the goods.

T F 9. If the buyer repudiates the parties' contract while the seller is in the process of manufacturing the subject goods, the seller must cease the manufacturing process and sell the uncompleted goods for their scrap or salvage value, in order to mitigate damages.

T F 10. The seller ordinarily will be entitled to recover the full contract price in a breach of contract suit against the buyer where the buyer's breach has left the seller in possession of specially manufactured goods that the seller cannot sell to another party.

Multiple Choice - Circle the best answer.

11. Bogus Corp. breached its contract with Shamco, Inc. by failing to deliver the agreed-upon goods to Shamco on the agreed-upon date of delivery or at any time thereafter. Accordingly, Shamco did not pay Bogus any part of the contract price of $56,000. As of the delivery date, the market price for such goods had risen to $67,000. Without attempting to purchase substitute goods, Shamco sued Bogus for breach of contract. Which of the following statements is accurate?
    a. Shamco is entitled to $67,000 in damages from Bogus, because that is the amount Shamco will have to pay if it decides to purchase substitute goods.
    b. Shamco's failure to attempt to purchase substitute goods means that Shamco cannot collect any damages from Bogus.
    c. On the facts given, Shamco is entitled to $11,000 in damages from Bogus even though Shamco made no attempt to buy substitute goods.
    d. The fact that Shamco did not find it necessary to seek substitute goods means that Shamco was not damaged by Bogus's breach; therefore, Shamco will lose the suit.

12. Retailer accepted and paid for a truckload of electric fans delivered by Manufacturer. Retailer soon discovered that the fans were defective, so Retailer promptly notified Manufacturer of the defects. On these facts, Retailer has a valid claim against Manufacturer for:

    a. an amount equal to the value the fans would have had if they had not been defective.

    b. an amount equal to the difference between the value of the fans received and the value they would have had if they had not been defective.

    c. specific performance, i.e., delivery of a truckload of nondefective fans.

    d. either a or c, at Retailer's option.

13. Hear Co. entered into a May 1, 1991 contract with Their Corp. for the sale of 10,000 widgets from Hear to Their. The contract called for a price of $3.50 per widget, payable at the time of delivery of the widgets. On July 1, 1991, when Hear attempted to deliver the widgets at Their's place of business in accordance with the parties' agreement, Their wrongfully refused to accept the widgets. Of course, Their also refused to pay Hear. Instead of attempting to resell the widgets, Hear sued Their for breach of contract. As of July 1, 1991, the relevant market price for widgets in Their's locality was $3.10 per widget. On these facts, Hear:

    a. should recover $35,000 in damages from Their, because that is the amount Hear would have received if Their had performed the contract.

    b. should recover $4,000 in damages from Their because that amount represents the difference between the contract price and the relevant market price.

    c. is not entitled to recover any damages from Their because Hear made no attempt to resell the widgets to another party.

    d. is not entitled to recover any compensatory damages for the reason stated in answer c, but should be awarded punitive damages because of Their's deliberate breach.

14. Throneberry contracted to supply Quisenberry 1000 jars of strawberry jelly at a price of $2.50 per jar. Throneberry repudiated the contract by notifying Quisenberry that he would not be providing the jelly, so Quisenberry paid nothing to Throneberry. Instead, Quisenberry bought 1000 jars of strawberry jelly from Mayberry at a price of $3.25 per jar, which was the lowest price Quisenberry could obtain under the circumstances. Quisenberry then made demand upon Throneberry for payment of damages for breach of contract. On these facts, what amount of damages is owed by Throneberry to Quisenberry?

    a. $3250

    b. $2500

    c. $750

    d. 0

15. When the seller has agreed to sell the buyer goods on credit but later discovers that the buyer is insolvent, the seller:

    a. may stop delivery of goods already shipped to and not yet received by the buyer, but only if the shipment qualifies as a large shipment.

    b. may immediately sue the buyer for the full purchase price.

    c. must still deliver the goods to the buyer but can then obtain rescission.

    d. may refuse to deliver the goods to the buyer unless the buyer pays cash.

16. If the buyer's breach of a contract for the sale of goods leaves the seller in possession of the goods, the seller:

    a. may be allowed to collect damages from the buyer even when the seller makes no effort to resell the goods to someone else.

    b. is generally allowed the option of collecting the full contract price from the buyer.

    c. may be allowed a remedy whose effect is to place him in a better position than he would have been in if the contract had been performed, because of the UCC policy of deterring parties from breaching valid contracts.

    d. will not be allowed to collect damages from the buyer unless the seller attempts to resell the goods to someone else.

17. Mindy Mork purchased a Jesfair brand refrigerator at a special factory clearance sale conducted on August 15, 1986 by the refrigerator's manufacturer, Jesfair Co. She took delivery of the refrigerator the same day. Jesfair warranted the refrigerator for three years from the date of purchase. The refrigerator ceased operating on June 1, 1989. Jesfair refused to remedy the problems. Mork waited until July 15, 1991 to sue Jesfair. On these facts, Mork's claim is:

    a. barred by the UCC's four-year statute of limitations, because her suit was filed more than four years after the date she took delivery of the refrigerator.

    b. allowable under the UCC statute of limitations, which extends for five years from the date of delivery of the goods.

    c. barred by the terms of the Jesfair warranty, because she failed to file her suit against Jesfair during the three-year warranty period.

    d. not barred by the UCC's four-year statute of limitations, which began to run on June 1, 1989, the date the breach of warranty occurred.

18. Les Wastem owns Wastem Guns, a retail firearms shop. Wastem and Awol Co. entered into a contract under which Awol was to supply Wastem with ten firearms of a particular type in return for payment of $3000 at the time of delivery. Awol, which was aware that Wastem intended to sell the firearms to his retail customers, breached the contract by failing to provide the firearms on the agreed delivery date (June 1, 1991) or at any time thereafter. Wastem, therefore, paid nothing to Awol. After diligent effort, Wastem finally found an alternate supplier on July 5, 1991. On that date, he purchased, for the sum of $3500, ten firearms of the type Awol was to have supplied. Wastem brought a breach of contract suit against Awol and proved at trial that between June 1 and July 4, 1991, he would have made $2400 in profits on sales that would have been accomplished if he had had the firearms Awol was to have supplied. In addition, Wastem proved that he incurred reasonable expenses of $250 in connection with locating the alternate supplier and securing the substitute goods. On these facts, what amount of damages is Wastem entitled to receive from Awol?

    a. $750

    b. $3150

    c. $3750

    d. $5650

19. Under UCC Article 2, a contractual limitation of remedy:

    a. is enforceable unless it fails of its essential purpose.

    b. is unconscionable and therefore unenforceable.

    c. cannot lawfully be employed in a contract for the sale of consumer goods.

    d. will be enforced by the courts unless it limits the buyer's remedies to repair and replacement.

20. Seller and Buyer had a valid contract for the sale of goods. Buyer wrongfully refused to accept the goods when Seller attempted to deliver them. Of the following remedies against Buyer, to which is Seller *least* likely to be entitled?

    a. Recovery of the contract price.

    b. Recovery of the profits Seller would have made if Buyer had not breached the contract.

    c. Recovery of the difference between the contract price and a lower price received by Seller upon resale of the goods to another party.

    d. Recovery of incidental damages caused by the breach.

21. On April 1, Seller and Buyer entered into a contract under which Seller was to provide Buyer with 2000 standard-sized toilets at a price of $20 per toilet. The contract called for payment to be made by Buyer at the time of delivery, which was to take place at Buyer's place of business on July 1. The volatile toilet market later changed significantly, so that as of July 1, the market price for standard-sized toilets in Buyer's geographic area had plummeted to $13 per toilet. Seller's manufacturing and labor costs and other overhead amounted to $9 per toilet. Buyer breached the parties' contract by refusing to accept and pay for the toilets when Seller tendered delivery on July 1. Without attempting to resell the toilets to another party, Seller filed a breach of contract suit against Buyer. On these facts, what amount of damages is Seller entitled to receive from Buyer? Explain the basis for your answer.

22. Marginal Co., a manufacturer, breached its contract with Risky Corp., a retailer, by failing to supply the subject goods on the agreed delivery date or at any time thereafter. Marginal was aware that Risky intended to resell the goods at a profit to its retail customers. Because Marginal failed to supply the goods, Risky, of course, did not pay the agreed purchase price of $14,000. As of the date delivery was to have taken place, the market price of goods of the sort Marginal was to have supplied was $18,000. Although Risky could have secured substitute goods with little difficulty and essentially no delay at approximately the market price just mentioned, it chose not to purchase substitute goods. Risky sued Marginal for breach of contract. At trial, Risky proved it lost certain sales that it would have been able to make if Marginal had made timely delivery of the goods. Risky also proved that it would have made $7000 in profits on those sales if they had been made. What amount of damages is Risky entitled to recover from Marginal? State the reasons for your answer.

23. Woody's Sales & Service Co. and Chuck Jerkman entered into a valid written contract under which Woody's was to sell Jerkman a television for the agreed price of $500, a VCR for the agreed price of $300, and a video camera for the agreed price of $450. On the agreed delivery date, Woody's attempted to deliver the three items, which conformed to the contract in all respects. Jerkman wrongfully refused to accept the goods and paid Woody's nothing. Thereafter, Woody's gave Jerkman notice of its intention to resell the items at private sale. By means of the private sale, which did not cause Woody's to incur any incidental expenses, Woody's sold the items to another buyer and received $500 for the television, $350 for the VCR, and $500 for the video camera. Woody's then sued Jerkman for breach of contract. In view of the facts and the governing legal principles, to what amount of damages is Woody's entitled, and why?

CHAPTER 23

PERSONAL PROPERTY AND BAILMENTS

True-False - Circle T for True and F for False.

T F   1.   Trademark rights are classified as intangible property.

T F   2.   Neither a gift *inter vivos* nor a gift *causa mortis* is revocable after delivery of the item.

T F   3.   An express contract is not necessary to the creation of a bailment.

T F   4.   Actual physical control is not always necessary in order for one to have legal possession of property.

T F   5.   A bailee in a bailment for the benefit of the bailee alone is held to a lower standard of care than is the bailee in a mutual benefit bailment.

T F   6.   Confusion is the mixing of goods belonging to different owners in such a way that the goods cannot later be separated.

T F   7.   The first person to take possession of wildlife or abandoned property does not necessarily become its owner.

T F   8.   One requirement for a valid gift is that the donor has irrevocably given up possession and control of the property to the donee or a third person.

T F   9.   Personal property may become part of real property, and is then known as intangible property.

T F 10.   A disclaimer that purports to relieve a bailee of liability for intentional harm to the property is unenforceable.

Multiple Choice - Circle the best answer.

11.   Fritz found a bicycle in the grass alongside a country road. Unbeknownst to Fritz, the bicycle belonged to Orville. It had fallen out of a fully loaded pickup truck that Orville had been driving on that road earlier in the day. Fritz took the bicycle home and improved it, incurring expenses in the process. Orville eventually learned that his bicycle was in Fritz's possession. He asked Fritz to return it but Fritz, citing the improvements he had made, declined because he considered himself the owner of the bicycle. Which of the following is an accurate statement?

a.   Orville is entitled to the bicycle, without any obligation to reimburse Fritz for the cost of the improvements.

b.   Orville has an absolute right to recover the bicycle after paying for the improvements.

c.   At the very least, Fritz is entitled to recover the cost of the improvements made to the bicycle.

d.   Under no circumstances would a court permit Fritz to keep the bicycle.

12.   Which of the following is an accurate statement about conditional gifts?

a.   They may be revoked at any time by the donor, even if the donee has partially complied with the conditions.

b.   They do not include gifts given in contemplation of marriage.

c.   They are the same thing as completed gifts.

d.   As a general rule, they may be revoked by the donor before the donee complies with the conditions.

13. "U 8 Yit?" is a restaurant located near the Atlantic coast of a southern state. U 8 Yit? operated a coatcheck room, above whose door was a sign stating that the restaurant "is not liable for loss or damage to checked items, regardless of cause." When Hurricane Jim Bob struck the coast with great force, the U 8 Yit? premises was leveled. All of the checked coats that had been in the coatcheck room were damaged beyond repair. Is U 8 Yit? liable to the owners of the coats?
    a. Yes, because its attempted disclaimer is unenforceable.
    b. No, because the damage to the coats was not caused by the restaurant's negligence or other fault.
    c. No, because its disclaimer would be enforceable in any instance of damage to checked coats, regardless of the the cause.
    d. No, because no bailment was created.

14. If a customer parks his car in a parking lot and keeps the keys:
    a. no bailment has been created.
    b. a bailment for mutual benefit has been created.
    c. a bailment for the sole benefit of the bailor has been created.
    d. a bailment for the sole benefit of the bailee has been created.

15. Which of the following is an accurate statement about a bailment?
    a. It occurs whenever the owner of goods surrenders possession of the goods to another.
    b. It is the delivery of personal property to another, who accepts it and is under an obligation to return it.
    c. It is any kind of intangible personal property.
    d. It may involve the delivery of real property to another.

16. Obtaining title to property by accession involves:
    a. revoking a gift of the property.
    b. finding lost property.
    c. increasing the value of property by adding labor or materials.
    d. holding misplaced property for the true owner until the statute of limitations runs.

17. In an ordinary bailment for mutual benefit, the bailee:
    a. is strictly liable for any damage to the bailed goods.
    b. owes the duty of the highest possible care to the bailor in looking after the goods.
    c. must use ordinary care in looking after the goods.
    d. owes the duty of somewhat less than ordinary care in looking after the goods.

18. Which of the following is an accurate statement about lost property?
    a. It is one type of mislaid property.
    b. The finder must return it to its true owner if the true owner claims it.
    c. Ownership of it cannot be acquired by the finder's possession of it for longer than the statute of limitations period.
    d. It is one type of abandoned property.

19. Gert purchased trees and shrubs and planted them in her yard. The trees and shrubs are now:
    a. ancillary property.
    b. personal property.
    c. intangible property.
    d. real property.

20. Delivery of an *inter vivos* gift:
    a. must be accomplished while the donor is alive.
    b. must be accomplished by manual delivery to the donee.
    c. must be supported by consideration to be effective.
    d. cannot be accomplished by symbolic means.

21. Harmon took five suits, which together were worth $1,000, to Ollie's 12-Hour Dry Cleaning, Inc. He gave the suits to an Ollie's employee and paid, in advance, the charges for the suits to be cleaned. The employee then gave Harmon a receipt. After he arrived at home, Harmon noticed that at the bottom of the receipt, the following statement appeared: "Maximum liability of Ollie's for loss of or damage to customers' clothing shall be $50." The Ollie's employee with whom Harmon dealt had said nothing to that effect. Harmon had no previous knowledge of any such policy. When Harmon returned the next day to pick up his suits, he learned that as a result of the negligence of an Ollie's employee in operating the dry cleaning equipment, Harmon's suits had been reduced to a pile of ashes. Ollie's refused to pay Harmon any more than $50. Is Ollie's liable for the remainder of Harmon's loss? Explain your reasoning.

22. Doyle loaned his car to Prudence without informing her that the car's brakes were bad. Doyle did not intend to endanger Prudence. Rather, he simply forgot to tell her about the brake problem. While driving the car, Prudence was injured in a collision that resulted from the bad brakes. Is Doyle liable to Prudence for his failure to tell her about the brake problem? Why or why not?

23. Bart Suave found a wallet in the pocket of the tuxedo he rented for the prom. Is the wallet lost, mislaid, or abandoned property? What would Suave's rights be under each of the foregoing classifications of property?

CHAPTER 24

REAL PROPERTY AND INSURANCE

True-False - Circle T for True and F for False.

T F 1. A fire that begins as a friendly fire may become a hostile fire, for purposes of determining whether a loss is covered by a fire insurance policy.

T F 2. In community property states, not all property owned by a married person is community property.

T F 3. The distinguishing feature of a joint tenancy is the right of survivorship.

T F 4. Coinsurance clauses apply only in cases of total losses of property.

T F 5. A transfer of real property will not also convey the fixtures located on the property unless the fixtures are mentioned in the transfer documents.

T F 6. An easement appurtenant is primarily designed to give a personal right to an individual property owner, rather than to benefit a certain parcel of property.

T F 7. Without an insurable interest on the part of the purchaser, an insurance contract would be an illegal wagering contract.

T F 8. The government may be required to pay compensation for a "taking" of private property even when it has not formally exercised the power of eminent domain.

T F 9. A quitclaim deed guarantees title to the subject property.

T F 10. A deed need not be recorded in order to be valid as between the grantor and the grantee.

Multiple Choice - Circle the best answer.

11. Gabrielle purchased, from Heartless Insurance Co., a fire insurance policy covering her home. The policy was a valued policy with a face amount of $113,000—the amount Gabrielle had paid for the property. Two years after the policy went into effect, the home was totally destroyed by fire. At the time of the fire, Gabrielle's home had a fair market value of $99,000, because of declining property values in the area where it was located. On these facts, how much must Heartless pay Gabrielle?

    a. $99,000
    b. $99,000 plus interest at the legal rate
    c. $113,000
    d. $106,000

12. In 1960, Ollie, the owner of Blackacre, conveyed his fee simple interest "to my brothers, Orville and Oscar, as joint tenants." In 1970, Orville died. In his will, Orville left interest in the property to "my son, Cedric, for life, then to Cedric's son, Sol, for life, and then to Sol's children and their heirs." In 1980, Oscar died. In Oscar's will, he left his interest in the property "to my friend Felix and his heirs." In 1982, Felix conveyed the property by deed to Sue, who wants to convey title to the land. Can she?

    a. Yes.
    b. Yes, but only if Cedric, Sol, and Sol's son join in the conveyance.
    c. No, because Sol may have additional children who have legitimate future interests in the land.
    d. No, because Ollie's intent was to keep the land in his family, so a fee tail was created by implication.

13. Which of the following is an accurate statement of the law in most community property states?
    a. A spouse who has never been employed outside the home takes a 40% share of property acquired by either during the marriage.
    b. Each spouse owns an equal interest in all property acquired through the efforts of either during the marriage.
    c. A husband or wife cannot dispose of his or her share of community property by will.
    d. Each spouse has an equal interest in all property owned by the other spouse.

14. When property is damaged and the insured has an open policy,
    a. the insurer cannot be given the option of restoring the property, regardless of what the policy purports to say.
    b. the insurer cannot be compelled to pay the insured more than the fair market value of the property.
    c. the insured will recover the amount stated in the policy, the property's fair market value notwithstanding.
    d. both a and c are accurate.

15. Duke and Wayne own adjoining parcels of farmland. Duke granted Wayne the right to install pipes across Duke's property in order to facilitate the pumping of water from a lake next to Duke's property, as well as the transmission of that water to Wayne's property for irrigation purposes. This grant is most likely to be:
    a. a negative easement.
    b. a profit.
    c. a license.
    d. an easement appurtenant.

16. Which of the following is *not* required in order for an easement by prescription to exist?
    a. Prior unity of ownership
    b. Use for a statutory period
    c. Adverse and hostile use
    d. Open, obvious, or apparent use

17. When the insured has purchased fire insurance policies from more than one insurer and there is a loss as to which each policy would appear to provide full coverage if it were the only policy in force at the pertinent time,
    a. the insured is entitled to collect the full amount of the loss from each insurer, assuming that the insured is current on the premiums for each policy.
    b. the loss must be paid by the insurer whose policy went into effect first.
    c. the loss must be paid by the insurer whose policy went into effect last.
    d. the loss will be apportioned among the insurers in accordance with the relationships the respective amounts of the individual policies bear to the total amount of insurance on the property.

18. Robinson purchased a house from Gelhorn under a contract which provided that Robinson was purchasing "all fixtures." After Robinson took possession, he found that Gelhorn had taken with him the electric garage door opener, a small oil painting that had been hanging on a hook in the living room, the built-in dishwasher, and a number of books that had been in built-in bookshelves in the library. Assuming that Robinson and Gelhorn had never discussed any of these items, which ones were fixtures that passed to Robinson upon sale of the house?
    a. The painting and the books.
    b. The built-in dishwasher only.
    c. The garage door opener and the built-in dishwasher.
    d. All of the items mentioned in the facts.

19. Otto began occupying land owned by Edith. He lived on the property as if it were his for 33 years. He also regularly paid taxes on the property. Edith did not like this, but she did nothing about it until the 34th year, when she went to see Otto and ordered him off the property. Must Otto go?

    a. Yes, because he only had a implied license to occupy the property—a license that was revocable by Edith.

    b. No, because he now possesses an easement appurtenant.

    c. Yes, because Edith never granted permission for him to occupy the property.

    d. No, because he owns the property.

20. Under which of the following circumstances would a tenant *not* be permitted to remove trade fixtures?

    a. If the tenant fails to remove them before the end of his lease for a definite period, or within a reasonable time after the expiration of a lease for an indefinite period.

    b. If the fixtures are used in the tenant's trade or business.

    c. If the fixtures are attached in any way to the leased premises.

    d. If removal of the fixtures would be obvious to the next tenant.

Short Essay

21. Overbearing Realty, Inc. purchased a fire insurance policy from Tight Insurance Co. The policy covered the building that housed the Overbearing business. The policy contained a 70 percent co-insurance clause. Although the building had a fair market value of $500,000, Overbearing purchased a policy with a face amount of $300,000. A fire caused $77,000 worth of damage to the building. How much must Tight pay Overbearing on Overbearing's claim under the policy? Explain how you arrived at your answer.

22. Ned and Norma Nimrod purchased a new home from Biltrong Construction Co, which had built the house. Within a month after moving into the house, the Nimrods noticed that numerous cracks had formed in the basement walls. These cracks allowed large amounts of water to accumulate in the basement during any rainfall. The roof of the house also leaked very badly, allowing large puddles of water to form in every room in the house. Significant amounts of moisture also came into the house because of poorly installed windows. The house was so consistently damp that mildew was forming in various rooms. When the Nimrods complained, Biltrong pointed out that it had not made any express guarantees regarding workmanship. Assume that Biltrong did not make made fraudulent representations when it sold the house to the Nimrods. Do the Nimrods have any recourse against Biltrong? If so, on what legal theory? If not, why not?

23. Quig has owned and operated a butcher shop in the same spot for 30 years. When he started in business, there were no zoning laws in effect. The town recently zoned Quig's neighborhood exclusively for residential uses. Butcher shops are not included as a permitted use. May Quig continue to operate his butcher shop? Why or why not?

CHAPTER 25

LANDLORD AND TENANT

True-False - Circle T for True and F for False.

T F 1. Constructive eviction occurs when a landlord ejects a tenant for nonpayment of rent.

T F 2. The tenant has a property interest in the leased premises that may be transferred to another person by the assignment of the lease unless the lease expressly provides that it shall not be assigned.

T F 3. The tenants are responsible for keeping the common areas in repair and in a safe condition for tenants and visitors to the property.

T F 4. As a general rule, a lease is ended by the tenant's surrender of the property to the landlord and the landlord's acceptance of the property.

T F 5. The implied warranty of habitability means that the tenant has the obligation to return the property to the landlord at the end of the lease in the same condition in which it was rented, normal wear and tear excepted.

T F 6. A lease may be created without an explicit agreement between landlord and tenant as to how long the lease will last.

T F 7. By virtue of being the owner of the property, a landlord has the legal right to enter leased premises for any purpose and whenever he wishes to do so.

T F 8. Many cities and states have enacted housing codes that impose duties on landlords with respect to the quality of leased residential property.

T F 9. A landlord may be liable for foreseeable criminal conduct committed against his tenants by third persons.

T F 10. A landlord is liable for all injuries suffered by tenants on the leased premises.

Multiple Choice - Circle the best answer.

11. Steve Slovenly, an Easy State University student, rented an apartment for one year from Jayvee Properties Co. After the first semester, Slovenly planned to transfer to a different school in a different city, but he still had six months to go on his lease. He therefore subleased the apartment to Todd Piercedear. Which of the following is true?
    a. If Piercedear does not pay the rent, Slovenly is liable to Jayvee for the amount of the rent.
    b. Slovenly could not lawfully sublease the apartment, even if his lease was silent on the matter of subleasing.
    c. Slovenly has no further liability to Jayvee.
    d. Slovenly could not lawfully sublease the apartment without the permission of Jayvee, even if his lease was silent on the matter of subleasing.

12. Which of the following would create a periodic tenancy?
    a. A lease for a period of nine months, from July 1, 1991 through March 31, 1992.
    b. Rental of a furnished apartment on a weekly basis.
    c. Tenant stays in possession after the expiration of a one-year lease and Landlord elects to treat him as a trespasser.
    d. Father allows his son and daughter-in-law to live in a cabin on his land indefinitely, without any agreement about paying rent or the length of time they will remain there.

13. Which of the following is/are true with respect to the implied warranty of habitability?
    a. It exists in every lease of real property for commercial use.
    b. It guarantees that property leased for residential use will be in habitable condition.
    c. If the warranty is breached, the tenant may be able to obtain a rent abatement reflecting the decreased value of the property.
    d. Both b and c.

14. Which of the following is/are necessary in order for constructive eviction to have occurred?
    a. The premises becomes uninhabitable because of acts of the landlord.
    b. The tenant must give the landlord a reasonable opportunity to correct the defect.
    c. The tenant must vacate the premises within a reasonable amount of time.
    d. All of the above.

15. Which of the following is an accurate statement about the legal responsibilities of landlords?
    a. A landlord is liable for all injuries that occur on property she has leased to a tenant for residential purposes.
    b. A landlord cannot be liable for trespass for entering leased premises without the tenant's permission, because the landlord owns the property.
    c. In many states, a landlord who leases residential property impliedly warrants that the leased premises will be fit for human habitation.
    d. Landlords have not yet been found liable for failure to protect their tenants from the foreseeable criminal conduct of third persons.

16. When a tenant subleases property to another party,
    a. the sublessee acquires all of the rights that the tenant had under the lease.
    b. the tenant is discharged from all obligations and liabilities under the lease.
    c. the tenant is legally liable for the rent if the sublessee fails to pay it.
    d. the sublessee has the same rights and obligations as an assignee of the lease would have.

17. A distinguishing feature of a tenancy for years is:
    a. that it can only be created by a written lease.
    b. that it automatically terminates at the ending date fixed in the lease.
    c. that one month's notice is necessary for termination of the tenancy.
    d. that a tenant may terminate the lease without legal liability if she gives three months' notice.

18. Which of the following is/are among the possible remedies for a tenant when the leased residential property has become uninhabitable?
    a. Repair and then deduct repair costs from rent.
    b. Termination of the lease.
    c. Rent abatement.
    d. All of the above.
    e. Both a and c, but not b.

19. Tenant rented an apartment in Landlord's building under a two-year written lease which provided that Landlord had the duty to repair any defects that arose during the term of the lease. After Tenant had lived in the apartment for one week, the toilet became stopped up and began to leak. It could not be used. Tenant told Landlord about this, and Landlord promised to fix it. Tenant waited for one month, but Landlord never came to fix the toilet despite Tenant's repeated reminders to Landlord. On these facts, Tenant:
    a. can move out, but he will be responsible for paying rent for the full term of the two-year lease.
    b. may move out within a reasonable time, and will not incur liability for further rent.
    c. must await Landlord's repair.
    d. is liable to Landlord for the cost of repairs.

20. Which of the following, if any, would create a tenancy at sufferance?
    a. Tenant stays in possession of an apartment after her one-year written lease has expired.
    b. Landlord leases property to Tenant on a month-to-month lease.
    c. Landlord orally leases property to Tenant for eight months.
    d. Tenant endures uninhabitable condition of leased property.

21. A landlord may be held liable for injuries on the premises when the injuries:
    a. have occurred in an area controlled by the landlord.
    b. resulted from the landlord's negligence in attempting to repair the property—even when the landlord had no duty to repair.
    c. resulted from a foreseeable criminal act as to which the landlord did not take reasonable steps of a preventive nature.
    d. occur under any of the above circumstances.

Short Essay

22. Substandard Properties, Inc. owns the Cockroach Heights apartment complex in Big City. The complex consists of three buildings. On January 31, Big City experienced heavy snowfall. Substandard cleared most of its sidewalks, driveways, and parking lots, but neglected to take any action to remove ice and snow in the parking lot and driveway leading to one of the Cockroach Heights buildings, Building A. That night, Oma Gosch happened to visit her son, who lives in Building A. As Gosch exited her car, which was parked in the lot near Building A, she slipped on an icy patch that was hidden beneath the snow. She fell to the pavement and severely injured her back. Gosch later filed a negligence suit against Substandard, which argues that it cannot be liable to Gosch because she was not a tenant. Is Substandard correct? Explain.

23. Biff rented an apartment near the campus of Easy State University. He pays his rent on the first day of each month. He and the landlord, however, have no explicit agreement about the duration of the lease. What sort of tenancy exists on these facts? If Biff wishes to move out, what must he do in order to terminate the tenancy properly?

24. Alvin leased an apartment from Prudence for a period of one year beginning Sept. 1, 1991. On Sept. 30, 1991, Prudence entered the apartment (using a passkey) while Alvin was at work so that she could see whether Alvin was keeping the apartment clean. Alvin came home early from work and found Prudence in the apartment. Does Alvin have a claim against Prudence? Why or why not?

CHAPTER 26

ESTATES AND TRUSTS

True-False - Circle T for True and F for False.

T F 1. A will whose execution violates the requirements of state law is void, not voidable.

T F 2. A person who takes property by will takes it free of all outstanding claims against the property.

T F 3. In a community property state, each spouse has a one-half interest in community property that cannot be defeated by a contrary will provision.

T F 4. A later will must expressly revoke the earlier will, or it will operate to revoke only those parts of the earlier will which it contradicts.

T F 5. A durable power of attorney does not terminate upon the incapacity of the person giving the power.

T F 6. Intestacy statutes attempt to distribute the property of the decedent to those most closely related to him.

T F 7. A trust must be created by use of an express trust instrument.

T F 8. The beneficiary of a trust generally may not assign his rights to the principal or income of the trust to another person.

T F 9. A trustee may only delegate the performance of discretionary duties to another.

T F 10. A constructive trust results when there has been an incomplete disposition of trust property.

Multiple Choice - Circle the best answer.

11. A will:
   a. can dispose only of property belonging to the testator at the time of his death.
   b. does not affect the disposition of property held in joint tenancy.
   c. does not control the disposition of life insurance proceeds.
   d. All of the above.

12. A holographic will:
   a. is a will written in the testator's handwriting.
   b. is an oral will.
   c. is an amendment of a will.
   d. is a will that has been revoked.

13. Ted Testator wishes to revoke his will. Which is a true statement?
   a. Ted may not revoke his will; wills are irrevocable once properly executed.
   b. Ted can revoke his will by executing a second will that does not mention the first will.
   c. Ted can revoke the will by shredding it with the intent to revoke it.
   d. Ted must revoke the will using formalities similar to those required for making a will.

14. What is the purpose of a "living will"?
   a. To give another person the legal authority to act on one's behalf in the case of mental or physical incapacity
   b. To state one's intention to forego extraordinary medical procedures to prolong one's life
   c. To remove the need for the will to be proved in court after one's death
   d. To distribute property owned by a decedent who did not execute a will

135

15. Intestacy statutes:
    a. provide for a disposition of property in accordance with the deceased's presumed intent.
    b. prevent property from escheating to the state in the event that no valid will governs the disposition of the property.
    c. distribute personal property according to the laws of the state in which the property is located.
    d. do not distribute property to adopted children of the deceased.

16. Edgar and Edna were married. They died simultaneously in a plane crash. Which is a true statement about the disposition of property after their death?
    a. Each person's property will go into the estate of the other spouse as if the other spouse had predeceased him or her.
    b. Each person's property will be distributed as though he or she had survived the other spouse.
    c. Both a and b are true statements.
    d. Neither a nor b is a true statement.

17. Which is a true statement about trusts?
    a. The beneficiary of the trust has both legal and equitable title to the trust property.
    b. A trust cannot be established in a person's will.
    c. A single person can be both the settlor of the trust and a beneficiary of the trust.
    d. A trust must be created by a declaration of the owner of the trust property.

18. Spendthrift clauses:
    a. operate to restrict the voluntary or involuntary transfer of a beneficiary's interest in a trust.
    b. give the trustee discretion concerning the amount of principal or income to be paid to a beneficiary.
    c. are designed to ensure that the trustee pays the beneficiary enough out of the trust to enable the beneficiary to live comfortably.
    d. are designed to give creditors the ability to reach trust property when the trustee has incurred debts on behalf of the trust.

19. Undue influence is present in the making of a will if:
    a. the named beneficiary was benefited because of the testator's maternal affection for him or her.
    b. a relative of the testator is named personal representative in the will.
    c. a named beneficiary improperly persuaded the testator with regard to the disposition of his or her property.
    d. the testator's attorney is named as a beneficiary in the will.

20. What is the difference between a resulting trust and a constructive trust?
    a. A resulting trust is expressly created by the settlor, while a constructive trust is created by operation of law.
    b. A constructive trust is based on the presumed intent of the settlor to create a trust, while a resulting trust is implied from circumstances.
    c. A constructive trust does not arise from any actual creation of a trust, while a resulting trust arises when there has been a trust created but an incomplete disposition of trust property.
    d. There is no practical difference between the two terms.

Short Essay

21. When will a spendthrift clause in a trust be ineffective?

22. Is it possible to disinherit one's spouse in one's will under modern legal principles? Was this possible at common law?

23. What is the purpose of a "self-proving clause" in a will?

CHAPTER 27

INTRODUCTION TO CREDIT AND SECURED TRANSACTIONS

True-False - Circle T for True and F for False.

T F 1. In an unsecured credit transaction involving the sale of goods, the seller is entitled to repossess the goods if the buyer fails to pay the agreed purchase price.

T F 2. Although there are technical distinctions between what constitutes *surety* status and what constitutes *guarantor* status, the rights and liabilities of the surety and the guarantor are substantially the same.

T F 3. Under the law of some states, the defaulting mortgagor has a right to redeem the property for a limited time after the property has been sold at a foreclosure sale.

T F 4. If the debtor has posted security for the performance of an obligation, the creditor may release the security without affecting the surety's liability for the debtor's debt.

T F 5. The right of a holder of an artisan's lien to possession of the subject property gives the lienholder the automatic right to sell the property if the debtor does not make the necessary payment.

T F 6. Under a mechanic's lien statute whose provisions are consistent with the Pennsylvania system, the general contractor's failure to perform his contract with the property owner does not directly affect the lien rights of materialmen.

T F 7. Courts are more protective of compensated sureties than they are of accommodation sureties because compensated sureties serve to expand commerce.

T F 8. In a state where foreclosure by action and sale is the required method of foreclosure, the mortgagee who gives proper notices of sale may sell the property without filing a foreclosure suit.

T F 9. If the creditor fails to inform the surety of a material fact concerning the risk involved, the surety may be relieved from liability for the debtor's obligation.

T F 10. Under most mechanic's lien statutes, the proper and timely filing of a notice of lien means that the lien is regarded as having attached to the property as of the date of the first work done (or first material supplied) by the lien claimant.

Multiple Choice - Circle the best answer.

11. Strict foreclosure:
    a. allows the creditor to sue the debtor for any deficiency remaining on the debt after the sale of the property.
    b. allows the debtor to recover any surplus after foreclosure sale proceeds have been applied to satisfy the debt.
    c. is normally restricted to situations in which the amount still owed on the debt exceeds the value of the property.
    d. occurs when the creditor, after taking possession of the property, sues the defaulting debtor for the amount by which the debt exceeds the property's value.

12. Duke Earl, a self-employed automobile mechanic, came to Del Dolt's home, at Dolt's request, to examine Dolt's disabled autmobile. Earl quickly determined what the problem was. He then performed the necessary repairs on the car in Dolt's garage. When Dolt failed to pay the bill Earl sent him, Earl returned to Dolt's home. Claiming a lien on Dolt's car, Earl demanded possession of the car. Dolt refused to relinquish it. On these facts, Earl:

   a. is entitled to possession of the car until Dolt pays the bill because of the repairman's lien that arose by virtue of his having performed work on the car.

   b. has the option of taking ownership of the car if he releases Dolt from liability for payment of the repair bill and takes the car in satisfaction of the debt.

   c. has no lien on the car because he did not inform Dolt, at the time he performed the repairs, that he intended to claim a lien.

   d. has no lien on the car despite having performed work on it, because he does not have (and indeed never did have) possession of the car.

13. Wilfred purchased a home for $92,000. He paid $10,000 down and financed the rest through Sincere Savings & Loan Co., which obtained a mortgage on the property to secure payment of the debt. Through an oversight on its part, Sincere failed to record the mortgage in the appropriate government office. Several years later, Wilfred sold the house to Olga, who paid him $101,000. At the time of the sale to Olga, Wilfred still owed Sincere $68,000. After Wilbur's house payment was not made for two months, Sincere learned that the property had been sold to Olga. Worse yet, Sincere discovered that Wilfred had lost the entire $101,000 in sale proceeds while on a gambling spree in Las Vegas. Sincere then commenced legal proceedings to foreclose the mortgage. What is Olga's best defense in the foreclosure action?

   a. That she did not assume personal liability for Wilfred's debt.

   b. That she had no notice of the mortgage's existence because Sincere failed to record the mortgage.

   c. That Sincere has no right to foreclose because she merely purchased the property subject to the mortgage.

   d. That a mortgage granted by a previous owner of property cannot bind a subsequent purchaser of the property.

14. The major purpose of a deed of trust is to:

   a. make it easier to liquidate the property than it would be if the property were subject to a mortgage.

   b. place legal title to the property in the name of the creditor.

   c. keep legal title to the property in the name of the debtor.

   d. provide the creditor the ability to employ the remedy of strict foreclosure in the event of a default.

15. A surety may avoid liability for a principal's default if the principal refused to pay the creditor because:

   a. the principal was a minor.

   b. the principal had filed for bankruptcy.

   c. the principal was induced to incur the debt because of fraudulent representations by the creditor.

   d. of any of the reasons set forth in answers a, b, and c.

16. Which of the following accurately sets forth a right or liability with regard to a mortgage?

   a. If the mortgagee assigns the right to receive payment of the debt giving rise to the mortgage, that assignment ordinarily entitles the assignee to the mortgagee's interest in the mortgaged property.

   b. If the mortgagee attempts to assign his interest in the mortgaged property without first securing the consent of the mortgagor, the mortgage becomes void.

   c. As a general rule, the mortgagor is not free to sell the mortgaged property without obtaining the prior consent of the mortgagee.

   d. If the mortgagor sells the mortgaged property without the mortgagee's prior consent, the purchaser automatically becomes personally liable for debt that gave rise to the mortgage.

17. Mechanic's lien statutes:
    a. provide protection to suppliers concerning materials they sell to general contractors for miscellaneous uses unrestricted to any particular project.
    b. contain provisions that must be strictly complied with if the claimed lien is to be valid.
    c. do not provide a workable remedy to the holder of such a lien, because they typically do not allow foreclosure as a means of enforcement.
    d. typically provide protection to suppliers of materials but not to subcontractors.

18. Kyle and Tara are cosureties on an obligation as to which their elderly aunt, Ruth, is the principal. When Ruth defaults, Kyle pays the entire debt. After having done so, Kyle:
    a. is automatically released from liability for any other obligations on which he is a surety and Ruth is the principal.
    b. acquires all the rights the creditor had against Ruth.
    c. acquires the right to call upon Tara to reimburse him for Tara's share of the obligation.
    d. acquires the rights referred to in answers b and c.

19. Land contracts generally:
    a. call for the seller to provide the buyer legal title to the property as of the time the contract is entered into, in exchange for the buyer's promise to pay the purchase price in installments.
    b. call for the buyer to take possession of the property and to assume various obligations that a property owner ordinarily has.
    c. require the seller to resort to the courts in order to gain legal title to the property if the buyer defaults on the payments.
    d. obligate the seller, upon default by the buyer, to follow the mortgage foreclosure procedure outlined by state law.

20. Mona Nitpick took her automobile to Lefty Wright's Body Shop to have a dented fender repaired. Wright performed the necessary or, and when Nitpick returned to pick up the car, Wright presented her with a bill for $250. Because she did not have the necessary funds with her, Nitpick promised to return the next day to make payment. Nitpick drove the car home. The next day, she telephoned Wright. She told him that the amount of his bill was outrageous and that she would not pay one cent more than $139.99. While Nitpick was at work, Wright towed her car back to his place of business and notified Nitpick that he would take the steps necessary to have the car sold, if she did not immediately pay the $250. Was Wright justified in taking the actions just described?
    a. Yes, assuming that his intent is to pay Nitpick any sale proceeds exceeding $250 plus expenses he incurs in selling the vehicle.
    b. No, because no court has determined that Nitpick owes him $250.
    c. No, because any lien he had on the car was lost when he gave up possession of the car to Nitpick.
    d. Yes, because Nitpick's promise to pay was the only reason he gave up possession of the car; therefore, he has a valid lien on the car.

21. Alice purchased a parcel of real estate known as Parcel A. The purchase was made subject to a preexisting mortgage on the property in favor of the Local National Bank. Boris purchased a parcel of real estate known as Parcel B. As part of the purchase of the property, Boris assumed a preexisting mortgage on the property in favor of Local National. After the two purchases took place, there were defaults on the debts giving rise to the above-referred-to mortgages on Parcels A and B. Local National instituted and completed foreclosure proceedings with regard to each of the mortgages. In each case, the foreclosure sale did not yield enough funds to pay off the debt in full. Therefore, Local made demand on Alice for payment of the deficiency owed in connection with the mortgage on Parcel A, and made demand on Boris for payment of the deficiency owed in connection with the mortgage on Parcel B. Is Local National entitled to receive, from Alice and Boris, the deficiencies it seeks from them? Why or why not?

22. Gilda agreed to be a surety for Henry on Henry's credit purchase of an automobile from Shaft Motor Co. Henry failed to make the payments called for in the purchase agreement. It was later determined that Henry was insane, and therefore lacking in capacity to enter into a contract, at the time he purchased the automobile. Shaft then made demand upon Gilda for payment of the debt but Gilda refused, claiming that as Henry's surety, she had the right to raise Henry's insanity as a defense. Is Gilda correct? Explain your answer.

23. Roxanne purchased a $315,000 house, financing 80 percent of the purchase price with a loan from Perpetual Infidelity Savings & Loan (hereinafter referred to as "PI"). She granted PI a mortgage on the house to secure repayment of the debt. A mixup by a PI employee resulted in PI's failure to record the mortgage in the appropriate government office. Two months after Roxanne purchased the house, Shark Loan Co. loaned her $15,000 and obtained, from her, a mortgage on the house to secure repayment of the debt. Shark promptly and properly recorded the mortgage. Roxanne later failed to make her house payments to PI and her agreed payments to Shark. PI instituted foreclosure proceedings. Roxanne argued that PI's failure to record the mortgage made the mortgage unenforceable against her, and that PI therefore had no right to seek foreclosure. Shark, which was made a party to PI's foreclosure suit, argued that if the court allows foreclosure, Shark should have first priority (ahead of PI) to the amount of foreclosure sale proceeds necessary to satisfy the debt owed to it by Roxanne. Evaluate the arguments made by Roxanne and Shark.

CHAPTER 28

SECURITY INTERESTS IN PERSONAL PROPERTY

True-False - Circle T for True and F for False.

T F 1. With regard to security interests, attachment is not effective unless the creditor has given something of value to the debtor.

T F 2. A security interest is an interest obtained by a creditor in personal property or fixtures, for the purpose of securing payment or performance of an obligation.

T F 3. Under the UCC's classifications of personal property for secured transactions purposes, an account receivable is considered a general intangible.

T F 4. When a store sells consumer goods on credit to a consumer, the store's security interest in the goods will be perfected without the store's maintaining possession of the goods and without the filing of a financing statement.

T F 5. With regard to competing security interests in the same collateral, the basic rule is that the respective priorities are determined in accordance with the order in which the security interests attached.

T F 6. In the commercial setting, a secured creditor cannot elect to keep the collateral in satisfaction of the debt on which the debtor has defaulted.

T F 7. If a security agreement purports to have a security interest cover future advances or to create a security interest in after-acquired property, it is unenforceable in those respects because security interests must be tied to matters that preceded or were contemporaneous with the security agreement.

T F 8. The holder of a security interest in fixtures may have a priority over the holder of a mortgage on the real estate to which the fixtures are attached, even if the mortgage interest was properly perfected before the holder of the security interest in the fixtures acquired her interest.

T F 9. Even though the filing of a financing statement in the appropriate government office is the most common way of perfecting a security interest, possession of the collateral is the means of perfecting a security interest in certain types of collateral.

T F 10. A Federal Trade Commission regulation prohibits the use of a waiver of defenses clause in any commercial contract.

T F 11. In a state that requires a certificate of title for motor vehicles, a creditor who takes a security interest in a motor vehicle is able to perfect his security interest only by having it noted on the certificate of title.

T F 12. If various creditors claim security interests in the same collateral but none of the security interests has been perfected, the security interest that attached first takes priority over the others.

T F 13. Under the UCC's bulk transfer provisions, sellers who intend to engage in a bulk transfer must give advance notice to their creditors.

Multiple Choice - Circle the best answer.

14. A creditor protects his security interest against third persons' competing claims of rights in the secured property by:
    a. foreclosing prior to default.
    b. granting a right to redeem.
    c. being certain that he has a security agreement signed by the debtor.
    d. taking appropriate action to perfect the security interest.

15. Of the following statements concerning the respective rights of the creditor and of the debtor following the debtor's default on a secured debt, which is *inaccurate*?

    a. Following the debtor's default, the secured creditor becomes entitled to possession of the collateral.

    b. Once the secured creditor gains possession of the collateral following the debtor's default, the debtor cannot redeem the collateral.

    c. Before the secured creditor sells repossessed collateral, he must give the debtor notice that the collateral will be sold.

    d. Following the debtor's default, the secured creditor must take court action to gain possession of collateral in the possession of the debtor, unless the creditor can obtain possession without a breach of the peace.

16. OK Sales & Service sold Fritz a large-screen color television, a dryer, and a portable dishwasher on credit. OK and Fritz agreed that OK would retain a security interest in the three items until the full purchase price had been paid. No financing statement was filed by OK. Fritz later borrowed money from Acme Finance Co. and agreed to give Acme a security interest in the television and the dryer. Acme filed a proper financing statement. Fritz then sold the dishwasher to Geraldine, who bought the dishwasher for her family's use and had no knowledge that OK claimed a security interest in it. When Fritz defaulted on his payments to OK and to Acme, both OK and Acme claimed a first-priority security interest in the television and the dryer. Upon learning that Fritz had sold the dishwasher to Geraldine, OK made demand on Geraldine for possession of the dishwasher. Of the following statements concerning the facts, which is accurate?

    a. OK's failure to file a financing statement means that its security interest in the television and dryer is inferior to that of Acme.

    b. Because OK has a valid purchase money security interest in the dishwasher, OK is entitled to obtain possession of it from Geraldine.

    c. OK's security interest in the television and dryer was perfected before Acme's was; therefore, OK's claim to the items prevails over Acme's.

    d. Because the respective security interests of OK and of Acme are of equal priority, OK is entitled to possession of the TV and Acme is entitled to possession of the dryer.

17. In order for a financing statement to be effective, it must:

    a. be signed by the debtor.

    b. be signed by the creditor.

    c. remain in the possession of the creditor.

    d. meet each of the requirements set forth above.

18. Hall borrowed money from Solvent National Bank and gave the bank a security interest in her business equipment, both present and after-acquired. She later borrowed money from Resilient Savings & Loan to purchase additional business equipment. Two weeks after Hall purchased the additional equipment and took possession of it, an employee of Resilient discovered the bank's recorded financing statement concerning its security interest in Hall's business equipment. On the same day its employee made the discovery just noted, Resilient recorded a financing statement, so as to perfect its purchase money security interest in the equipment. Hall then defaulted on the obligations owed to the bank and to Resilient. Who has the first priority security interest in the equipment purchased by Hall with the funds borrowed from Resilient, and why?

    a. Resilient, because purchase money security interests always take priority over other previously perfected security interests.

    b. The bank, because purchase money security interests necessarily are inferior to other parties' security interests in the debtor's after-acquired property.

    c. Resilient, because supposed security interests in after-acquired property are invalid, in view of the fact that the debtor did not have possession of the property at the time the supposed security interest was granted.

    d. The bank, even though some purchase money security interests may take priority over previously perfected security interests, because Resilient's security interest was perfected too late to give it priority over the bank's.

19. Following Clarice's default on a secured debt she owed to it, Open Palms Finance Co. lawfully repossessed, from Clarice, a television set and a grandfather clock in which it held security interests. Open Palms now intends to sell the clock at an auction and the television by means of a private sale. On these facts, Open Palms:

    a. need not give Clarice notice of its intent to sell the collateral, because its repossession of the collateral was lawful.

    b. will satisfy its obligations to give Clarice notice of its intended disposition of the collateral if it notifies her that it intends to sell the collateral.

    c. has notice obligations that include notifying Clarice of the time and place at which the auction is to be held.

    d. satisfies any notice obligations it has with regard to the television if it promptly notifies her of the fact of sale and the amount realized promptly after the sale of the television takes place.

20. Ed bought a watch from Ron at a garage sale. He gave Ron a $110 check in supposed payment of the purchase price, but the check bounced because Ed had insufficient funds in his checking account. Ron then orally informed Ed that he would take the watch back from Ed if Ed did not pay the $110 within one week. Before the expiration of a week, however, Ed sold the watch to Ollie. Upon learning of the sale to Ollie, Ron demanded that Ollie give him possession of the watch because of Ron's claimed security interest in it. Does Ron have a valid security interest in the watch?

    a. Yes, by virtue of his oral agreement with Ed; therefore, Ollie must turn over the watch.

    b. No, because Ron had neither a written security agreement nor continued possession of the watch.

    c. Yes, because the watch was a consumer good in which his security interest was automatically perfected.

    d. No, because the only way to perfect a security interest in a watch is to file a proper financing statement.

21. Mammoth Corp. held a properly perfected security interest in all of the inventory of Larry's Appliance Sales Co. Among the items in the inventory of Larry's were various stoves and refrigerators. Ward and June purchased one of the stoves and one of the refrigerators. Because they had done business with Larry's before, Ward and June knew that Larry's had purchased its inventory pursuant to a "floor plan" financing arrangement and that Mammoth had a security interest in Larry's inventory. At the time of the sale to Ward and June, Larry's was in default on its obligation to Mammoth. Because of the default, Mammoth began attempting to repossess the collateral. Mammoth therefore demanded that Ward and June turn over possession of the stove and refrigerator because of Mammoth's security interest. Is Mammoth entitled to possession of the stove and refrigerator?

    a. Yes, because Ward and June knew of the security interest held by Mammoth.

    b. Yes, because Larry's was in default on its obligation to Mammoth at the time of the sale to Ward and June.

    c. No, because by purchasing the appliances, Ward and June became holders of purchase money security interests.

    d. No, because Ward and June were buyers in the ordinary course of business.

22. First Bank loaned Biltrong Construction Co. $215,000 and obtained, by agreement with Biltrong, a security interest in all of Biltrong's present equipment plus any equipment it acquired in the future. The bank perfected its security interest on the day the loan was made. Several weeks later, Biltrong borrowed $18,000 from Legbreaker Loan Co. for the purpose of purchasing a bulldozer for the business. Biltrong and Legbreaker entered into a security agreement granting Legbreaker a security interest in the bulldozer. Legbreaker filed a financing statement on the same day Biltrong acquired the bulldozer. Biltrong later defaulted on its obligations to the bank and to Legbreaker. Which of the two creditors has a first priority security interest in the bulldozer, and why?

   a. Legbreaker, even though its purchase money security interest was not perfected until after the bank's security interest was perfected.

   b. The bank, even though Legbreaker's security interest was of the purchase money variety, because the bank's security interest was perfected first.

   c. Legbreaker, because purchase money security interests automatically take priority over conflicting security interests in the same collateral.

   d. The bank, because Legbreaker failed to wait to file its financing statement until the expiration of 10 days following Biltrong's acquisition of the bulldozer.

23. When a bank loans a consumer money to buy a stereo system,

   a. the bank has no valid security interest in the stereo system without the filing of a financing statement.

   b. other creditors will be able to gain a first lien on the stereo system to secure the payment of debts owed by the consumer, unless the bank has filed a financing statement.

   c. a subsequent bona fide purchaser of the stereo system who buys it for use in his home will acquire it free of the bank's security interest if the bank has not filed a financing statement before the purchase by the bona fide purchaser.

   d. all of the above are true.

Short Essay

24. Wally purchased a piano on credit from The Music Store (hereinafter referred to as "Store"). The agreed purchase price was $1999.99. The parties entered into a security agreement that gave Store a security interest in the piano until the full price was paid. After a year of making regular payments, Wally lost his job and ceased making payments to Store. He had reduced the amount of his debt to $450 with the payments he had made. While Wally was away from home one day, his butler allowed two Store employees to take possession of the piano. When Wally learned of this, he demanded that the piano be returned to him. Store refused, informing Wally that it intended to keep the piano in satisfaction of the debt. On these facts, what rights does Wally have? May Store keep the piano in satisfaction of the debt? Why or why not?

25. When Able opened his appliance store, he borrowed a large amount of money from Village Bank. To secure repayment of the loan, he gave the bank a security interest in all of his existing inventory and in all of the inventory he would later acquire. The security interest was properly perfected. Needing to expand his inventory, Able worked out an agreement with Solid Co., an appliance wholesaler. Under the Able-Solid agreement, Solid sold Able appliances on credit, with the appliances becoming part of Able's inventory. On the day of each shipment of appliances, Solid always filed a financing statement concerning its claimed security interest in the inventory. Able later defaulted on his obligations to the bank and to Solid. The bank then learned, for the first time, about Able's arrangement with Solid. Claiming a superior security interest, the bank refused to give Solid control over any of Able's inventory. Is the bank's security interest superior to Solid's? Why or why not?

26. Griede Finance Co. held a properly perfected security interest in a freezer owned by Mo Bile. Griede had perfected the security interest by filing a financing statement in the proper office in State A, where Bile lived and where the freezer was housed. Bile later moved to State B and took the freezer with him. During the first week he was in State B, Bile borrowed money from Easy Money Credit Union, which, by agreement with Bile, retained a security interest in the freezer. Easy Money properly perfected its security interest the same day. Six months later, Bile defaulted on his obligations to Griede and to Easy Money. Griede then learned, for the first time, that Bile had removed the freezer from State A. In view of the facts just stated, which creditor has the first priority claim to the collateral? Why?

CHAPTER 29

BANKRUPTCY

True-False - Circle T for True and F for False.

T F 1. Although individuals may obtain a voluntary liquidation under Chapter 7 of the Bankruptcy Act, they cannot have an involuntary bankruptcy proceeding thrust upon them.

T F 2. Among the duties of the bankruptcy trustee are to examine the proofs of claim filed by creditors and to object to claims that appear improper.

T F 3. Chapter 12 of the Bankruptcy Act provides a Chapter 13-like form of relief available to any party engaged in a farming operation.

T F 4. In a bankruptcy proceeding, the debtor may be permitted to void certain liens against exempt property if the liens impair his exemptions.

T F 5. Both the obligation to pay child support and the obligation to repay certain educational loans are nondischargeable in bankruptcy.

T F 6. In order for a debtor to be eligible to file a voluntary petition in bankruptcy, the debtor's debts must exceed his assets.

T F 7. A fraudulent transfer may be declared void if it was made by the debtor within a year prior to the filing of a bankruptcy petition against the debtor.

T F 8. When a farmer invokes the protections of Chapter 12 of the Bankruptcy Act, he is generally prohibited from operating his farm.

T F 9. For purposes of the Bankruptcy Act, a debtor is considered insolvent if she is unable to pay her debts as they come due.

T F 10. The federal supremacy doctrine notwithstanding, a state can forbid debtors subject to their laws from using the federal exemptions in bankruptcy proceedings.

Multiple Choice - Circle the best answer.

11. Assume that the bankruptcy trustee can show that an individual debtor's relative, having reason to believe that the debtor was insolvent, received a payment in excess of $600 from the debtor prior to the filing of the debtor's bankruptcy petition. The trustee can recover the payment if it was made:
    a. no more than 90 days prior to the filing of the bankruptcy petition.
    b. within one year prior to the filing of the bankruptcy petition.
    c. within two years prior to the filing of the bankruptcy petition.
    d. at any time prior to the filing of the bankruptcy petition.

12. Tax claims against the bankruptcy estate are paid:
    a. after secured creditors realize on their security and before most other unsecured claims are paid.
    b. before any other claims are paid.
    c. after all other claims are paid.
    d. after administration expenses are paid, but before secured creditors realize on their security.

13. Involuntary petitions in straight bankruptcy:
    a. are not possible unless the debtor has at least three creditors.
    b. are not possible if the debtor has more than 12 creditors.
    c. cannot be filed against farmers, regardless of how many creditors they have.
    d. automatically prohibit the debtor from continuing to operate her business.

14. A Chapter 11 reorganization:
    a. is not available to most business enterprises.
    b. may be instituted only by an individual person with a regular income.
    c. may be instituted either by the debtor or against the debtor by the debtor's creditors.
    d. is available only to farmers who meet certain requirements set out in the Bankruptcy Act.

15. Under a Chapter 13 proceeding,
    a. the debtor may receive extensions in the time by which debts otherwise would have to be paid.
    b. the debtor may receive reductions in the amounts owed on debts.
    c. the debtor must submit a plan for payment of her debts.
    d. all of the above are true.

16. Derwin recently filed a Chapter 7 petition. First State Bank held a lien on certain property of Derwin's, as security for a loan it had made to Derwin. The value of the property is less than the amount Derwin still owes on the loan. On these facts, the bank will be treated as having:
    a. a secured claim to the extent of the value of the property, but no valid claim for anything beyond that amount.
    b. a secured claim to the extent of the value of the property and an unsecured claim for the difference between the value of the property and the outstanding loan balance.
    c. an unsecured claim in the amount of the outstanding loan balance, in view of the fact that the loan was not adequately secured.
    d. a secured claim to the extent of the value of the property and, as to the amount of the loan balance exceeding that amount, an unsecured claim that receives priority over the claims of other unsecured creditors.

17. Dorothy received a discharge in her Chapter 7 proceeding. Her creditors received approximately 30 percent of what she had owed them. Two years after the discharge, Dorothy inherited a substantial amount of money. One of her former creditors, Augie, then persuaded Dorothy to agree to repay him the remaining 70 percent of the discharged debt that he had not received through the bankruptcy process. Several weeks later, Dorothy refused to abide by the agreement, even though the amount she had inherited would have enabled her to pay what Augie sought several times over. Is she bound by her promise to pay what Augie seeks?
    a. Yes, because her agreement with Augie amounted to a reaffirmation agreement.
    b. Yes, because she clearly has the ability to pay Augie and because it would be unjust to allow her to avoid fulfilling her promise.
    c. No, because the requirements necessary for an enforceable reaffirmation agreement were not fulfilled.
    d. No, because the Bankruptcy Act does not allow debtors to reaffirm debts.

18. The filing of a bankruptcy petition:
    a. must be done by the debtor if the debtor is an individual person.
    b. causes actions to perfect a lien against the debtor's property to be held in abeyance.
    c. has no impact on pending suits for the collection of debts owed by the debtor.
    d. discharges the debtor's obligations to unsecured creditors.

19. In Chapter 11 cases,
    a. the reorganization plan must receive the necessary approval of creditors and be confirmed by the court before it is effective.
    b. the debtor automatically is allowed to avoid having to comply with the terms of a collective bargaining agreement that existed before the filing of the Chapter 11 petition.
    c. the reorganization plan may treat individual creditors within the same class differently, regardless of whether the creditors of that class consented to such treatment.
    d. the debtor's business operation must cease, assuming the debtor wants the special benefits and protections of Chapter 11.

20. Last National Bank had loaned Skip $5000 for use in connection with his business. With $3500 still due on the loan, Skip became insolvent. Because the loan was unsecured and because it had heard rumors of a possible bankruptcy in Skip's future, Last National naturally became concerned. It therefore offered to extend Skip an additional $1000 on his loan if he would give Last National a security interest in his car to the extent of the new $4500 balance. Skip accepted the offer and the resulting agreement was performed. A month later, Skip filed for bankruptcy. On these facts,

   a. the debt owed by Skip to Last National is considered nondischargeable.

   b. Last National will be permitted to realize on its security, to the extent of $4500, before unsecured creditors are paid.

   c. Last National must pay the bankruptcy trustee $4500 because of its role in a fraudulent conveyance.

   d. the preferential nature of the lien granted to Last National means that at least $3500 worth of its claim is subject to reclassification as an unsecured debt.

Short Essay

21. Weak Corp. has filed a voluntary bankruptcy petition. Included among its numerous debts are the following, all of which are provable and allowed claims: an unsecured debt in the amount of $10,000, owed to Piranha Finance Co.; administration expenses and fees in the amount of $11,000; $6999 in back income taxes, owed to the state government; an unsecured debt in the amount of $1800, representing unpaid wages earned by a Weak employee during the month preceding the filing of the bankruptcy petition; and an unsecured debt in the amount of $2500, representing unpaid wages earned by another Weak employee during the month preceding the filing of the bankruptcy petition. Weak also has numerous other unsecured claims that are provable and allowed. In what order should the above-referred-to claims be paid? State the reasons for your answer.

22. Elroy has filed a Chapter 7 petition. Included among his numerous debts are the following: a $105,000 judgment entered against him as a result of injuries he caused to Darlene when he was operating a motor vehicle while under the influence of alcohol; $17,500 of past-due alimony owed to his former wife, Naomi; $1500 of cash advances received by Elroy on his Disastercard (a credit card) 30 days before the filing of the bankruptcy petition; $1000 on his Pisa card (a credit card) account for the purchase, made three weeks before the filing of the bankruptcy petition, of a diamond ring for himself; and a $57,000 judgment entered against him for injuries suffered by Orville, who was injured by a paint can that Elroy negligently dropped from atop some scaffolding on which Elroy was working. Of the specific debts just mentioned, which is/are nondischargeable in bankruptcy? Explain your answer.

23. Delbert was recently fired from his job. He does not anticipate being able to find another job for a substantial period of time. He has heard that under Chapter 13 of the Bankruptcy Act, he would be able to obtain protection from creditors' collection actions, have his debts reduced in amount, and receive extensions of the times within which the debts must be paid. He wonders whether these things are true and, if they are, whether a Chapter 13 proceeding is a viable option for him. How should Delbert's questions be answered?

CHAPTER 30

NEGOTIABLE INSTRUMENTS

True-False - Circle T for True and F for False.

T F 1. A "non-negotiable" instrument is unenforceable.

T F 2. Commercial paper is simply one type of contract for the payment of money.

T F 3. A draft is a form of commercial paper that involves an order to pay money rather than a promise to pay money.

T F 4. A holder in due course of a negotiable instrument takes the instrument free of all personal defenses and claims except those that concern the validity of the instrument.

T F 5. An instrument may be negotiable even if it is not in writing.

T F 6. An instrument that meets all of the formal requirements for negotiability is a negotiable instrument even if it is void, voidable, unenforceable, or uncollectible.

T F 7. An instrument is not negotiable unless the promise or order to pay is unconditional.

T F 8. The amount specified in a negotiable instrument may be payable either in money or in kind.

T F 9. If one cannot calculate the value of the instrument by merely looking at it, it is not negotiable.

T F 10. Commercial paper can be used either as a substitute for money or as a means of extending credit.

Multiple Choice - Circle the best answer.

11. Fred Farmer gave Gert Grocer an otherwise negotiable note promising "to pay to Gert's order ten bushels of apples."
    a. This is a negotiable instrument.
    b. This is not a negotiable instrument because it is not payable in money.
    c. This is not a negotiable instrument because it is not payable to the order of Gert.
    d. This is not a negotiable instrument because it is not payable to bearer.

12. If an instrument does not meet the formal requirements of negotiability, it is:
    a. a contract.
    b. a type of commercial paper.
    c. void.
    d. voidable.

13. Which is a consequence of negotiability?
    a. Payment is assured.
    b. The instrument is valid.
    c. Subsequent transferees may become holders in due course.
    d. Enforceability is assured.

14. A "draft" is:
    a. a two-party instrument.
    b. a promise to pay money.
    c. an order to pay money.
    d. exemplified by an I.O.U.

15. If an instrument is negotiable:
    a. the general rules of contract law control the rights and duties of the parties to the instrument.
    b. its transferee who is a holder in due course can obtain greater rights than his assignor had.
    c. it is also valid and enforceable.
    d. it will not substitute for money.

16. If there are ambiguous terms in a negotiable instrument:
    a. the instrument is not negotiable.
    b. typewritten and printed terms control handwritten terms.
    c. words control figures unless the words are ambiguous.
    d. printed terms control typewritten terms.

17. A "check":
    a. is a promise to pay money.
    b. is an order to pay money.
    c. may have any legal entity as its drawee.
    d. is not payable on demand.

18. Which of the following is not a negotiable instrument?
    a. A postdated check
    b. A note containing a clause permitting the time for payment to be accelerated at the option of the maker
    c. A note that is payable on the happening of an uncertain future event
    d. None of the above instruments is negotiable.

19. To be negotiable, an instrument:
    a. must be payable "to bearer."
    b. must be payable "to order."
    c. may be payable either "to order" or "to bearer."
    d. may be payable either "to cash" or "to order."

20. A certificate of deposit:
    a. is a type of draft.
    b. is a type of note.
    c. is an order to pay money.
    d. is not a type of commercial paper.

Short Essay

21. What is meant by the assertion that "negotiability is only a matter of form"?

22. What is required for a person to take a negotiable instrument free of all defenses except those affecting the validity of the instrument?

23. What is the reason for the requirement that a negotiable instrument must be payable either "to order" or "to bearer"?

CHAPTER 31

NEGOTIATION AND HOLDER IN DUE COURSE

True-False - Circle T for True and F for False.

T F 1. An instrument which is order paper can be negotiated only by delivery of the instrument after indorsement by the payee.

T F 2. No indorsement is necessary to negotiate an instrument payable to bearer.

T F 3. A person who indorses an instrument becomes liable to pay the instrument if the person primarily liable on it does not pay it.

T F 4. An instrument that is indorsed with a special indorsement becomes bearer paper.

T F 5. A check indorsed in blank needs an additional indorsement to be negotiable.

T F 6. A restrictive indorsement prevents further negotiation of an instrument.

T F 7. A qualified indorsement limits the contractual liability of the indorser, but does not affect the negotiability of the instrument.

T F 8. A holder in due course takes a negotiable instrument free of all real defenses.

T F 9. A person taking an instrument as a gift cannot be a holder in due course of the instrument.

T F 10. A regulation promulgated by the Federal Trade Commission makes the holder in due course doctrine inapplicable to certain consumer credit transactions in that the holder of certain consumer credit contracts is subject to all claims and defenses of the consumer.

Multiple Choice: - Circle the best answer.

11. Which of the following is order paper?
    a. A check indorsed to John
    b. A check issued payable to the order of John and indorsed in blank
    c. A note payable to the order of cash
    d. A note payable to bearer

12. Wanda has a check payable to her order. She wants to send it to her bank for deposit in her account. How can Wanda make sure that the check will be credited to her account?
    a. By indorsing the check "Wanda"
    b. By indorsing the check "for deposit only, Wanda"
    c. By indorsing the check "without recourse, Wanda"
    d. By not indorsing the check

13. Which of the following is a *personal* defense to payment of a negotiable instrument?
    a. Minority
    b. Duress
    c. Fraud in the essence
    d. Breach of warranty

14. Phil has a check that says "Pay to Phil." Phil sells the check to Jill without indorsing it. Is Jill a holder?
    a. No, because Phil did not indorse the check.
    b. Yes, because only delivery was necessary to negotiate the check.
    c. No, because Jill did not indorse the check.
    d. Yes, because Jill may supply the missing indorsement.

15. Smith indorses a check, "Pay Jones only if Jones delivers 1000 widgets, Smith." What type of indorsement is this?
    a. Blank and special
    b. Blank, special, and restrictive
    c. Special and restrictive
    d. Restrictive

16. Charlie, a maker of a $100,000 negotiable note due in 20 days, has a personal defense to payment of the note. John bought the note five days ago for $99,800. John does not know of Charlie's defense. The note is properly indorsed. Is John a holder in due course?
    a. No, because John is not a holder.
    b. Yes, John is a holder in due course.
    c. No, because John acted in bad faith.
    d. No, because John did not give adequate value for the note.

17. Marni Minor gives Larry a negotiable note for $1,000. Hank, a holder in due course, obtains the note. Marni refuses to pay Hank on the note. Must she pay Hank?
    a. No, because Marni has a real defense to payment.
    b. No, because Marni has a personal defense to payment.
    c. Yes, because a holder in due course takes an instrument free of all defenses.
    d. No, because Hank should have known that Marni was a minor.

18. Shana buys a $7,000 used truck to use in her lawn care business. She gives the seller, Truck Sales, Inc., a negotiable note for $7,000 due in six months. Truck Sales sells the note to Talbott Factors, a holder in due course. Talbott agrees to pay Truck Sales $6,800 for the note, $800 in cash immediately and $6,000 in four months. In one month the truck proves to be defective and Truck Sales refuses to repair it, despite the existence of an express warranty covering the defect. Shana tells Talbott that she will not pay the note when it comes due because of the unrepaired defect. Talbott goes ahead and pays Truck Sales the remaining $6,000 when it is due, and on the note's due date, Talbott demands that Shana pay it. Shana refuses. Which is a true statement?
    a. Talbott cannot collect anything from Shana.
    b. Talbott can collect only $800 from Shana.
    c. Talbott can collect only $6,800 from Shana.
    d. Talbott can collect the entire $7,000 from Shana.

19. Order paper that has been indorsed in blank is:
    a. order paper.
    b. bearer paper.
    c. nonnegotiable.
    d. not negotiated.

20. Which of the following indorsements affects the negotiability of the instrument to which it is attached?
    a. A qualified indorsement
    b. A restrictive indorsement
    c. A blank indorsement
    d. An indorsement never affects negotiability.

21. Dan makes out a note for $20,000 payable to the order of Todd and gives it to Todd in return for Todd's promise to loan him $20,000. Todd never loans the money to Dan. Then Todd sells the note for value but without any indorsement to Jen. Can Jen collect the face amount of the note from Dan?

22. If an indorsement is not necessary to negotiate an instrument made payable to bearer, why might the party who takes the instrument still insist on its indorsement?

23. What is the practical difference between a real defense and a personal defense? What do you think is the reason for this distinction?

CHAPTER 32

LIABILITY OF PARTIES

True-False - Circle T for True and F for False.

T F 1. A drawer is primarily liable on a draft until the draft has been accepted by the drawee.

T F 2. At the time a check or other draft is written, no one is primarily liable on it.

T F 3. A person who indorses a negotiable instrument is usually secondarily liable.

T F 4. An accommodation maker is primarily liable.

T F 5. Indorsers are liable to each other in the chronological order in which they indorsed, from the last indorser back to the first.

T F 6. An agent who signs a negotiable instrument is personally liable if he does not indicate he is signing as an agent and upon whose behalf he is signing.

T F 7. A person whose name is forged on a negotiable instrument is bound by the forged signature.

T F 8. The drawee bank is liable on a check until it certifies or accepts the check.

T F 9. If a note is dishonored, the holder can seek payment from any qualified indorser of the note.

T F 10. If a person drafts a negotiable instrument so carelessly that it can be easily altered, he cannot use the alteration as a reason for not paying a holder in due course.

Multiple Choice: - Circle the best answer.

11. Peter draws a check on his account in Third National Bank payable to the order of Stella and has it certified by the bank. When Stella presents the check to Third National Bank, it is dishonored. What result?
    a. Third National is primarily liable on the check and Peter is secondarily liable on the check.
    b. Third National is secondarily liable on the check and Peter is primarily liable on the check.
    c. Peter has no contractual liability on the check.
    d. Third National has no contractual liability on the check.

12. Who is primarily liable on a check when it is written?
    a. The payee
    b. The drawer
    c. The drawee bank
    d. No one

13. Which transferor warranty does an indorser in blank make?
    a. All signatures are genuine or authorized
    b. The instrument has not been materially altered
    c. No party has a valid defense against the indorser
    d. All of the above

14. Mack, Bertha's agent, is authorized to sign checks for her. Mack signs a check of Bertha's with only his name. Who is liable on the check?
    a. Bertha
    b. Mack
    c. Both Bertha and Mack
    d. Neither Bertha nor Mack

15. An indorser of a check is discharged from contractual liability if:
    a. the drawee bank pays the check to a holder.
    b. a thief cancels the check.
    c. the holder accidentally destroys the check.
    d. the indorser pays someone who stole the check.

16. The drawer of a check:
    a. is primarily liable on the check.
    b. is secondarily liable on the check if it is not paid by the drawee bank upon presentment by the holder.
    c. has the same contractual liability as the drawee.
    d. has the same contractual liability as a note's maker.

17. Susan stole three blank checks from Melanie and wrote each check for $500. Susan forged Melanie's signature on the checks and cashed them at various branches of Corner Cashing Service. Corner indorsed and deposited the checks at American Bank, and Corner withdrew the amount of the checks from its account in American Bank. When American Bank presented the checks for payment at National Bank, which was the drawee of the checks, National Bank refused payment on the ground that Melanie's signature had been forged. On what grounds may American Bank collect from Corner Cashing?
    a. Secondary liability only
    b. Secondary liability and breach of presentment warranty
    c. Secondary liability and breach of transferor's warranty
    d. Secondary liability, breach of presentment warranty, and breach of transferor's warranty

18. Hank holds a note issued by PC Corporation. The note has been indorsed and transferred by First Bank, while SC Corporation is an accommodation maker. When Hank presents the note to PC for payment, PC dishonors it. After he gives proper notice to all parties, who is liable to Hank on the note?
    a. PC, SC, and First Bank
    b. PC and SC
    c. PC and First Bank
    d. SC and First Bank

19. In the above scenario, who made transferor's warranties?
    a. SC
    b. First Bank
    c. SC and First Bank
    d. PC, SC, and First Bank

20. An accommodation indorser has the liability of:
    a. a drawer.
    b. an indorser.
    c. a maker.
    d. a payee.

21. Appleman signs a promissory note for $1000 payable to Bates. Bates indorses the note "Pay to the order of Crafty, signed Bates." Crafty alters the note, changing the $1000 to $100,000. Appleman and Bates find out about the alteration and refuse to pay Crafty anything on the note, and Crafty sues them to collect the $1000 for which the note was originally payable. What result, and why?

22. Ted Thief steals Goody Two Shoes' checkbook and signs Goody's name to a check. In the eyes of the law, whose signature is on the check, and who is liable on the check?

23. Evil Employee is employed by Gargantua Corporation. Evil prepares a check payable to Fern Parks, a fictitious payee, and Gargantua signs it. Evil cashes the check at First Bank after indorsing it in the name of Fern Parks. Is Gargantua liable to First Bank on the check? Why or why not?

CHAPTER 33

CHECKS AND DOCUMENTS OF TITLE

True-False - Circle T for True and F for False.

T F 1. If a bank wrongfully dishonors a check, it is liable for both direct and consequential damages caused to the drawer by the dishonor.

T F 2. A bank must pay any checks out of a drawee's account that are less than one year old.

T F 3. If a bank in good faith pays an altered check, it may charge the customer's account only for the amount of the check as originally drawn.

T F 4. If a bank which pays an originally incomplete check of a drawee which it knows has been completed by someone else, it can charge the amount to the drawee's account.

T F 5. If a person stops payment on a check and the bank honors the stop payment order, the person may still be liable to the holder of the check.

T F 6. A drawee bank is obligated to certify a check.

T F 7. A bank is primarily liable on a cashier's check at the moment it is drawn as both a drawer and a drawee.

T F 8. The death of a bank's customer immediately terminates the bank's authority to pay the checks of the deceased person.

T F 9. A bank may not charge its customer's account after it mistakenly honors a check with a forged signature of the customer.

T F 10. A document of title which provides for the delivery of the goods to bearer may be negotiated by delivery.

Multiple Choice: - Circle the best answer.

11. A person who acquires a negotiable document of title by negotiation acquires:
    a. title to the document.
    b. title to the goods.
    c. the right to the goods delivered to the bailee after the issuance of the document.
    d. all of the above rights.

12. The transferor of a negotiable document of title warrants to his immediate transferee:
    a. that the document is genuine.
    b. that he has no knowledge of facts that would impair the document's validity.
    c. that his negotiation or transfer is rightful and fully effective regarding title to the document and the goods.
    d. all of the above facts.

13. Which of the following is generally properly chargeable to a customer's account?
    a. A check with a forged drawer's signature
    b. A check with a forged payee's signature
    c. A check that has been materially altered
    d. None of the above is properly chargeable to the customer's account.

14. Steve stopped payment on a check made payable to Eleanor because she failed to deliver goods he had purchased from her. Steve's bank paid Hannah, a holder in due course, despite the stop payment order. Must the bank recredit Steve's account for the amount of the check?

    a. No, because Hannah took the check free of any defense Steve had.

    b. No, because Steve suffered no loss by the bank's paying Hannah.

    c. Yes, because Steve had a good defense against Hannah.

    d. Yes, because the stop payment order was in effect.

15. Boyd, an employee of Ace Corporation, forged a series of checks on the Ace account at First Bank over a period of two years. Ace discovers the forgeries, and can force First Bank to recredit its account for:

    a. all of the forged checks.

    b. all forged checks paid by the Bank before and for 14 days after Ace got its first statement containing forged checks.

    c. all forged checks paid for the first year.

    d. none of the forged checks since Boyd was its employee.

16. Ted died. His bank knew of his death. It also knew that Ted's account had only $600 in it. Nonetheless, eight days after Ted's death, the bank honored a check he had written for $2000, then sued Ted's estate for the $1400 overdraft. Can the bank recover from the estate?

    a. Yes.

    b. No, because a bank cannot overdraw a customer's account.

    c. No, because the bank had actual notice that Ted had died at the time it honored the check.

    d. No, because the check was honored more than five days after Ted died.

17. On an uncertified check, the drawee bank has liability to:

    a. the drawer.

    b. a holder of the check.

    c. the payee of the check.

    d. all of the above parties.

18. When a bank wrongfully dishonors a check, it is liable to its drawer customer for:

    a. the amount of the check only.

    b. direct damages only.

    c. both direct and consequential damages.

    d. treble the face amount of the check.

19. First Bank disobeyed Jane's stop payment order, paying the check to Sam, a holder in due course. Jane is mentally incapacitated. In a suit by Jane against First Bank to force the bank to recredit her account:

    a. Jane will win because her defense of incapacity is good against Sam.

    b. First Bank will win unless it was negligent in disobeying the stop payment order.

    c. First Bank will win because the defense of incapacity is not good against a holder in due course.

    d. First Bank will win because its payment to Sam is final.

20. Five days after Ken is adjudicated insane, his bank receives two checks he wrote before the adjudication. The bank knows that Ken has been adjudged insane, but pays the checks anyway. Must it recredit Ken's account if Ken's guardian so requests?

    a. Yes, because its authority to pay these checks terminated automatically upon the adjudication.

    b. Yes, because it knew about the adjudication.

    c. Yes, because it waited too long to pay the checks.

    d. No, because payment came within 10 days after the adjudication.

21. What is the difference between a cashier's check and a certified check?

22. If Buyer writes a check for $10,000 to Seller, and Seller presents the check to Buyer's bank where it is wrongfully dishonored, what can Buyer recover from his bank?

23. If a thief ships the stolen goods on a negotiable document of title and then negotiates the document of title, what kind of title to the goods does the purchaser of the document of title get?

CHAPTER 34

THE AGENCY RELATIONSHIP

True-False - Circle T for True and F for False.

T F   1.   Consideration is necessary for the creation of a principal-agent relationship.

T F   2.   If an agent had no actual authority to take a certain action, it necessarily follows that she had no apparent authority to take the action.

T F   3.   Although the agent ordinarily is obligated to obey instructions provided by the principal, the agent has no duty to obey an instruction calling for her to perform an act that is legal but unethical.

T F   4.   Although there is no sharp line between what is employee status and what is independent contractor status, an agent is generally classified as an independent contractor if the principal has the right to control the details of the agent's work.

T F   5.   A principal-agent relationship may be created even though the parties have expressly disavowed any intention to create such a relationship.

T F   6.   Either party to a principal-agent generally has the power to terminate the relationship even when doing so would violate the terms of the contract that created the relationship.

T F   7.   The agent has the duty to relay to the principal all information of whatever nature that he receives from a person with whom he has been dealing on behalf of the principal.

T F   8.   An agent may still be able to bind the principal even after the principal has informed the agent of the termination of the agent's authority.

T F   9.   If the principal discovers that his agent was acting not only as his agent but also as the agent of the other party in matters leading to a contract between the principal and the other party, the principal may sue the agent for damages but cannot rescind the contract.

T F 10.   The general rule is that even though the death of the agent terminates an agency relationship, the death of the principal does not do so.

Multiple Choice - Circle the best answer.

11.   Alf is an agent of Perry. If Alf justifiably believes that Perry would want him to take a certain action, what sort of authority would Alf have to take that action?
   a.   Ostensible authority
   b.   Quasi authority
   c.   Implied authority
   d.   Apparent authority

12.   Agnes acts as an agent for Prudence. Their agency agreement says nothing about compensation, if any, to be paid by Prudence to Agnes for her services as an agent. Which of the following is an accurate statement?
   a.   Prudence is obligated to reimburse Agnes for expenses incurred in the course of the agency, but is not obligated to pay Agnes for her services.
   b.   Prudence is likely to be obligated to pay Agnes at least the reasonable value of her services.
   c.   Agnes is entitled to half of the profits realized by Prudence in connection with matters as to which Agnes rendered services.
   d.   Agnes is a gratuitous agent and is therefore entitled to no compensation for her services.

13. While Woody was an employee at Sam's Grocery Store, Woody learned, from Sam himself, how to recognize truly fresh produce when farmers brought their produce to the store. After he ceased being Sam's employee, Woody opened his own grocery store and made good use of what he had learned about recognizing fresh produce. Woody's store became known for its fine produce. Many of Sam's customers began purchasing produce and other grocery items at Woody's store rather than at Sam's. Sam sued Woody for the damages allegedly resulting from the loss of customers. Sam should:

   a. lose the suit because the cessation of the principal-agent relationship between Sam and Woody meant that Woody could thereafter use any confidential information to which he acquired access as Sam's employee.

   b. win the suit because Woody's continuing duty of loyalty to Sam bars Woody from competing with Sam.

   c. lose the suit because in competing with Sam, Woody was not using any confidential information acquired while he was Sam's employee.

   d. win the suit because in competing with Sam, Woody used knowledge and skills he gained as Sam's employee.

14. Termination of an agency relationship can occur:

   a. only by agreement of both principal and agent.

   b. if subject matter critical to the agency is destroyed or lost.

   c. if the agent becomes insane, but not if the principal becomes insane.

   d. by means of the principal's decision to terminate the agency, but not by means of the agent's decision to that effect.

15. Which one or more of the following statements accurately sets forth something an agent is prohibited from doing?

   a. An agent cannot seize for herself a business opportunity concerning which the principal has interest and the ability to perform.

   b. An agent cannot under any circumstances make a purchase from herself for the principal.

   c. An agent cannot under any circumstances purchase for herself the property of the principal.

   d. All of the above.

16. Darnell, an assistant manager at F-Mart, was responsible for making a deposit of F-Mart funds every evening at the Second National Bank. On one evening, instead of driving directly to the bank, Darnell stopped at the Dismal Lounge. Darnell had agreed to sell his stereo to Evans, and had arranged to meet Evans at the lounge so that he could collect the $1000 purchase price from Evans. After receiving the $1000 in cash from Evans, Darnell placed it in the bank pouch along with $3000 of F-Mart cash that was to be deposited in the bank. Intending to deposit the F-Mart funds in F-Mart's account and the $1000 in his own account, Darnell left the lounge and walked toward his car. Before he reached the car, a thief snatched the bank pouch from him and ran away. A passerby grabbed the thief and struggled with him. During the struggle, $800 dropped from the pouch. The thief then broke away and escaped with the rest of the money, which was never recovered. On these facts, the $800 should:

   a. go to the passerby, without whose actions the thief would have escaped with all of the money.

   b. go to Darnell because in putting the funds together, he had no intent to abscond with F-Mart funds.

   c. be divided equally between F-Mart and Darnell, because each of them suffered a loss that was the fault of neither of them.

   d. go to F-Mart because Darnell's breach of his duty not to commingle personal funds with F-Mart funds caused a loss to F-Mart.

17. Which of the following is an accurate statement about express authority?

   a. It cannot be given to general agents.

   b. It is one form of actual authority.

   c. It cannot be given orally.

   d. It is the only form of actual authority.

18. An agency coupled with an interest:
    a. is not freely terminable by the principal prior to the accomplishment of the agency's purpose.
    b. is void as a matter of law in most states because of the potential conflict of interest inherent in it.
    c. is terminable at any time at the will of either party.
    d. is another term for a general agency.

19. Marlene is a loan officer employed by Shark Loan Co. Her employer has given her authority to receive loan applications and to approve the making of loans. In view of these facts, Marlene:
    a. is liable to Shark for monetary loss it experiences as a result of a debtor's failure to repay a loan approved by her.
    b. may approve a loan of Shark funds to herself without seeking the approval of company officials, if she charges herself the standard rate of interest.
    c. must take reasonable care to investigate the credit standing of prospective borrowers before approving loans.
    d. need not turn over to her employer a gift given to her by a Shark customer in appreciation of the courtesy and helpfulness she showed in processing his loan.

20. When an agent's breach of duty has caused harm to the principal,
    a. the principal may set off the amount of the loss against the compensation owed to the agent.
    b. the principal may have no duty to compensate the agent at all, if the agent's breach of duty was serious enough.
    c. the principal may have a damages claim as well as a claim for injunctive relief, depending upon the facts.
    d. all of the above are true.

Short Essay

21. Dewey Cheatem, owner of Dewey Cheatem Used Cars, employed several salespersons. Cheatem frequently appeared in television commercials in which he stated that he and his sales staff would not be undersold because they were dedicated to selling customers a Cheatem used car. At a sales meeting, Cheatem informed his salespersons that they were authorized to sell any car on the lot at any price, so long as they did not reduce the sticker price on the automobile by more than 20 percent. In addition, he noted that only he could make or approve a deal involving the reduction of the sticker price by more than 20 percent. Thereafter, during a particularly slow week, one of the salespersons, Salem Lemon, sold a customer, Sheldon Shrewd, an autombile at 30 percent below its sticker price. Cheatem did not know what had occurred until after Lemon had accepted Shrewd's cash payment and had relinquished the car to Shrewd. Cheatem promptly contacted Shrewd and informed him that he must either return the car or pay the additional 10 percent he had saved, because Lemon was not authorized to reduce the sticker price by more than 20 percent. Was Cheatem legally justified in taking this position? Why or why not?

22. Hank decided to sell his farm equipment, so he retained Slim as his agent to accomplish that purpose. After the equipment did not sell at the price Hank instructed Slim to insist upon, Slim arranged to sell the equipment to his stepson, Nunn, for a price that was $500 less than what Hank had initially set. Slim did not tell Hank that Nunn was his stepson. Hank approved the sale at the lower price. Assume that Slim was unaware of any other potential buyers and that he honestly did not think it was important to tell Hank about his relationship with Nunn. Did Slim breach his duty as an agent? Explain your reasoning.

23. How is it possible that a principal's former agent may take actions that bind the principal even though the agency relationship has terminated? What should the principal do to minimize this danger?

CHAPTER 35

THIRD-PARTY RELATIONS OF THE PRINCIPAL AND THE AGENT

True-False - Circle T for True and F for False.

T F 1. The effect of a ratification is to make the principal liable for the agent's unauthorized action, just as if the agent had possessed authority at the time he took the action.

T F 2. If the principal neither instructed the agent to make false statements to third parties nor intended that such statements be made, the principal cannot be held liable for the consequences of the agent's false statements to third parties.

T F 3. If an agent, with authority, enters into a contract on behalf of an undisclosed principal, the agent is entitled to indemnification from the principal in the event that the agent is held liable in a breach of contract suit brought by the other contracting party.

T F 4. Because an agent's implied authority is an extension of her express authority, there is no implied authority concerning a subject if there is no relevant grant of express authority concerning that subject.

T F 5. An agent acting within the scope of her employment will generally be immune from liability for the torts she commits, because her employer will be held liable instead.

T F 6. Although a principal generally is not liable for the tort of an independent contractor he has retained, the principal may be held liable for the independent contractor's negligent failure to take suitable precautions normally associated with conducting inherently dangerous activities.

T F 7. If an agent had no authority to make a contract on behalf of a principal, the third party with whom the agent dealt is generally able to hold the agent liable on a theory that he made and breached an implied warranty of his authority to contract.

T F 8. In an agency involving a disclosed principal, the third party may, at his option, hold either the principal or the agent legally responsible for performing the obligation owed to the third party.

T F 9. If the court finds that both the principal and agent are liable to the plaintiff, the plaintiff becomes entitled to a double recovery of damages.

T F 10. An agent who acted at the principal's direction in committing what ordinarily would be considered a crime will not have criminal liability for the act.

T F 11. A agency is one involving a partially disclosed principal when the third party knows that she is dealing with someone's agent but neither knows nor has reason to know the identity of the principal.

Multiple Choice - Circle the best answer.

12. Under the doctrine of *respondeat superior*,
    a. an employee or independent contractor involved in the commission of a tort is relieved from liability to the injured third party if the employee's or independent contractor's principal is held liable for the tort.
    b. the principal is held liable for the torts committed by an independent contractor if the principal was negligent in retaining the independent contractor.
    c. an employer cannot be held liable for an employee's intentional tort.
    d. an employer is liable for her employee's tort if the tort was committed within the scope of employment.

13. The following statements pertain to a situation in which Agent, purportedly acting on behalf of Principal, entered into a contract with another party. Which of the statements is *inaccurate*?

   a. If Agent had no actual authority to enter into the contract on Principal's behalf, Principal cannot be held liable on the contract.

   b. Under certain circumstances, Principal could be held liable on the contract even if Agent had no authority to enter into the contract on Principal's behalf.

   c. Agent had actual authority to enter into the contract on Principal's behalf if Agent, under all the facts and circumstances, had a reasonable belief that the actions resulting in the contract were actions Principal wanted him to perform.

   d. An effective ratification by Principal of Agent's actions cannot have taken place if Principal merely remained silent and failed to repudiate the contract.

14. Bar owner Wally Wimpner instructed his employee, Biff Oafley, to beat up wisecracking college student (and bar patron) Todd Punk. Oafley did his employer's bidding. Which of the following is an accurate statement?

   a. Oafley will face imputed liability to Punk.

   b. The only liability Wimpner would have to Punk would be under respondeat superior.

   c. Oafley's having simply done what his employer instructed him to do would not be a defense for Oafley if Punk sued him.

   d. Neither Wimpner nor Oafley should be liable on these facts, because Punk's wisecracking was what created the problem.

15. Portnoy was engaged in the business of fixing up older cars and selling them for a profit. Portnoy often complained that because many persons in the area where he lived knew of his business operation, they tended to hold out for higher prices before selling their older cars to him. To remedy the problem, Portnoy retained several persons to make purchases of cars for him. Roth, an agent retained by Portnoy for the purpose just mentioned, contracted to purchase a car from a used car dealer, "Good Buy" Columbus, without disclosing that he was acting on behalf of Portnoy. On these facts,

   a. Roth faces potential liability on the contract if a dispute later arises.

   b. Roth has committed fraud by failing to reveal his status as an agent for Portnoy.

   c. Portnoy does not face potential liability on the contract with Columbus, because Portnoy was an undisclosed principal.

   d. both a and c are true.

16. Under the legal rules governing tort liabilities of principals and agents,

   a. the principal has direct liability whenever he/she/it has imputed liability.

   b. the principal cannot have direct liability unless the principal specifically instructed the agent to commit the tort committed by the agent.

   c. an employee cannot be regarded as having committed a tort within the scope of employment if the commission of the tort occurred outside the employee's designated working hours.

   d. an employee may have committed a tort within the scope of employment even if at the time of the commission of the tort, the employee was not solely motivated by a desire to advance the employer's interests.

17. Willkie was an employee of Dewey, a painting contractor. Dewey had verbally authorized Willkie to charge necessary purchases of paint on Dewey's charge account at Stevenson's paint store, with the limitation that Willkie was to charge no more than 10 gallons of paint at a time without first checking with Dewey for approval. Despite Dewey's instructions, Willkie charged from 10 to 20 gallons at Stevenson's store on each of several different occasions without ever getting Dewey's prior approval. Each time, Dewey had paid the bill submitted by Stevenson. No discussions of any kind had ever taken place between Dewey and Stevenson concerning the extent of Willkie's purchasing authority. After Willkie had charged more than 10 gallons without prior approval on several occasions, Dewey reminded Willkie of the limitation on his authority and specifically instructed him that he should never again charge more than 10 gallons without

176

Dewey's prior approval. Shortly thereafter, Willkie charged 15 gallons of paint at Stevenson's store. Once again, Willkie did not check with Dewey first. This time, Dewey refused to pay the bill submitted by Stevenson for the 15 gallons. On these facts, Dewey:

a. has no obligation to pay Stevenson for the last 15 gallons because Dewey has already over-paid Stevenson for numerous gallons of paint that Willkie was never authorized to charge.

b. is obligated to pay Stevenson for only 10 of the last 15 gallons charged by Willkie, because Stevenson had a duty to inquire concerning the extent of Willkie's purchasing authority.

c. is obligated to pay Stevenson for the last 15 gallons charged by Willkie, because Willkie had apparent authority to charge the 15 gallons.

d. is obligated to pay Stevenson for the last 15 gallons charged by Willkie, because Willkie had implied authority to charge the 15 gallons.

18. In which of the following situations would the party in the position of the agent probably be held liable on the contract made with the third party? (*Note*: assume in each instance that the agent had authority to enter into the contract on behalf of his or her principal.)

a. Alice Amoral, president of an existing corporation known as Barbaric, Inc., signs a written contract with a third party in this manner: "Barbaric, Inc., by Alice Amoral, President."

b. Alfred Alpo, an officer of an existing corporation known as Rancid Corp., negotiates a written contract with a third party. The contract pertains to Rancid's restaurant, which is located in Indianapolis and is operated under the name "The Indy Gestion." During the negotiations, Alpo has referred only to the restaurant's name and has not mentioned Rancid Corp. The third party does not know of Rancid's existence. Alpo signs the contract in this manner: "The Indy Gestion, by Alfred Alpo."

c. The same facts as in answer b, except for these differences: 1) that the third party knows Rancid Corp. is the owner of the restaurant even though Alpo did not tell the third party that and even though Alpo signed the contract in the manner set forth in answer b; and 2) that the third party intended to deal with Rancid Corp.

d. None of the above.

19. Chip Sahoy was employed by Ruinit Cleaners, Inc. His duties involved driving a company van along a designated route and picking up, from customers, items that needed to be dry cleaned. His work hours were 8 a.m. to 5 p.m., Monday through Friday. Sahoy had been instructed by his employer that he must not be negligent while driving the van. In addition, Ruinit had a policy that employees were not to eat or drink anything inside company vans, so that the interiors of the vans could be kept clean. On a recent Friday at 5:12 p.m., Sahoy had just completed his designated route and was driving a fully loaded Ruinit van back to Ruinit's place of business to drop off the items he had just picked up. Sahoy was eating a fig newton as he drove. Some of the filling dropped on his pants, and as he looked down at his pants, Sahoy negligently allowed the van to cross the center line of the street. A head-on collision with another vehicle resulted. Which of the following statements is accurate?

a. Because he was disobeying instructions not to drive negligently and not to eat anything while in the van, Sahoy was outside the scope of employment when the accident occurred.

b. Sahoy was acting within the scope of employment when the accident occurred, despite the time when it occurred and despite the fact that he was disobeying his employer's instructions.

c. The fact that Sahoy was eating a fig newton while driving the van indicates that he was partially motivated by his own interests; therefore, he was outside the scope of employment when the accident occurred.

d. Even though his regular work hours had expired, Sahoy was acting within the scope of employment because whenever an employee is negligent, the scope of employment test is satisfied.

20. Notice given by a third person to an agent is:
    a. binding on the agent's principal if the agent had either actual or apparent authority to receive the notice.
    b. not considered to have been received by the agent's principal regardless of the nature or subject of the notice.
    c. binding on the agent's principal if the agent had authority to receive it, but not until the agent actually relays the message to the principal.
    d. not effective to bind the agent's principal under any circumstances, although it may be effective to bind the agent.

21. Sean Smooth, an unemployed business school graduate, decided he would like to work as a salesperson at a local store, Hi Fye Stereo Sales. Unable to obtain an interview with the store's owner, Hiram Fye, Smooth devised a scheme to catch Fye's attention and to demonstrate his considerable marketing skills in the process. For several weeks, Smooth regularly conducted social gatherings at his apartment. During these gatherings, Smooth always played his stereo and extolled its virtues. At the conclusion of each of these affairs, Smooth would offer to sell the same type of stereo system and to personally install it, for no additional charge, at the buyer's home. Smooth eventually informed Fye of what he had done and said at the gatherings just mentioned, and pointed out to Fye that he had secured orders for 10 stereo systems. An overjoyed Fye agreed to the sales and allowed Smooth to install the systems in the buyers' homes. Fye later billed each of the buyers for installation charges, because it was not Fye's usual business practice to do installation work at no charge. Is Fye entitled to recover the installation charges from the buyers?
    a. Yes, because Smooth had no authority from Fye to make a promise of free installation.
    b. Yes, because when Smooth dealt with the buyers and took their orders, he was not Fye's agent.
    c. No, because when Smooth communicated with the buyers and took their orders, he had apparent authority to make binding representations on Fye's behalf.
    d. No, because Fye ratified Smooth's actions and in doing so became bound by both the beneficial and the burdensome aspects of Smooth's actions.

Short Essay

22. Butch Lugnut was an employee of Bigrig Co., a small trucking firm. Lugnut was driving a Bigrig truck down Interstate 80 on a Bigrig-authorized trip to Des Moines, Iowa. Near the outskirts of Des Moines, he fell asleep at the wheel and lost control of the truck. The truck left the highway, rumbled across an open field, and crashed through a wall of the Griese Truckstop (owned by Griese, Inc., a large corporation). Fortunately, no one was physically injured, but the truckstop sustained approximately $20,000 worth of damage. In falling asleep at the wheel, Lugnut violated a specific Bigrig directive that forbade employees from sleeping while on the job. Of course, Lugnut is liable to Griese for the consequences of his negligence. Is Bigrig also liable to Griese? If so, why? If not, why not?

23. Jackie Steinbeck owns a bookstore. Before leaving on a one-month vacation, she informed one of her sales clerks, Scotty Fitzgerald, that she wanted him to serve as acting manager of the store during her absence. Steinbeck instructed Fitzgerald to do the standard sorts of things managers do to keep businesses operating, but specifically told him not to purchase any books for the store, under any circumstances, while she was away. Assume, however, that in the area in which the bookstore was located, it was customary for bookstore managers to have authority to purchase additional inventory for the business. While Steinbeck was gone on vacation, Fitzgerald was approached by Billy Faulkner, a book salesman who proposed to sell the bookstore certain books at a special discount price. Thinking that very favorable terms had been proposed by Faulkner, Fitzgerald entered into a contract, allegedly on behalf of Steinbeck, for the purchase of the books. Faulkner, who was aware that bookstore managers customarily have the authority to make purchases of books, knew nothing of Steinbeck's instruction to Fitzgerald that he was not to purchase any new books. When Steinbeck returned and learned what had occurred, she denied that she was liable on the contract. Is she correct? Why or why not?

24. Marla Mousse owned and operated the House of Hair, a hairstyling salon. She hired Trevor Trendy as a hairstylist after noticing, on Trendy's application, that he had worked as a hairstylist at other salons. Contrary to the general pre-hiring practices of salon owners in Mousse's area, Mousse did not check with any of Trendy's references or former employers before putting him to work, and did not do any sort of background check on Trendy. She also did not ask Trendy to demonstrate his hairstyling skills before assigning him to a customer. If Mousse had checked with Trendy's former employers, she would have learned that Trendy had a history of not paying proper attention to his work, and as a result, causing serious damage to the hair and scalp of customers. On his first day of work at the House of Hair, Trendy was assigned to apply a nice blue tint to Edna Elderly's hair. Unfortunately for Elderly, Trendy carelessly retrieved the wrong bottle and, without examining its label, applied the contents of the bottle to Elderly's hair. Instead of containing the blue tint, the bottle contained an anti-psoriasis solution to which Elderly was allergic. The application of the anti-psoriasis solution caused all of the hair on Elderly's head to fall out, not to mention severe damage to Elderly's scalp. On these facts, who is liable to Elderly, and on what basis or bases? State the reasons supporting your answer.

CHAPTER 36

INTRODUCTION TO FORMS OF BUSINESS AND FORMATION OF PARTNERSHIPS

True-False - Circle T for True and F for False.

T F 1. A partner's liability for partnership debts is limited to the amount of his capital contribution to the partnership.

T F 2. If persons are engaged in a nonprofit venture, their venture cannot be carried on as a partnership.

T F 3. A written agreement is essential to the creation of a partnership.

T F 4. Each partner has the right to use partnership property for his own personal purposes unless the partnership agreement forbids such use.

T F 5. Under federal tax law, income tax is imposed on the partnership rather than on the individual partners who have profited from the partnership business.

T F 6. If the actions of parties indicate that they have a partnership, the parties' decision to call the relationship something other than a partnership is not determinative of what the relationship is.

T F 7. If a partner in a mining partnership transfers her partnership interest to another party (the transferee) without the consent of the other partners, the transferee nevertheless becomes a partner in the mining partnership.

T F 8. Either sharing profits or sharing management is, by itself, ordinarily considered conclusive evidence of a partnership.

T F 9. A person may have the liability of a partner even though she is not in fact anyone's partner.

T F 10. The primary difference between a joint venture and a partnership is that each participant in a joint venture ordinarily will have greater implied authority than will the partners in a partnership.

Multiple Choice - Circle the best answer.

11. Partnership property:
    a. includes all property used in the partnership business, regardless of who owns it.
    b. ordinarily includes property purchased with partnership funds for use by the partnership.
    c. must be titled in the partnership name.
    d. includes property originally contributed to the partnership, but not property purchased later on with partnership funds.

12. Wanda and Eno agreed to operate a clothing store together and to split the profits made thereby. Although they began operating the store together and splitting the profits, they never signed a formal partnership agreement. Are they partners?
    a. No, because they did not have an agreement in writing.
    b. No, because they did not specifically intend to create a partnership.
    c. Yes, unless they labeled their relationship as something other than a partnership.
    d. Yes, in all likelihood, even if they did not expressly call their relationship a partnership.

13. Of the following statements concerning sole proprietorships, which is accurate?
    a. A sole proprietorship has no existence apart from the existence of the owner of the business.
    b. A sole proprietor's liability for business-related debts is limited to the value of the assets of the business.
    c. If a sole proprietor begins operating her business under a trade name, the business becomes a separate entity for income tax purposes.
    d. If a sole proprietor hires one or more employees, the business becomes a joint venture rather than a sole proprietorship.

14. Zack and Jill have been partners in a used car business for five years. Last year, Jill bought ten used cars with her own money and then sold them on her own time. She made profits totaling $8000 on the sales. Is Zack entitled to an appropriate share of the $8000?

    a. No, because Jill bought the cars with her own money.
    b. Yes, because Jill owed Zack and their partnership a duty not to compete with the partnership business.
    c. No, because the profits were not profits made by the partnership business.
    d. Yes, because when two persons are partners, any income made by one of them must be shared with the other.

15. Jimmy and Debra agreed that they would become partners in a photography business. The never conducted the business together, however. Instead, Jimmy operated the photography business by himself and Debra kept her job as a salesperson for another business. In order to obtain photography supplies on credit, Jimmy told the supplier that Debra was his partner. The supplier extended credit to the business in reliance on Jimmy's statement that he and Debra were partners. When the photography business failed and Jimmy did not pay the supplier what was owed, the supplier sued both Jimmy and Debra in an effort to collect payment of the debt. Is Debra liable to the supplier?

    a. No, because a partner is liable only for the partnership debts she actually incurs.
    b. Yes, because Jimmy and Debra had agreed to become partners.
    c. No, because Jimmy and Debra never operated the business together.
    d. Yes, because of the operation of the partnership by estoppel doctrine.

16. A partnership:

    a. may own property in its own name.
    b. is considered, for most purposes, an employer of the partners.
    c. ordinarily may sue or be sued in its own name.
    d. is regarded under the law as primarily a separate entity, rather than as an aggregate of its partners.

17. According to the law governing partnerships,

    a. partners own partnership property in individual proportionate shares.
    b. loans made by a partner to the partnership are considered partnership capital.
    c. a partner's rights in partnership property pass to her heirs upon her death.
    d. property used in the partnership's business need not be owned by the partnership.

18. Which of the following cannot be a partner in a partnership?

    a. A minor
    b. A person who has been declared insane by a court
    c. A corporation
    d. All of the above

19. Olive is a partner in Oil Ltd. One of Olive's personal creditors, Castor, has obtained a judgement against Olive, as well as a charging order against Olive's interst in Oil Ltd. What right(s) does Castor have?

    a. The right to receive Olive's share of the partnership profits
    b. The right to engage in management of the partnership business
    c. The right to inspect partnership books and records
    d. Each of the rights set forth above

20. Feeble operates a toy store. As a means of repaying debts owed to Weak, Feeble granted Weak a share of the profits made in the toy store business. In addition, Feeble and Weak agreed that Feeble would consult Weak before incurring any additional business-related debt from other sources. Are Feeble and Weak partners?

   a. Probably, because of their agreement to divide the profits in some manner.
   b. Probably, because Weak has been granted a voice in management of the business.
   c. Probably not, because the Feeble-Weak relationship is that of debtor and creditor.
   d. Probably not, because nothing in the facts indicates that Feeble and Weak called their relationship a partnership.

Short Essay

21. George Walton, Sr., the sole owner of a small retailing business, was attempting to arrange a credit purchase of goods from a wholesaler with whom he had not previously done business. While talking in person to the wholesaler's representative, Mr. Walton pointed to his son, George-Boy (a famous musician who was home visiting his parents for a few days), and stated that "my partner and I have always paid our bills on time." George-Boy saw and heard what his father had done and said, but made no comments in the presence of the wholesaler's representative. George-Boy later informed his father that he had no intention of assuming liability for any of his father's debts. The wholesaler sold goods to Mr. Walton on credit, in reliance on the notion that Mr. Walton and the well-known George-Boy were partners. Mr. Walton failed to pay for the goods when payment was due. After various efforts to collect payment from Mr. Walton proved unsuccessful, the wholesaler sued Mr. Walton and George-Boy in an effort to collect the debt. Is George-Boy liable for the debt? Why or why not?

22. Ace Deuce owns Ace Deuce Hardware, a sole proprietorship. One of his customers was injured when she slipped on a banana peel that Deuce negligently failed to remove from the floor of the store. The customer has sued Deuce, who claims that he has no personal liability and that the customer may recover damages only out of the business assets of the hardware store. Is Deuce correct? State the reasons for your answer.

23. Quentin and two other persons were partners in a firm known as PDQ Enterprises. Because he had made some poor personal investments, Quentin had numerous creditors, all of whom were eager for payment. Among Quentin's creditors was Clara. In an effort to pay the debt he owed Clara, Quentin assigned Clara his interest in PDQ Enterprises. Clara then contacted the other two partners in PDQ Enterprises and demanded access to PDQ books and records, but they refused her demand. Was Clara on sound legal footing in making her demand? State the reasons for your answer.

CHAPTER 37

OPERATION OF PARTNERSHIPS AND RELATED FORMS

True-False - Circle T for True or F for False.

T F 1. A restriction on a partner's express or implied authority does not necessarily prevent the partner from having apparent authority.

T F 2. In order for a partnership to guarantee the debt of another party, all of the partners must agree to do so, if the giving of guarantees is outside the partnership's ordinary course of business.

T F 3. Partners must share the losses of the partnerships in the same percentages that they share the firm's profits.

T F 4. A partner may, for his own financial benefit, engage in the same business as that of the partnership if he does so on his own time.

T F 5. If a partner causes the partnership to experience a loss as a result of a transaction concerning which she had apparent authority but neither express nor implied authority, she is liable to the partnership for the amount of the loss.

T F 6. Many states have statutes that, contrary to the Uniform Partnership Act, allow partnerships to sue and be sued in their own name.

T F 7. A partnership's business may be shifted from hardware sales to book publishing whenever a majority of the partners agrees to do so.

T F 8. Although in certain instances partners may be held liable for the negligence of another partner, such vicarious liability is not imposed concerning any intentional torts committed by a partner.

T F 9. Absent a special provision to the contrary in applicable state law, if a partnership creditor sues less than all of the partners in an attempt to enforce a contract claim, the creditor cannot compel any individual partner to pay a judgment rendered on the claim.

T F 10. If a partner's exercise of judgment concerning a transaction caused the partnership to experience a loss, that partner necessarily will be liable to the partnership for the amount of the loss.

T F 11. The broad implied authority of a partner necessarily includes the implied authority to sell the partnership's real property on behalf of the partnership.

Multiple Choice - Circle the best answer.

12. Braggart, Palwell, and Takker formed a partnership. They made no express agreement concerning how profits were to be divided. Of the $50,000 initial capital of the firm, Braggart and Palwell each contributed $20,000. Takker contributed $10,000. The partnership had a profit of $30,000 during the first year the partnership business was in operation. What is Palwell's share of the profit?
    a. $10,000
    b. $12,000
    c. $15,000
    d. $17,500

13. Partners have a duty to account for:
    a. any purchases they make for the partnership.
    b. any sale of partnership property.
    c. any funds received by them as agents of the partnership.
    d. all of the above.

14. Mavis is one of the partners in a retail toy store business. The partnership frequently must borrow money in order to purchase inventory and satisfy other operating requirements. Needing money to pay some personal debts, Mavis recently borrowed $10,000 from Local National Bank. She signed the name of the partnership on all documents connected with the loan. She informed Local National that the money was for the firm, but she actually used the money for herself only. Mavis is now unable to repay the debt. Is the partnership liable to Local National for the debt?

   a. No, because Mavis was acting outside the scope of her authority when she borrowed the money.

   b. No, because Mavis committed a fraud upon Local National and upon the partnership.

   c. Yes, because the partnership is a trading partnership for which borrowing is in the ordinary course of business.

   d. Yes, because Mavis was negligent in failing to tell Local National the real purpose of the debt, and because the negligence of a partner is imputed to the partnership.

15. Joe Bill, a partner in Acme Stereo Sales, was authorized by his partners to repossess stereos from purchasers who had failed to make the agreed installment payments. While repossessing a stereo from Rex Punk, Joe Bill convinced an initially reluctant Punk to be cooperative by shoving him against a wall. Punk sustained a brain concussion as a result of Joe Bill's shove. If Punk sues for damages stemming from Joe Bill's battery, will the other partners in Acme be held liable?

   a. Yes, because partners are always liable for the torts committed by their fellow partners.

   b. Yes, because the tort was committed while Joe Bill was within the scope of an action for the partnership.

   c. No, because only the individual partner who committed the tort can be held liable.

   d. No, because the other partners obviously would not have authorized Joe Bill to commit a battery.

16. Roy, Rhonda, and Reggie are partners in Triple R Investments. Roy has proposed to sell the partnership an office building he personally owns. Rhonda and Reggie have agreed that the partnerhsip should make the purchase. The office building is located in another city and will not be inspected by Rhonda and Reggie before the purchase takes place. Roy is aware, but Rhonda and Reggie are not aware, that the building needs a complete electrical rewiring job whose cost would be several thousand dollars. The price Roy has agreed to accept for the building is $275,000—a fair price given the building's location, condition (including the need for the rewiring), and other pertinent factors. On these facts, Roy

   a. is free to sell Triple R the building without violating his duty not to self-deal, because he is asking a fair price and is therefore proceeding in good faith.

   b. has violated his duty of loyalty and good faith, because partners cannot engage in any self-dealing transactions with their partnership.

   c. must disclose the need for the rewiring before the purchase takes place; otherwise, he will violate his duty not to self-deal.

   d. has not engaged in prohibited self-dealing because his partners' agreement to purchase the building constitutes approval of the transaction.

17. Of the following statements concerning criminal liability of partners and partnerships, which is/are *inaccurate*?

   a. Most modern criminal codes allow partnerships to be convicted of crimes.

   b. If a partner commits a crime within the course and scope of transacting partnership business, the other partners are usually held criminally liable.

   c. If one partner actually commits a crime that the remaining partners authorized, all of the partners will have criminal liability.

   d. a, b, and c.

18. A partner has implied authority to bind the partnership:

    a. on contracts that are usually appropriate for the business in which the partnership is engaged.

    b. only on those contracts that he, according to the terms of the partnership agreement, is expressly authorized to make.

    c. only if the partnership agreement specifically states that he will have such implied authority.

    d. whenever a third person justifiably believes that the partner has authority to enter into a contract with her on behalf of the partnership.

19. Agnes, Burl, and Cletus were partners in the ABC Partnership. Their partnership agreement stated that Agnes would bear 50 percent of partnership losses, with Burl and Cletus each bearing 25 percent of partnership losses. ABC's business failed, with various partnership debts being left unpaid. After all partnership assets had been exhausted for the benefit of the firm's creditors, $48,000 remained due and owing to the creditors. On these facts, how much may the creditors lawfully collect from Burl?

    a. 0

    b. $12,000

    c. $16,000

    d. $48,000

20. W, X, Y, and Z are partners in WXYZ Partnership. W committed a tort upon Plaintiff. Assume that under applicable law, X, Y, and Z are vicariously liable for the tort as well. Of the following statements concerning the facts, which is accurate?

    a. If Plaintiff wishes to enforce her tort claim, she must sue all four of the partners.

    b. In most states, the only individual partner Plaintiff can sue is W, with the partnership being a permissible additional defendant.

    c. Plaintiff would be permitted to sue only X, Y, and Z and enforce her claim against them if she so chooses.

    d. None of the above.

21. Which of the following may be done without the unanimous consent of the partners?

    a. Assigning partnership property for the benefit of creditors

    b. Selling items of the the partnership's inventory in the ordinary course of business

    c. Submitting a dispute involving the partnership to arbitration

    d. Confessing a judgment against the partnership in favor of a creditor

Short Essay

22. Lonnie and Myrna are partners in L & M Maid Service, a business whose specialty is the furnishing of cleaning services. The partnership's assets have a value of approximately $10,000. Lonnie went to Friendly Savings & Loan and requested that Friendly loan L & M $8,000 so that L & M could purchase a used car for use in connection with the firm's business. Friendly chose to make the loan, so it issued Lonnie an $8000 check made payable to the order of L & M Maid Service. Lonnie then cashed the check, took the $8,000, and fled for parts unknown, never to return. A month later, when the initial loan payment was not made, a Friendly employee called the L & M office. Asserting that the debt was a partnership debt, the Friendly employee made demand upon Myrna for payment. The demand constituted Myrna's first knowledge of the loan. She refused to make any payments on the loan. Is Myrna justified in refusing to pay the debt? State the reasons for your answer.

23. Arthur, Eunice, LeRoy, and June formed a partnership. Arthur and Eunice each made a capital contribution of $10,000. LeRoy and June each contributed $5000 in capital. Although the parties did not agree concerning how to split profits, they agreed that Arthur and Eunice would each bear 30 percent of partnership losses, and that LeRoy and June would each bear 20 percent of partnership losses. During the partnership's first year, the partnership business made a profit of $21,000. What is Eunice's share of the profit? Explain your reasoning.

24. Boyd Boring is a partner in the accounting firm Dull, Dry & Boring. Boring performed extensive accounting services for a client of the firm. The client was quite appreciative, because the work performed by Boring enabled him to obtain a large income tax refund. Dull, Dry & Boring billed the client $2100 for the work performed by Boring. Besides promptly paying the bill, the client sent, to Boring's home, a separate $700 check made payable to the order of Boyd Boring. Along with the $700 check, the client sent a note stating that he was grateful for the work Boring had done and that the $700 check was meant for Boring personally, as further compensation for the accounting services performed. May Boring keep the $700 for himself, or must he turn it over to the firm? State the reasons for your answer.

CHAPTER 38

DISSOLUTION, WINDING UP, AND TERMINATION OF PARTNERSHIPS

True-False - Circle T for True and F for False.

T F 1. When a partnership is dissolved, any partner who did not wrongfully cause the dissolution may demand winding up.

T F 2. A partner who wrongfully causes a dissolution of the partnership nevertheless remains entitled to share in the goodwill of the business.

T F 3. Any partner has the power to dissolve the partnership before the expiration of the duration established in the partnership agreement.

T F 4. Dissolution ends the business of a partnership.

T F 5. The addition of a new partner causes a dissolution of the former partnership, as well as the creation of a different partnership, because the addition of the new partner brings about a change in the composition of the former partnership.

T F 6. The value of an outgoing partner's interest in the partnership is determined as of the time of dissolution.

T F 7. The insolvency of a partner does not cause the dissolution of the partnership.

T F 8. A new partner who has joined an existing partnership has no liability for partnership debts that existed before he became a partner.

T F 9. A partner who conducts the winding up of partnership affairs ordinarily is not entitled to special compensation for conducting the winding up process.

T F 10. A partner who withdraws from an existing partnership remains liable for all partnership obligations that existed as of the time of her withdrawal, but her liability is limited to the extent of partnership assets.

Multiple Choice - Circle the best answer.

11. In winding up the affairs of a partnership, the partners doing the winding up:
    a. are prohibited from electing to perform partnership contracts on which performance had not begun before dissolution of the partnership.
    b. are prohibited from borrowing money and creating a partnership obligation to that effect.
    c. may enter into contracts for wholly new business if it is not necessary to borrow money in order to perform the obligations created by the contracts.
    d. may borrow money and create an accompanying partnership obligation if doing so would preserve partnership assets or enhance their sale value.

12. If a partner causes a wrongful dissolution of the partnership,
    a. the innocent partners acquire the right to continue the partnership business by themselves, but not with new partners.
    b. he loses the right to demand that the partnerhsip business be wound up.
    c. he is entitled to receive the value of his partnership interest plus his share of the partnership's goodwill, less damages caused by the wrongful dissolution.
    d. each of the above consequences is triggered.

13. The liability of an incoming partner for partnership obligations arising after she became a partner:
    a. is limited to the amount of her capital contribution.
    b. begins when notice of her joining the partnership is given.
    c. is unlimited in extent and scope.
    d. is limited to the extent of partnership assets.

14. Absent a contrary provision in the partnership agreement, a partnership becomes dissolved without a court order to that effect if:
    a. a partner dies.
    b. a partner becomes insane.
    c. a partner becomes permanently disabled.
    d. any one of the above circumstances occurs.

15. The order of distribution of partnership assets is:
    a. first to satisfy creditors' claims; then to repay partners' loans to the firm; then to pay partners their shares of profits; then to return partners their capital contributions.
    b. first to satisfy creditors' claims; then to return partners their capital contributions; then to repay partners' loans to the firm; then to pay partners their shares of profits.
    c. first to satisfy creditors' claims; then to repay partners' loans to the firm; then to return partners' capital contributions; then to pay partners their shares of profits.
    d. not accurately set forth in any of the above answers.

16. Hamlet, Ophelia, Othello, and Desdemona were partners in a dissolved partnership, HOOD Enterprises, whose business was the manufacturing and sale of widgets. Ophelia is conducting the winding up of the partnership business. HOOD has a contract to supply 20,000 widgets to the We R Widgets chain of stores. Performance of the contract has not yet begun. In addition, HOOD has 35,000 unsold widgets in stock. HOOD also owns the building in which its manufacturing operation has been conducted. For which of the following does Ophelia possess express or implied authority during winding up?
    a. Painting the building in preparation for selling it
    b. Selling the 20,000 widgets to We R Widgets
    c. Selling the building
    d. Each of the above

17. Johnnie, Ollie, and Eddie were partners in JOE Co., a partnership that has been dissolved. When JOE was formed, Johnnie contributed capital of $60,000, Ollie contributed capital of $30,000, and Eddie contributed capital of $10,000. The three partners agreed to share profits and losses in this manner: 50 percent to Johnnie; 30 percent to Ollie; and 20 percent to Eddie. Following liquidation of all partnership assets and distribution of the proceeds to creditors, there remains $24,000 due and owing to partnership creditors. Among Johnnie, Ollie, and Eddie, which amount represents Johnnie's proper share of the amount still owed to creditors?
    a. $2000
    b. $8000
    c. $12,000
    d. $14,400

190

18. Orville and Otto have been partners in a car wash business for a number of years. Their partnership agreement sets forth a duration that will not expire for five more years. Orville has found that it takes considerable effort to get along with Otto, who is a moody person with a gruff manner. The two of them have had numerous disagreements through the years. Tired of dealing with Otto, Orville has filed suit against him in an effort to obtain a court-ordered dissolution of the partnership. Will the court grant the requested dissolution?
    a. Yes, because the partnership is a partnership at will.
    b. No, if the business is a profitable one.
    c. No, regardless of whether the business is profitable or unprofitable.
    d. Yes, regardless of whether the business is profitable or unprofitable.

19. Under the Uniform Partnership Act, what notice, if any, must be given concerning the dissolution of a partnership to: 1) prior creditors of the partnership; and 2) noncreditors who had previously done business with the partnership without extending credit, or who otherwise had knowledge of the partnership's existence?
    a. Actual notice to those fitting in category no. 1, and no notice to those fitting in category no. 2.
    b. Constructive notice to those fitting in category no. 1, and no notice to those fitting in category no. 2.
    c. Actual notice to those fitting in category no. 1, and constructive notice to those fitting in category no. 2.
    d. Constructive notice to those fitting in category no. 1 and category no. 2.

20. When may the nonwithdrawing partners continue the partnership business?
    a. When the partnership agreement permits it.
    b. When the withdrawing partner has dissolved the partnership in violation of the partnership agreement.
    c. When the withdrawing partner dissolved the partnership nonwrongfully, and he and all of the nonwithdrawing partners agree to the continuation.
    d. In each of the above situations.

Short Essay

21. Prudence, Deidre, and Quincy were partners in PDQ Associates. When PDQ was formed, Prudence contributed capital of $50,000 and Deidre and Quincy contributed capital of $20,000 each. The partners agreed that Prudence would receive 50 percent of the firm's profits and that Deidre and Quincy would each receive 25 percent of the profits. Their partnership contained no provision concerning how losses would be allocated among the three of them. The three partners unanimously agreed that PDQ should be dissolved. After all partnership assets were liquidated and the proceeds therefrom distributed to creditors, PDQ still owed creditors $24,000. Among Prudence, Deidre, and Quincy, what amount represents Prudence's proper share of the $24,000 still owed to creditrs? Explain your reasoning.

191

22. Womble and three other persons owned and operated a sporting goods store as partners. Womble died. Pursuant to a provision in the partnership agreement, the surviving partners elected to continue the partnership business. They sent partnership creditors a notice stating that the partnership and the surviving partners would assume any liability Womble's estate otherwise would have had on partnership obligations that existed prior to Womble's death. Among the partnership creditors receiving the notice was Bigcorp, Inc., which was owed a substantial amount of money on a partnership debt that existed before Womble died. When it came time for the debt to be paid to Bigcorp, neither the partnership nor any of the surviving partners paid it. Bigcorp then filed suit against the partnership, the surviving partners, and Womble's estate in an effort to collect the debt. The personal representative of Womble's estate argues that the estate has no liability on the debt because the giving of the notice referred to above constituted a novation. Is the personal representative correct? Why or why not?

23. XYZ was a partnership whose business was performing all types of painting jobs. Before the partnership was dissolved, XYZ had entered into a contract under which it was to paint every room in the local courthouse. At the time of the dissolution, XYZ had not yet performed the work called for by the contract just mentioned. Regarding the contract as one that could bring in substantial revenue, the partners conducting the winding up of the firm's business elected to perform the contract. They also decided the work would go more quickly if they subcontracted part of the work to another party, so they entered into a new contract to that effect with another painting contractor. In addition, the partners conducting the winding up entered into a new contract with a paint supplier for the purchase of the substantial amount of paint necessary for completion of the courthouse project. Were the above-described actions of the winding up partners proper? State the basis for your answer.

CHAPTER 39

LIMITED PARTNERSHIPS

True-False - Circle T for True and F for False.

T F 1. A proper certificate of limited partnership must state the name of each limited partner.

T F 2. Although a limited partnership cannot be created except pursuant to state statute, substantial compliance with the statute's requirements for creation ordinarily is sufficient for the creation of a limited partnership.

T F 3. A limited partner may assume personal liability on a specific partnership obligation without forfeiting her limited liability on other partnership obligations.

T F 4. A general partner who does not actually participate in the management of a limited partnership has the same liability to partnership creditors that a limited partner has.

T F 5. The RULPA's provision on post-dissolution distribution of limited partnership assets allows the partners to eliminate the priority position of creditors by agreeing unanimously that creditors' claims will be paid after the partners have received the return of their capital.

T F 6. Absent a contrary provision in the limited partnership agreement, a limited partner's withdrawal from the firm does not result in dissolution of the limited partnership.

T F 7. Although a corporation may serve as a general partner in a limited partnership, it cannot serve as a limited partner.

T F 8. In a limited partnership, a general partner's liability to partnership creditors is limited to the amount of his capital contribution.

T F 9. Although the addition of a new limited partner does not cause a dissolution of the former limited partnership, the addition of a new general partner does have that effect.

T F 10. When a limited partnership is dissolved and there are no general partners who have not wrongfully dissolved the firm, a limited partner may perform the winding up of partnership affairs.

Multiple Choice - Circle the best answer.

11. Roy and Woody are the only general partners in R-W Limited Partnership. Each has contributed capital of $20,000. Archibald and Priscilla are the only limited partners in the firm. Archibald has contributed capital of $20,000. Priscilla has contributed capital of $40,000. R-W has a profit of $90,000 to distribute. Under the RULPA rule for sharing of profits, what is Priscilla's share of the profit?
    a. $22,500
    b. $45,000
    c. $40,000
    d. $36,000

12. Assuming that the limited partnership agreement is silent on the subject of what constitutes dissolution, which of the following dissolves the limited partnership?
    a. The death of a general partner
    b. The bankruptcy of a limited partner
    c. The death of a limited partner
    d. All of the above

13. Arthur and Alan decided to open a retail store and to operate the business as a partnership. Because they needed additional funds to get the business in operation, they asked Jayne whether she would like to invest money in the business and become a limited partner. Assuming that Jayne becomes a limited partner, which of the following statements is/are accurate?

    a. Jayne's status as a limited partner gives her a substantial stake in the operation of the business; therefore, she is entitled to participate in the management of the business.

    b. Jayne will not have personal liability for partnership debts, although it is possible that partnership losses may be so significant that she will lose the money she invested in the business.

    c. If Jayne later becomes an employee of the limited partnership in addition to being a limited partner, she will lose the advantage of the limited liability that ordinarily accompanies limited partner status.

    d. All of the above.

14. The following statements pertain to the RULPA's approach to post-dissolution distributions of limited partnership assets. Which statement is accurate?

    a. Under the RULPA, the rules governing the order in which limited partnership assets are distributed following dissolution are the same as the rules governing distribution of general partnership assets following dissolution.

    b. Under the RULPA, previously withdrawn partners' claims to a return of their capital contributions are given a higher priority, in a post-dissolution distribution of limited partnership assets, than are the claims of partners for a return of their capital contributions.

    c. If a limited partnership agreement contains a distribution of assets provision that purports to alter, among the partners, the order of distribution of assets called for by the RULPA, the RULPA-established order controls and the partnership agreement's provision is unenforceable.

    d. If a partner extended a loan to a limited partnership that later dissolved, the partner's claim for repayment of the loan is given a lower priority, in the post-dissolution distribution of assets, than the priority given to nonpartner creditors' claims.

15. In order for a limited partnership to be formed, there must be at least how many general partners and at least how many limited partners?

    a. At least one general partner and at least two limited partners

    b. At least two general partners, but there is no minimum number of limited partners

    c. At least one general partner and at least one limited partner

    d. At least two general partners and at least one limited partner

16. Chip is one of the limited partners and Skip and Bambi are the general partners in a certain limited partnership. The business of the limited partnership is investing in works of art. Chip has received reliable information indicating that Skip and Bambi have been buying and selling some works of art on their own, without making the opportunities available to the limited partnership. Although Chip would like to bring a derivative suit against Skip and Bambi on the theory that they breached their fiduciary duties, he is concerned that by doing so, he may forfeit his limited liability. Will he lose his limited liability if he brings the derivative suit?

    a. Yes, because the decisions of Skip and Bambi not to have the partnership involved in certain purchases and sales were ordinary business decisions.

    b. No, because limited partners have the same voice in management decisions that general partners have.

    c. Yes, because the filing of the suit would be an impermissible attempt to exercise control over the limited partnership's business.

    d. No, because a limited partner's attempt to enforce other partners' fiduciary duties does not constitute exercising control over partnership business.

17. Arnold, Barbara, and Claudette attempted to create a limited partnership with Arnold as general partner and Barbara and Claudette as limited partners. Arnold filed an inaccurate certificate of limited partnership that listed himself, Barbara, and Claudette as general partners. Dorf, a supplier, extended credit to the business on the good faith belief that Arnold and Claudette were general partners, but without any knowledge or belief concerning any interest Barbara had in the business. After the extension of credit by Dorf, Barbara and Claudette discovered that they had been listed incorrectly in the certificate as general partners. Both of them promptly withdrew from future equity participation in the firm by filing a certificate to that effect in the secretary of state's office. The debt owed to Dorf went unpaid when it came due, so Dorf sued Arnold, Barbara, and Claudette in an effort to collect the debt. Who is liable to Dorf?
    a. Arnold only
    b. Arnold and Claudette
    c. Arnold, Barbara, and Claudette
    d. No one, because no limited partnership was created

18. Which of the following may a limited partner do and retain her limited liability to partnership creditors?
    a. Allow the use of her surname in the limited partnership's name if her father, who has the same surname, is a general partner in the firm.
    b. Attempt to enforce the limited partnership agreement against a general partner who arguably has breached it.
    c. Propose to the partners that there be a sale of substantially all of the assets of the limited partnership.
    d. All of the above.

19. Nimble was a general partner in Shaky Limited Partnership prior to the firm's dissolution. Before the dissolution, Nimble loaned the firm $10,000. The loan was not repaid before the dissolution took place. Shaky also owes debts to creditors X, Y, and Z. When Shaky's assets are liquidated and distributed, what priority does the RULPA give to Nimble's claim for repayment of the loan, in relation to the priority given to the claims of X, Y, and Z?
    a. The same priority given to the claims of X, Y, and Z, because Nimble is considered a creditor of the firm.
    b. A lower priority than what is given to the claims of X, Y, and Z, because the loan by Nimble is considered a contribution of capital.
    c. A higher priority than what is given to the claims of X, Y, and Z, because Nimble is a partner-creditor.
    d. No priority whatsoever, meaning that Nimble's claim will paid only if assets remain after all other claims of whatever nature are paid.

20. Wally is a limited partner in Beaver Limited Partnership. His capital contribution to the firm was $40,000. Because he wishes to use the $40,000 for another business venture, Wally would like to withdraw his capital contribution. Which of the following statements accurately sets forth Wally's rights concerning withdrawal of his capital contribution?
    a. Wally cannot withdraw his capital contribution unless he obtains the consent of the other partners in Beaver.
    b. Wally cannot obtain repayment of his capital contribution until the winding up of Beaver's affairs.
    c. Wally may withdraw his capital contribution by giving six months' advance written notice to the other partners, assuming that creditors' claims would not be impaired by the withdrawal.
    d. Wally may withdraw his capital contribution only if all of the firm's creditors have been notified of his intention to do so and, after having received such notification, have given their consent.

21. The KT Limited Partnership has two general partners, Kyle and Tara, and five limited partners. Kyle's capital contribution to the firm was $15,000. Tara's capital contribution was $10,000. Each of the five limited partners contributed capital of $15,000. KT has profits of $70,000 ready for distribution. Under the RULPA rule for sharing of profits, how much should each partner receive? Explain the basis for your answers.

22. Joe Stallings was a limited partner and Karla Marks and Nikki Lennon were the general partners in Pinko Limited Partnership. The capital contribution of Stallings was $10,000. Marks and Lennon each contributed capital of $2000. Other partnership assets had a total value of $5000. The partnership's business was the operation of a small retail store. Originally, Marks and Lennon performed all management tasks concerning the store. Because he wanted to be certain that his investment would be protected, Stallings gradually became heavily involved in management of the business. A wholesaler, Lee Ontrotsky, came to the Pinko store one day in hopes of establishing a new business relationship with the store. While waiting to speak with Marks, Ontrotsky overheard a conversation involving Marks, Lennon, and Stallings. The conversation, which pertained to Pinko business decisions, gave Ontrotsky the impression that Marks, Lennon, and Stallings were partners in the operation of the store. Later that morning, when Ontrotsky and Marks met, Marks agreed on behalf of Pinko to purchase $30,000 worth of goods on credit from Ontrotsky. Pinko failed to pay the debt to Ontrotsky when it came due. What is the extent of liability that Marks, Lennon, and Stallings, respectively, have to Ontrotsky? Explain your reasoning.

23. Weeble and various other persons reached an agreement or the creation of a limited partnership. A cerificate of limited partnership was prepared. The certificate contained everything required by law, plus the signatures of each general and limited partner and all of the terms of the parties' limited partnership agreement. Weeble, designated as a limited partner, was among the signers. The certificate recited that Weeble had contributed capital of $25,000 and would be making an additional capital contribution of $15,000 on July 1, 1991. The business of the supposed limited partnership was put into operation. July 1, 1991 came and went without Weeble's making the additional capital contribution just mentioned. After the various partners began pressing Weeble for payment, Weeble discovered that the certificate of limited partnership had never been filed in the appropriate government office designated by state law. Weeble therefore argued that the agreement set forth in the certificate was unenforceable, and that he had no obligation to make the additional contribution of capital. Is Weeble correct? Why or why not?

CHAPTER 40

HISTORY AND NATURE OF CORPORATIONS

True-False - Circle T for True and F for False.

T F   1.   A principal advantage, to shareholders, of the corporate form of business is that the money they have invested in the corporation is not at risk of being lost because of the claims of creditors of the corporation.

T F   2.   If a foreign corporation sends a delivery truck driven by an employee into a state, the corporation will be subject to a suit in that state's courts, assuming the suit is based upon the truck driver's negligence while operating the truck in that state.

T F   3.   Because corporations are artificial legal entities rather than natural persons, they do not obtain the benefit of the due process guarantees given by the U.S. Constitution.

T F   4.   Because the federal government has control over interstate commerce, a business that wishes to conduct business in interstate commerce and under the corporate form must become incorporated pursuant to federal incorporation statutes.

T F   5.   Although publicly held corporations and close corporations are generally treated alike under the various states' corporation laws, some states give close corporations greater latitude in regulating their internal affairs than is given to publicly held corporations.

T F   6.   A state cannot constitutionally impose its health and safety regulations on a corporation that was incorporated under the law of another state, because an attempt to do so would necessarily deny the corporation due process.

T F   7.   Unlike shareholders of a publicly held corporation, shareholders of a close corporation do not have limited liability for corporate debts.

T F   8.   A foreign corporation must qualify to do business in a state if the foreign corporation owns, for passive investment purposes, a piece of real property in that state.

T F   9.   If a corporation was incorporated in Delaware but does most of its business in Iowa, the corporation is nevertheless considered a foreign corporation in Iowa.

T F 10.   A shareholder may be held personally liable to the corporation's creditor if the corporation and the shareholder have depleted corporate assets by engaging in less-than-arm's-length transactions with each other.

Multiple Choice - Circle the best answer.

11.   A state may impose a tax:
   a.   on the property of a foreign corporation if the property is located within the state.
   b.   on the income derived from a foreign corporation's making sales contracts in the state through the use of a sales agent there, even if the goods sold are prepared and shipped from outside the state.
   c.   in both the situations described in answers a and b.
   d.   in neither of the situtations described in answers a and b.

12.   Shareholders of a corporation:
   a.   ordinarily play little role in management of the corporate business.
   b.   will lose their limited liability if they engage in management of the corporate business.
   c.   cannot serve as officers of the corporation.
   d.   cannot also be creditors of the corporation.

13. Realbig Corp., an Ohio corporation, has received numerous orders from customers located in Illinois. It plans to ship the ordered goods by its own trucks from Ohio to Illinois. In order to do so, the Realbig trucks must proceed across Indiana highways. Must Realbig qualify to do business in Indiana before it may ship the goods to Illinois in the manner just described?

    a. Yes, because the fact that there have been numerous orders means that the passage of the Realbig trucks through Indiana will be more than merely an isolated transaction.

    b. Yes, because when the Realbig trucks enter Indiana, Realbig is engaged in intrastate business within Indiana.

    c. No, because Indiana cannot constitutionally require a corporation of another state to qualify to do business in Indiana.

    d. No, because Realbig is engaged only in interstate business and is merely using Indiana's highways for that purpose.

14. Warmco, Inc., a South Dakota corporation that manufactures portable electric heaters, has retail dealers in South Dakota, North Dakota, and Minnesota. A Warmco dealer in South Dakota sold Chuck Charles a Warmco heater. Charles took the heater to his home in Texas and began using it there. A defect in the heater caused it to catch on fire, and Charles was seriously burned as a result. A similar defect in a Warmco heater caused severe burns to Jerry Gerald, who had purchased his heater from a Warmco dealer in Minnesota and was using the heater at his Minnesota home when he was injured. Assume that Charles has filed a product liability suit against Warmco in a Texas court, and that Gerald has done the same in a Minnesota court. In addition, assume that the long arm statutes of Texas and Minnesota allow the assertion of jurisdiction over out-of-state corporations to the fullest extent permitted by the Due Process Clause. In which of the two suits would the court's assertion of jurisdiction over Warmco be constitutional?

    a. In Charles's suit, because in today's mobile society, it should have been foreseeable to Warmco that its heaters would be used in other states, including Texas.

    b. In Gerald's suit, because Warmco placed its heaters into the stream of commerce with the expectation that they would be purchased and used in Minnesota.

    c. In both of the suits, for the reasons stated in answers a and b.

    d. In neither of the suits, because the minimum contacts requirement is not satisfied under the facts of the two cases.

15. Courts will allow piercing of the corporate veil:

    a. whenever there is a parent-subsidiary relationship between two corporations.

    b. whenever the parent corporation dominates its wholly-owned subsidiary corporation.

    c. whenever a corporation has only one shareholder.

    d. whenever a parent corporation's domination of its wholly-owned subsidiary was for an improper purpose.

16. Which one or more of the following constitutes "doing business," for the purpose of whether a foreign corporation must qualify to do business within a state?

    a. Soliciting orders by mail within the state, and accepting and filling the orders from outside the state.

    b. Soliciting orders through the use of an employee within the state, and accepting and filling the orders from outside the state.

    c. Maintaining a stock of goods within the state for the purpose of filling orders, but accepting the orders outside the state.

    d. Both b and c.

17. A corporation:
    a. must be organized for the purpose of making a profit.
    b. does not obtain constitutional protection against unreasonable searches and seizures because it is not a *person* under the U.S. Constitution.
    c. must use shareholders as its officers and directors.
    d. is a legal entity separate from those who own the corporation even if the corporate ownership consists of a single shareholder.

18. Bilkem Corp., a Delaware corporation, solicited purchase offers for its products in Arkansas through the use of a sales agent in Arkansas. All offers were subject to acceptance by Bilkem at its home office in Delaware. When sales contracts were made, Bilkem manufactured the products in Delaware and shipped them from that state. May Arkansas impose an income tax on the profits made by Bilkem in connection with sales to Arkansas residents?
    a. Yes, because Bilkem was transacting business in Arkansas.
    b. No, because any sales contracts between Bilkem and Arkansas residents were not made in Arkansas.
    c. Yes, because Bilkem's contacts with Arkansas are sufficient to satisfy the minimum contacts requirement.
    d. No, because Bilkem did not not have any property located in Arkansas.

19. If a foreign corporation is obligated to qualify to do business in a state but fails to do so,
    a. it is barred from defending a suit brought against it in that state's courts.
    b. its shareholders will lose the limited liability they otherwise would have had.
    c. it may become obligated to pay a fine.
    d. all of the above consequences are possible.

20. Which of the following is an accurate statement concerning Subchapter S corporations?
    a. They are treated much as partnerships are treated for federal income tax purposes.
    b. They must have at least 35 shareholders.
    c. They pay income taxes in the same manner that ordinary corporations do.
    d. None of the above.

Short Essay

21. After several years as sole proprietor of a tavern known as Butch's Bucket, Butch decided to incorporate the business. He proceeded to form Bucket, Inc., a corporation of which he was the president and majority stockholder. All shares of Bucket stock not owned by Butch were owned by his wife, Pixie. Because they were Bucket's only shareholders, Butch and Pixie mixed Bucket funds and their personal funds in the same bank accounts. They regularly drove a truck titled in the name of the corporation and did not pay the corporation anything for the use of the truck. During the first four years the corporation was in existence, no directors' meetings or shareholders' meetings were held, with the exception of initial meetings shortly after incorporation took place. The corporation always made a timely filing of its corporate income tax return. A Bucket creditor has now discovered that Bucket does not have sufficient assets to satisfy his past-due claim. On these facts, what remedy does the creditor have? Why is that remedy appropriate?

22. Roller World, Inc., a family-owned corporation organized under Missouri law, operated a single roller skating rink in a small Missouri town. All of the corporation's business activities were confined to the state of Missouri, although sometimes persons from other states were customers at the rink. On one occasion, a nine-year-old girl, who lived in Idaho and was passing through Missouri while on vacation with her parents, was skating at the Roller World rink. She sustained serious injuries as the result of a fall. Her parents, claiming that the fall and the ensuing injuries were caused by Roller World's negligence in maintaining the rink, filed suit against Roller World in an Idaho court. Assume, for purposes of this question, that Idaho has a long-arm statute that allows the assertion of jurisdiction over out-of-state defendants to the fullest extent allowed by the U.S. Supreme Court's *International Shoe* decision. Roller World's president occasionally travels through Idaho while on his way to visit his grandparents in Washington. On the basis of these facts, may the Idaho court assert jurisdiction over Roller World? Why or why not?

23. The Griese brothers, Gus and Gil, operated an automobile service and repair business. They incorporated the business under the name Griese Service, Inc. Gus owned 60 percent of the corporation's stock and Gil owned the other 40 percent. Corporate assets, all contributed by Gus and Gil, totaled $1000. The corporation carried no liability insurance. After the business was incorporated, Bart Suave took his late model Porsche to Griese Service for an oil change. As the result of negligence on the part of a Griese Service employee, Suave's Porsche fell off a Griese Service hoist. Several thousand dollars worth of damage was caused to the Porsche. If you were Suave's attorney, from whom would you seek recovery, and on what theories?

CHAPTER 41

ORGANIZATION, FINANCIAL STRUCTURE, AND DISSOLUTION OF CORPORATIONS

True-False - Circle T for True and F for False.

T F   1.   If preferred stock is by its terms redeemable, it is subject to being purchased by the corporation from the shareholder, even against the wishes of the shareholder.

T F   2.   In some states, a corporation's shareholders, rather than a board of directors, will have the power to manage the corporation, if the corporation has properly elected close corporation status.

T F   3.   A promoter will remain liable on a contract made by him on behalf of a proposed corporation only if the corporation is never formed.

T F   4.   Modern corporation statutes give corporate boards of directors broad latitude concerning the types of consideration that will support the issuance of stock to a shareholder.

T F   5.   The difference between *issued* shares and *outstanding* shares is that issued shares are those currently held by shareholders, whereas outstanding shares are those that have not yet been issued by the corporation.

T F   6.   The special nature of close corporations has caused many states to adopt statutes that prohibit close corporations from employing transfer restrictions concerning shares of their stock.

T F   7.   In some states, those who make wholly defective and ineffective attempts to incorporate a business may be treated as partners with unlimited liability for the obligations of the business.

T F   8.   Even if the corporation first pays the holders of cumulative preferred shares the current year's dividends, it is not necessarily free to proceed with payment of dividends to the holders of common shares.

T F   9.   If a corporation is solvent but has not paid a particular creditor, the unpaid creditor may obtain a judicial dissolution of the corporation.

T F 10.   Under the MBCA, the secretary of state's issuance of a certificate of incorporation to a firm creates a presumption of corporate existence that any third party may rebut by other evidence showing a lack of corporate existence.

T F 11.   A corporation's existence does not terminate until the winding up process has been completed.

T F 12.   Debentures and bonds are long-term debt securities that differ in the sense that the debts created by debentures are secured debts, whereas the debts created by bonds are unsecured debts.

T F 13.   *Capital surplus* consists of an amount equal to the number of outstanding shares multiplied by the par value of each share.

T F 14.   In states that recognize the de jure corporation concept, a de jure corporation is treated as a corporation for all purposes even though not all incorporation requirements set forth by state law were met by the corporation.

T F 15.   As a general rule, the owners of a corporation's common shares do not possess voting rights with regard to the election of corporate directors.

Multiple Choice - Circle the best answer.

16.   Under the MBCA, the articles of incorporation must include:
    a.   the name of each person who will serve as an initial director of the corporation.
    b.   a statement of the number of shares of stock that the corporation has authority to issue.
    c.   a statement of the par value of the shares of stock to be issued by the corporation.
    d.   each of the above.

17. Prior to the incorporation of Pyle Co. (a manufacturing business), Gomer, who was acting as a promoter for Pyle, negotiated a contract for the purchase of manufacturing equipment from Sergeant-Carter Corp. The contract was entered into on behalf of and in the name of Pyle Co. Shortly thereafter, a certificate of incorporation was issued to Pyle Co. In view of the facts just stated, which of the following statements is accurate?

    a. Gomer is liable on the contract with Sergeant-Carter Corp.

    b. When Pyle Co. received its certificate of incorporation, it became liable on the contract with Sergeant-Carter Corp.

    c. The contract is void, because Pyle Co. was not in existence at the time the contract was formed.

    d. If Pyle Co.'s board of directors issues a suitable resolution, Gomer will be relieved from all liability on the contract.

18. Of the following statements concerning buy-sell agreements, which is/are accurate?

    a. Modern corporation law restricts the use of buy-sell agreements to situations in which the death or retirement of a shareholder is the triggering event.

    b. If a buy-sell agreement imposes on the remaining shareholders the obligation to purchase the shares of the departed shareholder, it is classified as a redemption agreement.

    c. Because a funding source often is necessary to make a buy-sell agreement workable, such agreements often are funded by a life insurance policy.

    d. All of the above.

19. On April 15, Thelma Lou signed a preincorporation subscription to purchase 1000 shares of common stock in Barney Co. following its incorporation. On December 1 of the same year, Thelma Lou revoked her subscription because she had decided she did not wish to be a shareholder. Barney Co. was incorporated shortly thereafter. Barney's board of directors promptly accepted all preincorporation subscriptions, including Thelma Lou's. When the board attempted to force Thelma Lou to purchase the shares, she refused. If the Model Business Corporation Act is in effect in the state whose law controls, is Thelma Lou liable for refusing to purchase the shares?

    a. Yes, because preincorporation subscriptions create legally binding contractual obligations.

    b. Yes, because her change of mind concerning whether she wanted to be a shareholder is not sufficient cause to support a revocation of the subscription.

    c. No, because a preincorporation subscriptions is of no effect even if it is later accepted by the corporation's board, because the corporation was not in existence when the subscription was made.

    d. No, because her revocation occurred more than six months after she made the subscription and before the board accepted it.

20. Nimrod served as promoter concerning Flaky Industries, Inc. prior to its incorporation. During the preincorporation period, Nimrod purchased manufacturing equipment in contemplation of selling it to the corporation once it was formed. After Flaky was properly incorporated, Nimrod sold it the equipment for $90,000. He did not tell the Flaky directors that the equipment had cost him only $50,000. In light of the facts, which of the following statements is accurate?

    a. Once Flaky came into existence, Nimrod's fiduciary duty ceased and he became entitled to receive the highest price he could command for the equipment without disclosing his actual costs.

    b. Because Flaky was already incorporated before Nimrod's sizable profit came to light, Flaky cannot bring an action against him to recover monetary compensation.

    c. Nimrod's continuing fiduciary duty was violated when he failed to make a full disclosure concerning what he had paid for the equipment; therefore, Flaky may rescind the purchase or recover Nimrod's profit.

    d. The secret profit received by Nimrod amounts to watered shares, meaning that he is liable to each Flaky shareholder in the amount by which his secret profit reduced the value of that shareholder's investment in the corporation.

21. A corporation's bylaws:
    a. provide the basic source from which the corporation's powers are derived.
    b. may supplement the articles of incorporation by more precisely defining rights and responsibilities of parties involved in the corporate structure.
    c. are controlling when they conflict with the articles of incorporation, in keeping with the legal principle that specific provisions control general provisions when the two appear to be in conflict.
    d. can be amended only by the corporation's board of directors.

22. Dissolution of a corporation:
    a. occurs when all corporate assets have been liquidated and distributed to creditors and shareholders.
    b. may be decreed by a court if the majority shareholder has sold her shares against the wishes of minority shareholders.
    c. may occur by means of a vote to that effect by a majority of the corporation's initial directors if the corporation has begun doing business but has not yet issued shares.
    d. may be decreed by a court against the will of the corporation's directors and at the request of creditors of the corporation, under appropriate circumstances.

23. Jim acted as a promoter for Tammy Co. prior to its incorporation. He negotiated a contract with Plaster, Inc. Under the contract, which Jim signed in the name of Tammy Co., Plaster was to supply Tammy with essential ingredients and substances that Tammy would use in its makeup manufacturing operation. At the initial board of directors meeting following the incorporation of Tammy, the Tammy board adopted the contract Jim had negotiated with Plaster. After Plaster had performed its contract obligation but before Tammy paid what was called for by the contract, Tammy became insolvent and unable to make payment. Plaster is now looking to Jim for payment. Is Jim liable to Plaster?
    a. No, because once Tammy Co. was actually incorporated, any liability he may have had on the contract was discharged.
    b. Yes, because he committed fraud by entering into a contract on behalf of a nonexistent party.
    c. No, because Tammy Co.'s adoption of the contract had the effect of releasing him from liability on the contract.
    d. Yes, because nothing in the facts indicates that Plaster has released Jim from liability on the contract.

24. If the right of first refusal exists concerning a shareholder's stock,
    a. the corporation and the other shareholders are given a right to purchase the stock at the price offered by an outsider willing to purchase it.
    b. the shareholder is barred from selling her stock to an outsider.
    c. the corporation's board of directors may refuse to give its consent to a shareholder's proposed sale of her shares.
    d. the corporation's board of directors may refuse to pay dividends to that shareholder, even if dividends are being paid to other holders of shares of the same class.

25. Of the following statements concerning shares of stock issued by a corporation, which is *inaccurate*?
    a. The par value of a share of stock is not necessarily equal to the fair value of the share of stock.
    b. A corporation must not issue shares of stock for an amount less than par value.
    c. A corporation is barred by law from issuing shares of stock for an amount greater than par value.
    d. None of the above.

26. Sam Sham promoted Pharaoh Co. prior to its incorporation. He spent a considerable amount of time, as well as $3500 of his own money, in promoting the corporation. Pharaoh has now been incorporated and its business is in operation. On these facts, Pharaoh is:

   a. obligated to reimburse Sam for his expenses but is not obligated to compensate him for his time and services.

   b. neither obligated to reimburse Sam for his expenses nor obligated to compensate him for his time and services.

   c. obligated to reimburse Sam for his expenses and to compensate him according to the reasonable value of his time and services.

   d. obligated to compensate Sam according to the reasonable value of his time and services, but is not obligated to reimburse him for his expenses.

Short Essay

27. BIG Co. was the name chosen by Bo, Ingrid, and Geoff for a corporation they intended to form. Not all of the incorporation requirements were met, so incorporation did not take place before the parties' business, a hardware store, went into operation. Bo, a purported shareholder who had been the promoter of the business and had taken primary responsibility for handling the incorporation requirements, actively participated in management and policy decisions concerning the business. He was aware that the incorporation requirements had not been satisfied and that the corporation did not exist. Ingrid, also a purported shareholder, participated in management and policy decisions concerning the business, but was not aware of the defective incorporation. Geoff, the other purported shareholder, neither participated in management and policy decisions concerning the business nor knew of the defective incorporation. Rusty's Hardware Supply Co. extended credit to the BIG business. When the large debt went unpaid, Rusty's did some checking on BIG and learned that because of the defective incorporation, BIG Co. had no legal existence. Rusty's then filed suit against Bo, Ingrid, and Geoff in an effort to hold them personally liable for the debt. Assume that the revised MBCA is in force in the state where suit was filed. On these facts, who will be held liable to Rusty's? State the reasons for your answer.

28. Duke Windsor, a promoter for Regal Co. prior to its incorporation, negotiated a preincorporation contract with Crown Corp. Windsor signed the contract in the name of Regal Co. Regal subsequently was incorporated, but the Regal board of directors refused to adopt the contract. Are Windsor and Regal liable on the contract? State the reasons for your answer.

29. Zeke served as a promoter prior to the incorporation of Rancid Corp. After Rancid became properly incorporated, it issued Zeke 2000 shares of its no-par stock in payment for the services performed by him as a promoter. Another shareholder later brought a derivative suit to have the issuance of stock to Zeke declared unlawful and void on the ground that the stock was issued in return for improper consideration. The revised MBCA is in effect in the state in which Rancid was incorporated. Was there improper consideration for the issuance of the stock to Zeke? State the reasons for your answer.

30. After Small Corp., a close corporation, was incorporated and all shares of stock had been issued to shareholders, Small's board of directors adopted a resolution stating that no shareholder could transfer his shares of stock without first securing the approval and consent of the board. No such provision was contained in Small's articles of incorporation. The shareholders had not entered into an agreement to that effect. Nevertheless, the board, after careful thought, concluded that the resolution was necessary to preserve the nature of the corporation. One of the corporation's minority shareholders, Sterling Small (who was not a member of the board), attempted to sell his shares to an outsider, Hugh Mongous, without first securing the approval of the board. When the board learned of this, it threatened to take appropriate action to block the sale. Is the restriction on transfer of shares enforceable against Sterling? State the reasons for your answer.

CHAPTER 42

MANAGEMENT OF CORPORATIONS

True-False - Circle T for True and F for False.

T F   1.   Corporate directors may cause corporate funds to be contributed to charity only if the shareholders have voted to make such a contribution.

T F   2.   One result of pressures and proposals for changes in corporate governance is that corporate boards of directors tend to have more outside directors, and hence fewer inside directors, than they once had.

T F   3.   In the modern corporation, the board of directors makes most of the day-to-day management decisions.

T F   4.   A freeze-out plan that does not satisfy the total fairness test may subject the directors to liability for breach of the fiduciary duty they owe even to minority shareholders.

T F   5.   Although the MBCA has eliminated the use of the *ultra vires* doctrine as a defense to the enforcement of a contract, it does allow shareholders to seek an injunction to stop a corporation from carrying out a proposed action that is beyond the corporation's powers.

T F   6.   Because of the importance of keeping qualified directors on the board, most states' statutes allow shareholders to remove directors only when the shareholders show just cause for doing so.

T F   7.   By virtue of the title of her office, a corporation's treasurer has inherent authority to borrow money on behalf of the corporation.

T F   8.   If an officer or director engages in personal purchases or sales of the subject corporation's securities on the basis of nonpublic, inside information, he may face liability under federal and state law.

T F   9.   Although many powers of the board of directors may be delegated to a board committee, the approval of an issuance of shares of stock must be approved by the board as a whole.

T F   10.   Directors may forfeit the protection of the business judgment rule if their decision to oppose a tender offer resulted from an inability on the part of the directors to separate their own interests in remaining directors from the best interests of the corporation.

T F   11.   The major effect of management's solicitation of proxies from shareholders is that shareholders' varying viewpoints on matters of corporate governance are more strongly expressed than they otherwise would be.

T F   12.   Supermajority voting requirements for board actions are employed more frequently in publicly held corporations than in close corporations because there is usually less need, in the close corporation setting, for concern about whether the directors will adequately represent the interests of all shareholders.

Multiple Choice - Circle the best answer.

13.   Without seeking shareholder approval, the board of directors may:
   a.   declare dividends.
   b.   fill vacancies on the board.
   c.   establish the sale price at which shares of stock are to be issued.
   d.   do all of the above.

14. Hoping to gain an edge in the highly competitive electric razor market, the directors of Cutting Edge Corp. (CEC) voted to have CEC develop and market a revolutionary type of electric razor to replace the conventional electric razor sold by CEC for years as its flagship product. Before so voting, the CEC directors studied past price and sales data, future projections in those regards, and considerable technical information concerning the new type of razor. In addition, they consulted economists and various financial experts. The new razor was a commercial flop. CEC lost many millions of dollars as a result. Although it eventually went back to producing the type of razor it formerly produced and thereby regained some customers that had been lost along the way, CEC's market position was badly, and probably permanently, weakened. A group of disenchanted CEC shareholders has now sued the directors in an attempt to hold them liable to CEC for the consequences just mentioned. Will the directors be held liable?

   a. Yes, because directors' fiduciariy duties make them liable for the consequences of management decisions that cause severe damage to the corporation.

   b. Yes, because shareholders have a right to a determination of whether directors have acted in the best interests of the corporation.

   c. No, because the business judgment rule insulates the directors from liability here, despite the harm their decision caused the corporation to experience.

   d. No, because directors will not be held liable for the negative consequences of their management decisions unless they intended to cause the corporation harm.

15. Marginal Corp.'s directors left all management and policy decisions to the discretion of the corporation's officers. The directors held annual meetings, but made no detailed inquiries into operation or performance of the corporate business. Marginal suffered heavy losses for three successive years, until it was discovered that the officers in charge of daily management of the business had been diverting substantial portions of corporate assets for their own personal use. Will the directors face liability to the corporation for losses experienced by the corporation?

   a. Yes, if their approach to management amounted to a failure to act as ordinarily prudent directors would have acted under the same or similar circumstances, and if the exercise of due care by the directors would have resulted in an earlier discovery of the officers' improper actions.

   b. Yes, because the doctrine of respondeat superior imposes liability on corporate directors for the wrongful and injurious acts committed by corporate officers and employees in connection with their corporate duties.

   c. No, because the directors' lack of familiarity with the operation of the corporation meant that they had no reason to believe the officers were engaged in improper activities; therefore, the directors did not possess the level of knowledge necessary to make them liable for losses experienced by the corporation.

   d. No, because nothing in the facts indicates that any director had personal involvement in the impermissible diversion of corporate assets for personal gain; therefore, no director possessed the requisite intent to harm the corporation.

16. Under the MBCA, the board of directors may take formal action without a meeting:

   a. if the action pertains to a routine matter and two-thirds of the directors have agreed to waive the need for a meeting.

   b. if all of the directors consent in writing to take a certain action.

   c. if a director polls the other directors by separate telephone calls and determines that the directors have unanimously agreed to take a certain action.

   d. in the situations described in answers b and c.

17. Under the MBCA, a corporation may indemnify a director for the cost of defending and/or settling a civil suit brought against him
    a. only if the director was not found liable to the plaintiff.
    b. only if the director acted in good faith and with a reasonable belief that his actions were in the best interests of the corporation.
    c. in any case except one in which the director was held liable to the corporation itself.
    d. only if the director was found liable to the plaintiff in connection with a personal matter unconnected with his duties as a director.

18. Which of the following matters must the board of directors submit to shareholders for their approval?
    a. The proposed firing of the corporation's president and chief executive officer
    b. Proposed amendments to the corporation's bylaws
    c. A proposed merger of the corporation with another corporation
    d. All of the above

19. Warren Windbag III is a director of Overbearing, Inc. Needing additional office space, Overbearing sought to purchase a new corporate headquarters. Windbag owned a suitable building that he had purchased for $250,000 several years earlier. The six directors other than Windbag voted to purchase the property after fully inspecting it for suitability and after Windbag informed them of what he had paid for the property. The sale was then completed at a price of $430,000, the fair market value of the property as of the time of the sale. An Overbearing shareholder later brought a derivative suit against Windbag in an effort to recover, for the benefit of the corporation, the profit made by Windbag on the sale of the building. Is Windbag liable to the corporation for the profit he made?
    a. Yes, because he violated his duty not to engage in self-dealing.
    b. Yes, because his actions amounted to usurpation of a corporate opportunity.
    c. No, because the other directors' approval of a transaction conclusively releases the self-dealing director from liability to the corporation.
    d. No, because he made a full disclosure to a disinterested board, which approved a transaction that was fair to Overbearing.

20. A corporation has committed a crime if:
    a. its salesperson coerces a customer into buying the corporation's product.
    b. its president agrees with competitors to fix prices in violation of the antitrust laws.
    c. its assembly line employee intentionally sabotages a product to make it dangerous to users.
    d. any of the above occurs.

21. Of the following statements concerning corporate officers, which is accurate?
    a. The same person usually may hold more than one corporate office, except for the dual holding of the offices of president and secretary.
    b. Most states' corporation statutes call for the corporation's president to be elected by the shareholders.
    c. As a general rule, the board of directors cannot remove a corporate officer unless the board demonstrates just cause for doing so.
    d. The title of "vice president" vests the holder of that office with substantial inherent authority to act on behalf of the corporation.

22. Margaret is one of the 11 directors of Specific General, Inc. Although they had not so informed the board of directors, top officers of Specific General were giving serious consideration to obligating the company on a long-term contract that would involve the expenditure of millions of dollars of company funds. Margaret learned of the officers' intentions through a reliable source. Because she opposed the plan, she sought to examine Specific General's books and records in order to gain information that would support her position. The officers refused her inspection request because the request did not come from the full board. May Margaret obtain a court order requiring the corporation and its officers to produce the books and records for her examination?

    a. No, because individual directors have no authority to act on their own.

    b. No, because individual directors are not agents of the corporation.

    c. Yes, because the books and records contain information essential to the performance of her duties.

    d. Yes, because each individual director has managerial authority with regard to the corporation.

Short Essay

23. Alf is an officer of Nouveau Riche Kids, Inc. (NRK), which engages in the manufacturing and sale of clothing designed for infants and children up to approximately the age of five years. While at his office one day, Alf received a telephone call from a representative of We R Young People, Inc. (WRYP), which manufactured clothing designed for children of elementary school age. The WRYP representative asked whether NRK would be interested in purchasing approximately one-third of the outstanding shares of WRYP. Alf responded by stating that he did not believe NRK would be interested, because NRK's business focused on clothing for younger children. NRK had the financial ability, at the time, to purchase the WRYP shares. Alf, for whom money was no problem, then purchased the WRYP shares for himself. A year later, he sold them for a considerable profit. When NRK's directors learned about Alf's purchase and sale of the WRYP shares, they sued him on behalf of NRK. Does Alf have liability to NRK? State the reasons for your answer.

24. Loretta is a director of Amorphous Co. She entered into a contract with the corporation for the sale of certain property from Loretta to Amorphous. The contract was approved by a majority of the disinterested Amorphous directors. A disgruntled shareholder has brought a derivative suit (on behalf of the corporation) against Loretta, however, on the theory that she engaged in self-dealing. What effect, if any, does the board's approval of the contract have on whether Loretta will be held liable? In view of the facts stated, who has the burden of proof on the issue of the contract's fairness or unfairness? Why?

25. Assume that corporate directors have made a decision that turned out to have disastrous consequences for the corporation. If the directors wish to avoid liability to the corporation by relying on the shield provided by the business judgment rule, what requirements must have been met by the directors during their decisionmaking process?

26. Fleecem Co. is a corporation whose principal business is the manufacturing and sale of items of clothing. Dobie is the manager in charge of the employees in Fleecem's product delivery division. Maynard, a truck driver, is one of the employees in that division. Recently, while Maynard was en route to a retailer's place of business (where he was to make a delivery of a large quantity of Fleecem-manufactured items), Maynard negligently operated the Fleecem truck he was driving and caused an accident in which a pedestrian was seriously injured. In driving negligently, Maynard violated a specific Fleecem directive that employees were not to be negligent while performing their employment duties. The injured pedestrian has now filed suit against Maynard, Dobie, and Fleecem. As to which defendant(s) will the pedestrian prevail? Why?

CHAPTER 43

SHAREHOLDERS' RIGHTS AND LIABILITIES

True-False - Circle T for True and F for False.

T F 1. A corporation may issue a class of stock that carries with it no right to vote for corporate directors.

T F 2. Even if a shareholder is consistently dissatisfied with the day-to-day operational decisions made by corporate management, the shareholder is not entitled, on that basis, to enforce the right of appraisal.

T F 3. In a share exchange involving two corporations, the shareholders of both corporations must approve the exchange.

T F 4. Majority shareholders may owe minority shareholders certain duties of a fiduciary nature even in corporations that are not close corporations.

T F 5. When the board of directors or its shareholder litigation committee decides whether a corporate claim should be pursued in court, the decision does not carry the potential protection of the business judgment rule because a decision whether to pursue litigation is not an ordinary business decision.

T F 6. A shareholder is liable, under the MBCA, for the amount of a dividend received by her with the knowledge that the corporation was insolvent when it declared and paid the dividend.

T F 7. If an extraordinary corporate transaction such as a merger is to be voted on at a shareholders' meeting, notice of the merger proposal and the meeting must be given to all shareholders, except those shareholders whose stock is of a class that is not entitled to voting rights.

T F 8. It is per se unlawful for a majority shareholder to sell his shares for a premium that exceeds the fair market value of minority shares.

T F 9. A corporation may repurchase its shares from a willing shareholder on the open market even if the articles of incorporation say nothing about the corporation's having such a power or right.

T F 10. Under the MBCA, a dividend amount is prohibited if, after payment of the dividend, the corporation's assets would not be sufficient to cover the corporation's liabilities plus the liquidation preference of shareholders having a liquidation priority over the shareholders who would receive the dividend.

T F 11. Although share splits affect all authorized shares, share dividends affect only outstanding shares.

T F 12. Under the MBCA, a proxy is irrevocable unless the proxy is expressly made revocable.

13. Acme Corp.'s board of directors unanimously approved a merger agreement under which Acme and Generic, Inc. would merge, with Generic continuing as the surviving corporation. The MBCA is in effect in the state where both corporations were incorporated. As the two corporations were about to begin performance of the duties set forth in the merger agreement, certain Acme shareholders instituted suit in an effort to block the merger agreement from being implemented. The shareholders claimed, in their suit, that the proposed merger should have been submitted to them for their approval. Nothing in Acme's articles of incorporation required the directors to submit such matters to the shareholders. The directors argued that the merger was carefully considered and investigated and was agreed to by the board on the basis of a justifiable belief that the merger was in the best interests of Acme and its shareholders. Will the shareholders' suit be successful?

    a. No, assuming the court agrees with the directors' decision that the merger is in the best interests of Acme and its shareholders.

    b. No, because the articles of incorporation did not require the directors to submit the proposed merger to the shareholders.

    c. Yes, because what the supposed merger agreement really contemplated was not a true merger, but instead a consolidation.

    d. Yes, because under the MBCA, the Acme board was required to submit the proposed merger to the shareholders.

14. Cumulative voting is a procedural device that:

    a. assures minority shareholders a position of influence within the corporate structure.

    b. is now required by the corporation statutes of all states.

    c. is designed to give minority shareholders a chance to elect a director of their choice.

    d. can be employed only when directors, for election purposes, have been divided into classes.

15. If preemptive rights exist,

    a. shareholders are allowed, collectively, to veto actions taken by the board of directors.

    b. current shareholders may refuse to allow the directors to issue any new shares of stock.

    c. current shareholders have an option to buy their proportionate part of a new issue of stock.

    d. the corporation is entitled to force shareholders to sell their shares back to the corporation for a fair price.

16. Declaration of dividends:

    a. is a subject entrusted to the business judgment of the directors.

    b. is a subject customarily reserved for a vote of the shareholders.

    c. must occur on at least an annual basis, if the corporation is profitable.

    d. is a subject accurately referred to in answers a and c.

17. Gaffe Co.'s chief executive officer called a special meeting of the company's shareholders. The notice issued by the CEO listed only the time and place of the meeting. The meeting was held to have the shareholders vote on a proposed sale of substantially all of the assets of Gaffe. At the meeting, the shareholders voted to approve the sale. Ernest, a Gaffe shareholder who attended the meeting and voted against the sale, later objected to the sale and sought to have the shareholders' approval of it declared invalid on the theory that the notice of the meeting was defective. Is Ernest correct in his argument that the action taken at the meeting was invalid?

    a. Yes, because the notice of the meeting failed to state the purpose of the special meeting; therefore, the notice was defective.

    b. No, because the notice contained what was required by law; therefore, it was not a defective notice and the action taken at the meeting was valid.

    c. Yes, because no valid action can be taken at a meeting concerning which defective notice was given to the shareholders.

    d. No, because by participating in the meeting without objecting to the notice, he waived his right to argue later that the defective notice invalidated the action.

18. Roland Astute, a shareholder of Steamroller, Inc., acquired evidence demonstrating, in his view, that Steamroller's treasurer had embezzled corporate funds. Uncertain whether Steamroller's board of directors would agree with his assessment of what the evidence showed, Astute did not discuss the matter with the board. After conferring with his attorney, Astute filed a derivative suit against the treasurer in an effort to recoup, for Steamroller, the funds converted by the treasurer. Is Astute's suit properly before the court?

    a. No, because shareholders cannot sue to enforce rights that belong to the corporation.

    b. No, because Astute failed to make the requisite demand upon the board to pursue the claim.

    c. Yes, because demanding that the board authorize suit against the treasurer would have been futile.

    d. Yes, because the board might have disagreed with his view of the evidence if he had consulted the board.

19. Of the following statements concerning voting trusts, which is *inaccurate*?

    a. The voting trust agreement may give the voting trustee directions concerning how to vote the shares that are subject to the agreement.

    b. The voting trust can be used with regard to the election of directors, but not as to other matters on which shareholders are entitled to vote.

    c. Under the MBCA, voting trust agreements are limited in duration to 10 years, but they may be renewed, by agreement of the participating shareholders, for another 10-year period.

    d. The voting trust may be used by a group of shareholders to ensure control of the corporation by that group.

20. Terminal Corp.'s meeting of shareholders is being held. Principles of cumulative voting apply to the election of directors. If 400 shares are being voted at the meeting and four directors are to be elected, how many shares are needed to elect one director?

    a. 100

    b. 80

    c. 101

    d. 81

21. Crude Corp. currently has 100,000 outstanding shares and another 20,000 authorized. The MBCA is in effect in the state in which Crude was incorporated. The Crude directors plan to issue the other 20,000 shares. Norm Nifty, a Crude shareholder, claims that with regard to the 20,000 to-be-issued shares, he should be given the right to purchase a percentage of those shares that equals the ratio between the number of shares he currently owns and the number of shares currently outstanding. The Crude articles of incorporation are silent concerning whether any such right exists with regard to new issuances of shares. Is Nifty correct?

    a. Yes, because a right of that nature exists unless it is expressly eliminated in the articles of incorporation.

    b. Yes, because Nifty's investment in Crude stands to be jeopardized unless such a right is recognized.

    c. No, because Nifty is claiming a preemptive right that does not exist unless it is established in the articles of incorporation.

    d. No, because the MBCA has abolished any such right, on the ground that it interferes too greatly with the authority of corporate directors.

22. Ruby is a shareholder of Tuesday Co., a large corporation having thousands of shareholders. The MBCA is in effect in the state in which Tuesday Co. was incorporated. Because she wished to communicate with other shareholders concerning matters related to corporate business, Ruby made a written request that Tuesday Co.'s management provide her access to a list containing the names of all Tuesday Co. shareholders. Citing the administrative burden that would be created if requests of that nature were granted routinely, Tuesday Co.'s management informed Ruby of a company policy that shareholders could not review such records. Which of the following statements is/are accurate?

    a. Tuesday Co.'s policy notwithstanding, Ruby has an absolute right to obtain access to a list of the sort referred to above.

    b. Ruby has only a qualified right to examine a list of the sort referred to above, meaning that the administrative burden that would be created by her request may be sufficient reason for Tuesday Co. to deny her request.

    c. Ruby's request properly may be denied by Tuesday Co. if her written request did not state, with particularity, the purpose she had in mind in making her request.

    d. Both b and c.

Short Essay

23. Jack Flash is a holder of Jumpin' Corp. common stock. Pursuant to a proposal instituted by Jumpin' directors and approved by the shareholders, Jumpin' is to merge with Gas, Inc. Flash objected to the merger because he believes Gas, Inc. is a poorly managed company. Before the Jumpin' shareholders voted on the proposed merger, Flash notified Jumpin' management of his opposition to the proposal. When the shareholders voted, he voted against the proposal. The Jumpin' directors made all pertinent disclosures to Jumpin' shareholders concerning the merger proposal. In all respects, the directors acted fairly. On these facts, what recourse, if any, does Flash have? Explain your reasoning.

24. Notbad Corp. is considering declaring a dividend for holders of its common stock. Notbad's assets total $18,000,000 in value. Its liabilities total $7,000,000. It has stated capital of $1,300,000, capital surplus of $2,500,000, and earned surplus of $4,800,000. Notbad has $3,600,000 in excess cash that it does not need to pay current debts as they come due. Under the MBCA, what is the maximum amount of the dividend that Notbad may declare and pay? State the reasons for your answer.

25. Mammoth Corp.'s directors voted unanimously to expend $20,000,000 of corporate funds to acquire a manufacturing plant that would enable Mammoth to expand its product lines. The decision turned out to be a losing proposition for Mammoth. A Mammoth shareholder has now brought a derivative suit against the directors in an effort to recover, for the corporation, the losses stemming from the directors' decision. The directors have filed a motion with the court in which they request that the suit be dismissed because the shareholder improperly filed suit without making the necessary demand upon the board to pursue the claim. Should the court sustain (i.e., grant the request in) the directors' motion? Why or why not?

CHAPTER 44

SECURITIES REGULATION

True-False - Circle T for True and F for False.

T F 1. Among the powers of the Securities and Exchange Commission is to prosecute persons for criminal violations of the federal securities statutes.

T F 2. Any security traded on a national securities exchange must be registered by its issuer pursuant to the Securities Exchange Act of 1934.

T F 3. The Securities Act of 1933 and the Securities Exchange Act of 1934 both establish periodic, continuing disclosure requirements for issuers of securities.

T F 4. When a private plaintiff wins a Rule 10b-5 suit against a defendant who has engaged in insider trading, the plaintiff is entitled to recover three times the amount of profit realized by the defendant as a result of the insider trading.

T F 5. Although the Williams Act does not clearly define a tender offer, it does indicate that there is no tender offer if the bidder does not intend to become the holder of at least 5 percent of the subject company's shares.

T F 6. During the period prior to the filing of a registration statement for an offering subject to the Securities Act of 1933, the prospective issuer is prohibited from publishing any notices concerning the prospective offering.

T F 7. If a tender offer has been made, the bidder is prohibited by law from increasing the offered price during the term of the tender offer.

T F 8. Trading in securities on the basis of inside information may violate Rule 10b-5 even if the buyer and seller neither met nor had any direct communication with each other.

T F 9. The Securities Act of 1933 establishes a rule that every transaction in securities be registered with the SEC or be exempt from registration.

T F 10. Although the Securities Act of 1933's definition of *security* includes a specific reference to "stock," a court may determine in an appropriate case that an interest denominated by the involved parties as "stock" was not actually a security for purposes of the 1933 Act.

T F 11. Under the small offering exemption provided by Rule 505, an issuer cannot rely on that rule's exemption from registration if the offering would involve more than 35 accredited investors.

T F 12. Even if an offering of securities is exempt from registration under the Securities Act of 1933, fraud committed in connection with the sale of the securities will violate provisions of the 1933 Act.

T F 13. The Foreign Corrupt Practices Act may be violated by an offer to make a prohibited payment, even if the payment is not actually made.

T F 14. If the plaintiff's suit is brought under Section 18 of the Securities Exchange Act of 1934 because of a false statement in a document filed with the SEC pursuant to the 1934 Act, the plaintiff need not prove that he relied on the false statement when purchasing the subject securities.

T F 15. During the waiting period following the filing of a registration statement with the SEC, the issuer of the securities may neither offer nor sell the securities.

Multiple Choice - Circle the best answer.

16. Capital Corp. is a California corporation engaged in manufacturing. Approximately half of its assets are in California, where it has a large manufacturing plant. The remainder of its assets are in Washington, where it has another plant. Capital needs to raise $50,000,000 to finance the expansion of its California plant. Therefore, it has decided to issue stock to its employees who work in the California plant and to other California residents. Is Capital entitled to rely on the intrastate offering exemption as a means of avoiding the registration requirement of the Securities Act of 1933?

    a. Yes, because Capital intends to sell the stock only to purchasers in the same state in which Capital is located.

    b. No, because Capital has approximately half of its assets outside California.

    c. Yes, because Capital intends to use all of the sale proceeds in California.

    d. No, because the amount of money Capital seeks to raise is too large to permit it to rely on the intrastate offering exemption.

17. Portly, a resident of Illinois, has brought a Rule 10b-5 suit against Dorfman, a resident of Indiana. Portly's claim is that in a letter sent by Dorfman to Portly, Dorfman made false statements about Tiny Corp. stock that Dorfman wished to sell to Portly. In addition, Portly claims that he purchased the stock from Dorfman without knowing the statements were false, and that he was damaged as a result. Tiny Corp. stock is not required to be registered (and is not registered) under the Securities Act of 1933 and the Securities Exchange Act of 1934. Which of the following arguments, if made by Dorfman, will absolve him from liability in the 10b-5 suit?

    a. That this is not an insider trading case; therefore, Rule 10b-5 does not apply.

    b. That Rule 10b-5 does not apply because Tiny Corp.'s securities are not required to be registered under the federal securities statutes.

    c. That Rule 10b-5 does not apply because Tiny Corp.'s shares are not traded on a national securities exchange.

    d. None of the above.

18. The federal securities statutes are designed to:

    a. require the disclosure necessary to permit securities investors to made informed investment decisions.

    b. establish the SEC as the authoritative determiner of whether investment ventures are meritorious enough to be made available to the public.

    c. ensure that investors in federally registered securities make a reasonable profit.

    d. do all of the above.

19. Ann Oldcodger, an officer of Aged Corp., signed an Aged registration statement filed with the SEC pursuant to the Securities Act of 1933. The registration statement failed to mention a material fact: that Aged recently had made substantial loans to officers other than Oldcodger. Jerry Atric, an Aged shareholder, sued Oldcodger for an alleged violation of Section 11 of the 1933 Act. Atric proved the following: that he purchased the shares after the filing of the registration statement; that the registration statement was defective because of the failure to mention the loans to the officers; that the omission was material; and that he was damaged as a result. Atric neither alleged nor proved that Oldcodger was negligent in connection with what the registration statement did or did not say. Should the court dismiss Atric's suit against Oldcodger?

    a. No, because officers who sign registration statements are strictly liable for defects therein.

    b. Yes, because Atric has failed to prove that Oldcodger's failure to exercise due diligence accounted for the registration statement's omission of the material fact.

    c. Yes, because nothing in the facts indicates that Oldcodger had any reason to know about Aged's loans to other Aged officers.

    d. No, because rather than Atric's having to prove Oldcodger's negligence, Oldcodger must prove her due diligence if she wishes to escape liability.

20. ZYX Co.'s equity securities are registered under the terms of the Securities Exchange Act of 1934. If a bidder privately seeks a controlling block of ZYX's shares in face-to-face dealings with a few of the company's shareholders, the bidder:
    a. must be certain to have filed a tender offer statement with the SEC prior to undertaking such action.
    b. must keep any offers to purchase shares open for 20 days.
    c. need not give advance notice of his desire to the SEC or to the other ZYX shareholders.
    d. must adhere to the requirments set forth in answers a and b.

21. The SEC's proxy rules:
    a. contain requirements about proxy content, so that the shareholder will know how the proxy will be voted.
    b. must be complied with by corporate management but not by shareholders' groups that wish to solicit proxies.
    c. require corporate management to include, in its proxy statement, any proposals shareholders wish to have included therein.
    d. apply regardless of whether the shareholders whose proxies are being solicited are holders of securities registered under the Securities Exchange Act of 1934.

22. In a Rule 10b-5 case,
    a. the plaintiff may be a person who was deterred, by the defendant's false statements, from purchasing a security.
    b. the plaintiff must prove that the defendant acted with an intent to deceive, manipulate, or defraud.
    c. negligence on the part of the defendant is enough to make the defendant liable.
    d. it is not necessary for the plaintiff to prove that she relied on the defendant's false statement.

23. Adventure Co. has built numerous cabins in a mountainous area that is frequented by tourists. In nationally circulated publications, Adventure has advertised the cabins as being for sale under the following terms: that each purchaser may use his or her cabin for three weeks each year; that Adventure will seek to lease each cabin for the remaining weeks of the year; and that all rental income from the cabins will be combined and prorated among the cabin owners according to the respective square footages of the owners' cabins. Does the SEC have jurisdiction over the cabin venture just described?
    a. No, because the cabin purchasers are purchasing real estate.
    b. No, because the cabin purchasers would be deriving income from efforts other than their own.
    c. Yes, because Adventure is proposing and promoting investment contracts.
    d. Yes, because Adventure's interstate venture may mislead purchasers if the SEC does not determine its merits.

223

24. Huge Corp., an American corporation with business operations around the world, must obtain an identification number from the government of Miniscule, a small foreign nation, before Huge lawfully may engage in a certain business activity in Miniscule. Under Minisculean law, all applicants for required identification numbers are issued numbers if they fill out the necessary application and pay the fee specified by law. The official in charge of the application process has no discretion to deny a proper application that is accompanied by the prescribed fee. Nevertheless, because of the volume of applications, there are often considerable delays in the processing of the paperwork. Besides delivering a proper application and the necessary fee, a Huge executive paid the Minisculean official, personally, Minisculean currency equivalent to $500 in American money. The purpose of the $500 payment was to speed up the processing of Huge's application. On these facts, has Huge violated the Foreign Corrupt Practices Act?

a. Yes, because the $500 payment was made to influence the action of an official of a foreign government.

b. No, because the $500 payment to the Minisculean official was a permissible grease payment.

c. Yes, because the $500 payment was given to a government official in an effort to gain Huge an identification number sooner that it otherwise would have had one.

d. No, because the $500 payment was merely an attempt to convince the official to exercise his discretion in a manner favorable to Huge.

25. Ted Tedious, a certified public accountant, certified Foible, Inc. financial statements that were included as part of a registration statement Foible filed with the SEC. The financial statements contained false assertions as to material matters. Although Tedious did not deliberately cause the financial statements to contain the falsehoods, he did fail to perform as a reasonable accountant would have performed under similar circumstances. In a suit brought by an allegedly injured purchaser of Foible stock, does Tedious face potential liability for a defective registration statement under Section 11 of the Securities Act of 1933?

a. No, because he is neither an officer nor a director of Foible.

b. No, because the plaintiff will not be able to meet the requirement of proving privity between Tedious and herself.

c. Yes, but only if the plaintiff proves that she actually relied on the defective registration statement in making the decision to purchase Foible stock.

d. Yes, unless he proves that the plaintiff knew of the falsehoods in the financial statements when she purchased her Foible stock.

26. Of the following statements concerning cases brought under Rule 10b-5, which is *inaccurate*?

a. When the SEC is the plaintiff in a 10b-5 suit, proof of reliance is not an element of the plaintiff's case.

b. When a private plaintiff brings a 10b-5 suit on the basis of the defendant's omission to state a material matter of fact, the plaintiff generally is not required to prove reliance.

c. With regard to 10b-5 suits based on the defendant's publicly-made false statements concerning matters pertinent to securities that are traded in an open market, the Supreme Court has ruled that the fraud-on-the-market theory creates an irrebuttable presumption of reliance by the plaintiff on the false statements.

d. None of the above.

27. Largesse, Inc. proposes to issue $15,000,000 worth of securities without offering the securities to the public. The corporation plans to deal with 43 purchasers, all of whom are knowledgeable, experienced, sophisticated investors who are able to make a meaningful evaluation of the investment. The intended purchasers are residents of various states. On these facts, must the proposed offering be registered with the SEC under the Securities Act of 1933?

a. No, because of the private offering exemption.

b. Yes, because of the dollar amount of the offering.

c. No, because it will be an interstate offering.

d. Yes, because more than 35 purchasers will be involved.

28. Ordinary Computer Co. (OCC) is at work on a personal computer that, if perfected, will revolutionize the industry. All previously manufactured computers will become obsolete. Rumors about a breakthrough by OCC have been circulating in the business community, but OCC has made no public statements. Instead, OCC has decided to sit on the news until the computer is perfected. Is OCC risking a violation of Rule 10b-5 by not commenting on the rumored invention? State the reasons for your answer.

29. Gem Co.'s securities are registered under the Securities Exchange Act of 1934. Harris Tweed began his duties as president of Gem on May 5, 1988. The next day, Tweed purchased 200 shares of Gem stock for a price of $9 per share. On December 2, 1988, while he was still Gem's president, he sold the 200 shares for a price of $22 per share. On these facts, is Gem entitled to recover from Tweed the profit he made on the purchase and subsequent sale of the Gem stock? Why or why not?

30. Because he was preparing a report for use within XYZ Co., Al Truistic, a junior vice president of XYZ, was given access to a confidential piece of information. The information was such that if it were available to the investing public, the price and value of XYZ stock would soar. Truistic revealed the confidential information (representing it as such) to his friend, Phil Anderer, in return for Anderer's performance of repairs on Truistic's BMW. Anderer then purchased 100 shares of XYZ stock from Shari Holder without informing her of what Truistic had told him. When the information was made available to the public, the value of XYZ stock indeed soared. Anderer later sold, at a substantial profit, the shares he had purchased from Holder. Holder then brought a Rule 10b-5 suit against Anderer in a effort to recover the profit he made on the purchase and subsequent sale. Anderer argued that because he was not an officer, director, or employee of XYZ, he had done nothing wrong and therefore had no liability to Holder. Analyze and evaluate Holder's claim and Anderer's argument.

CHAPTER 45

LEGAL RESPONSIBILITIES OF ACCOUNTANTS

True-False - Circle T for True and F for False.

T F 1. Although punitive damages may be awarded in a fraud action against an accountant, they generally are not available in a breach of contract or negligence action against an accountant.

T F 2. A nonclient who sues an accountant for negligence will be allowed by most courts to win the suit if the nonclient was a foreseeable user of the accountant's work and was monetarily damaged as a result of relying on it.

T F 3. An accountant is not liable under the Securities Act of 1933 for false or misleading information he furnished for a securities registration statement unless the plaintiff proves that the accountant failed to exercise due diligence.

T F 4. When the issue to be determined by the court is whether an accountant exercised reasonable care in the performance of her professional responsibilities, the standard applied today is a national standard rather than a standard tied to the accountant's locality.

T F 5. An accountant cannot delegate, without the consent of his client, the responsibility for performing professional services that the accountant agreed to perform for the client.

T F 6. Under SEC Rule 10b-5, an accountant may be held liable for having negligently misstated a material fact.

T F 7. The working papers an accountant prepares during the course of an audit for a client are considered the property of the accountant rather than the property of the client.

T F 8. In most states, the confidential communications between an accountant and client are privileged from forced disclosure in court.

T F 9. A suit against an accountant for an alleged violation of Section 11 of the Securities Act of 1933 may be brought at any time within three years after the accountant's misstatement or omission was or should have been discovered.

T F 10. An accountant's issuance of an unaudited financial statement is treated by the courts as an implied disclaimer of the financial statement's accuracy.

Multiple Choice - Circle the best answer.

11. The accounting firm Rippum, Auf & Billem (RAB) prepared and certified a financial statement concerning its client, Sham Corp. When Sham's president retained RAB to perform the work just mentioned, she informed RAB that Sham personnel would be providing the financial statement to Perpetual Infidelity Savings & Loan Co. so that Perpetual Infidelity could decide whether to make a loan to Sham. Sham personnel in fact showed the financial statement not only to Perpetual Infidelity but also to another prospective lender, Open Palms Savings & Loan, Inc. Impressed by what the financial statement appeared to indicate about the financial state of Sham, Open Palms made a substantial loan to Sham. RAB had been negligent in the preparation and certification of the financial statement. As a result, the precarious financial position that Sham actually was in did not become apparent to Open Palms until later (after the loan had been made), when Sham "folded the tents" and filed for bankruptcy. Upset because the loan is now uncollectible, Open Palms has brought a negligence suit against RAB. If the state whose law controls is among the states that adhere to the *primary benefit* test, Open Palms:

    a. cannot win the suit, despite the injury it claims to have sustained.

    b. will win the suit because its status as a lender places it within the class of foreseen users.

    c. cannot win the suit, even though RAB acted with scienter.

    d. will win the suit because the financial statement was prepared for the primary benefit of prospective lenders.

12. Of the following statements concerning an accountant's potential liability to her client, which is/are accurate?

    a. If an accountant is conducting an audit for a client, the accountant's failure to discover embezzlement by the client's employee constitutes negligence on the part of the accountant.

    b. If an accountant fails to perform as agreed in the contract between herself and the client, the accountant is liable for all damages experienced by the client as a result.

    c. If an accountant, while conducting an audit for a client, develops a reasonable suspicion that the client's employee has engaged in embezzlement, the accountant's subsequent failure to report the suspicion to the client constitutes negligence.

    d. All of the above.

13. Bob Carp retained accountant Wanda Trout to prepare his federal income tax return. During the course of working on the return, Trout had several conferences with Carp. Trout made detailed notes during these conferences. Trout prepared and filed the tax return. The federal government ultimately brought suit against Carp, in an appropriate federal court, on the theory that he had substantially underpaid his actual tax liability for the year concerning which Trout prepared the tax return. The government arranged for a subpoena to be served on Trout. According to the subpoena, Trout was to produce, in court, the working papers she used in preparing the tax return, as well as the notes she made during her conferences with Carp. Uncertain about whether she was obligated to abide by the subpoena, Trout telephoned attorney Nick Shark for advice. Shark told her to resist the subpoena because their state had a statute creating an accountant-client privilege. Assuming that their state does have such a statute, was Shark's advice sound?

    a. No, because the working papers in Trout's possession do not belong to her; they belong to Carp.

    b. No, because the privilege will not be honored by the court in the pending federal tax litigation.

    c. Yes, because Carp provided confidential information to Trout during their conferences.

    d. Yes, because the information provided by Carp to Trout would be considered privileged if Trout were an attorney.

14. Les Scruem, a certified public accountant, certified a client's financial statement because he believed the financial statement was accurate, based on his proper use of standard auditing and accounting practices. Later, while doing additional work for the same client, Scruem discovered information leading him to the conclusion that the financial statement he had certified was false and misleading. On these facts, Scruem:

    a. has a duty of loyalty to his client that prevents him from revealing, to third parties, the unreliability of the financial statement.

    b. cannot be liable to a third party if he chooses not to reveal the unreliability of the financial statement, because he when he certified it, he had good reason to believe it was accurate.

    c. has a duty to inform his client of what he has discovered, but has no duty to inform any third parties.

    d. must disclose the unreliability of the financial statement to anyone he knows is relying on the financial statement.

15. Accountant Dee Ductible prepared the 1988 income tax return for her client, Cap Gaines. Exercising at all times the degree of care and skill that a reasonable accountant would have exercised in preparing the return, Ductible claimed certain deductions that arguably were appropriate and supportable for Gaines. The Internal Revenue Service later disallowed the deductions, however, creating the result that Gaines had underpaid his tax liability for 1988. Recognizing the arguable validity of the disallowed deductions, the IRS agreed to accept the additional tax in full satisfaction of its claims against Gaines, and to waive any penalties that might otherwise have been owing from him. It became necessary for Gaines to borrow money (and thus incur interest charges) in order to pay the additional tax. Gaines has now brought a negligence suit against Ductible in an effort to collect from her the additional tax he had to pay, as well as the interest charges he has incurred with regard to the borrowed funds referred to above. Gaines should

    a. win the suit because he experienced economic loss as a result of Ductible's preparation of the tax return.

    b. lose the suit even though he had to pay additional tax and incur the interest charges referred to above.

    c. win the suit because Ductible's negligence caused him to have to expends funds he would not otherwise have had to expend.

    d. lose the suit even though Ductible was negligent in claiming the deductions, because Ductible acted in good faith.

16. If an accountant commits fraud in the course of performing professional services, the accountant is:

    a. liable for resulting injury experienced by any party.

    b. not liable to injured nonclients unless they fall within the category of foreseen users.

    c. liable to injured nonclients who fall within the category of foreseeable users.

    d. not liable to an injured party unless that party and the accountant were in privity with each other.

17. The following statements pertain to suits against accountants, under Section 18(a) of the Securities Exchange Act of 1934, for false statements of fact in a report or document filed with the SEC under the 1934 Act. Which of the statements is *inaccurate*?

    a. If the accountant's negligence resulted in the false statements' presence in the report or document, the accountant will be held liable even though she had no intent to deceive.

    b. In order to prevail in such a suit, the plaintiff must prove that the securities' price was affected by the false statements.

    c. If the plaintiff is to prevail in such a suit, the plaintiff must prove that he actually relied on the false statements in deciding to purchase the securities.

    d. Whether the false statements pertained to material matters is relevant to a determination of the accountant's liability.

Questions 18 and 19 are based on the following facts:

Hulk Co. retained Duncan Debit, a certified public accountant, to prepare and certify a financial statement concerning Hulk. Hulk's president informed Debit that the financial statement would be provided to Village Bank officials so that they could decide whether the bank should make a loan to Hulk. Because of Debit's negligence in performing the work, the financial statement set forth a false and unrealistically positive economic position for Hulk. Hulk officials made the financial statement available not only to Village Bank for the purpose stated above, but also to Slick Corp., so that Slick officials could decide whether to enter into a long-term contract with Hulk. Under the contract, Hulk would manufacture goods especially suited to the needs of Slick, which would then resell the goods to Slick's customers.

Village Bank made the loan to Hulk, largely on the basis of the false picture painted by the financial statement. Slick Corp. chose to enter into the contract with Hulk rather than another party because of the impression created by the financial statement. Hulk later defaulted on the loan, ceased making the goods for Slick, and filed for bankruptcy. Village Bank was left with a substantial monetary loss. There was a substantial delay before Slick, despite its best efforts, was able to locate another supplier that was available to produce the goods Slick was to have received from Hulk. As a result, Slick lost many sales that it otherwise would have been able to make.

18. Assume that Village Bank brings a negligence suit against Debit in an effort to recoup its losses, and that the state whose law controls the case adheres to the *primary benefit* test. Village Bank will:

    a. lose the suit because Debit's work was intended to help Hulk obtain a loan; therefore, the work was done primarily to benefit Hulk.

    b. win the suit even though under the facts Village Bank was only a foreseeable user that happened to be injured as a result of Debit's work.

    c. lose the suit because nothing in the facts indicates that Debit committed fraud.

    d. win the suit even though there was no privity between Village Bank and Debit.

19. Assume that Slick brings a negligence suit against Debit. This time, assume (contrary to the assumption you were asked to make in question 8) that the state whose law controls the case adheres to the *foreseen users and foreseen class of users* test. Slick:

    a. will win the suit.

    b. may win the suit if the court considers Slick a foreseeable user of the financial statement.

    c. will lose the suit.

    d. may lose the suit because of its contributory negligence in relying on a financial statement that was not prepared primarily for its benefit.

20. Which of the following may cause criminal liability to be imposed on an accountant?

    a. The accountant's negligent preparation of a client's tax return.

    b. The accountant's willful misrepresentation of the earnings of a client in a document filed with the SEC pursuant to the federal securities statutes.

    c. The accountant's grossly negligent preparation and certification of a financial statement included as part of the registration statement filed by his client with the SEC.

    d. Each of the above.

Short Essay

21. Bilkem, Inc. retained the accounting firm Dolittle, Hockett & Steele (DHS) to certify a Bilkem financial statement for inclusion in a Securities Act of 1933 registration statement. DHS did not conduct investigations to determine the validity of figures and statistics provided verbally by Bilkem officials, because the Bilkem officials appeared to be trustworthy. Instead, DHS accepted the figures, many of which were false, and used them in the financial statement. As a result, the financial statement indicated that Bilkem's financial position was far stronger than it really was. Shortly after the Bilkem registration statement (containing the misleading financial statement) became effective, Fred Furd purchased 100 shares of Bilkem stock, which was being traded on a national securities exchange. Furd did not read the misleading financial statement before purchasing the shares. Two months after Furd's purchase of the shares, Bilkem filed for bankruptcy. Furd has sued DHS for damages on two alternative theories: first, that DHS is liable under Section 11 of the Securities Act of 1933; and second, that DHS violated SEC Rule 10b-5. Discuss and evaluate Furd's chances of success on the alternative claims.

22. At the request of its client, Andre Preneur, the accounting firm Dewey, Cheatem & Howe (DCH) prepared and certified a financial statement concerning Preneur's business. When he requested that the work be done, Preneur informed DCH that he would be furnishing the financial statement to Legbreaker Loan Co. as part of a loan application. Preneur did so, but he also provided a copy of the financial statement to Glen Gullible, who was trying to decide whether to purchase Preneur's business. Largely on the basis of what the financial statement showed, Gullible purchased the business from Preneur. It later became apparent that DCH had been negligent with regard to the financial statement and that as a result, the financial statement made the business look much stronger than it really was. Claiming to have suffered financial injury because of DCH's negligence, Gullible has brought suit against DCH. Discuss and evaluate Gullible's chances of success under each of the following alternative tests employed in cases such as Gullible's: first, the *primary benefit* test; second, the *foreseen users and foreseen class of users* test; and third, the *foreseeable users* test.

23. Assume that Charles purchased a corporation's securities in reliance on a false impression about the corporation's soundness. The false impression was created by negligently performed work of the corporation's accountant. If Charles lost all or part of his investment when the corporation failed shortly after he purchased the stock, and if applicable state law has departed from the holding in the *Ultramares* case, why might Charles rather sue the accountant under principles of state tort law instead of under SEC Rule 10b-5?

CHAPTER 46

ADMINISTRATIVE AGENCIES

True-False: Circle T for True or F for False.

T F 1. The Fifth Amendment privilege against self-incrimination applies in the regulatory context if the regulatory sanction is punitive in intent or effect.

T F 2. An administrative agency may conduct a warrantless search of private property without having probable cause to do so.

T F 3. The burden of proof in administrative proceedings, even when a respondent is charged with violating the law, is the civil preponderance of the evidence standard.

T F 4. Constitutional procedural safeguards such as the exclusionary rule do not protect the respondent in an administrative proceeding.

T F 5. The decision of an administrative law judge is not subject to judicial review.

T F 6. Despite the American constitutional principle of separation of powers, administrative agencies combine investigative, legislative, and judicial functions in one entity.

T F 7. Administrative agencies possess only ministerial powers.

T F 8. An adminstrative agency's legislative rules have the effect of law.

T F 9. All administrative agency actions are judicially reviewable.

T F 10. Congress cannot amend the enabling legislation that was used to establish an administrative agency once the agency has begun operation.

Multiple Choice: Circle the best answer.

11. Administrative agencies may be created:
   a. only by a legislature.
   b. by a legislature or by the executive branch.
   c. by the judiciary only.
   d. by the executive branch only.

12. The following statements pertain to types of agencies. Which statement is accurate?
   a. The Senate may refuse to confirm a presidential appointment to the board or commission of an independent agency.
   b. Administrative heads of executive agencies are removable only for cause.
   c. Federal administrative agencies that reside within the office of the President are called independent agencies.
   d. None of the above.

13. When an agency makes interpretive rules,
   a. it must follow the formal rulemaking process.
   b. it specifies procedural standards for how agency hearing will be conducted.
   c. it sets forth legal standards that are binding on businesses and are subject to judicial enforcement.
   d. it typically provides guidance regarding the circumstances under which it is likely to take formal enforcement action.

14. The adjudicatory power of a major federal agency includes:
    a. the power to investigate alleged violations.
    b. the power to produce regulations that have legal effect.
    c. the power to instigate and hold proceedings to determine whether regulatory or statutory violations have occurred.
    d. all of the above powers.

15. Which of the following is an accurate statement about a *de novo* review of an administrative law judge's decision?
    a. It will be conducted by a appropriate federal court.
    b. The agency's governing body must accept the ALJ's findings of fact if they were supported by the evidence presented at the initial hearing over which the ALJ presided.
    c. The agency's governing body will empanel a jury whose function is to determine whether there was an adequate legal and factual basis for the ALJ's decision.
    d. None of the above.

16. Which is a true statement about judicial review of administrative agency actions?
    a. No agency actions may be reviewed by the courts.
    b. The Administrative Procedures Act creates a strong presumption in favor of reviewability.
    c. All agency actions are subject to judicial review.
    d. Only those who have suffered economic loss from agency actions have standing to sue.

17. The "exhaustion" requirement for judicial review of agency actions requires that:
    a. the dispute be fully developed.
    b. the ALJ decision has been reviewed by a court.
    c. the aggrieved party has pursued all of its available administrative remedies.
    d. the agency's actions be subjected to *de novo* review.

18. The judicial standard of review used in cases involving informal agency adjudications or rulemaking is:
    a. the "arbitrary and capricious" test.
    b. the "substantial evidence" test.
    c. the *de novo* test.
    d. the "preponderance of the evidence" test.

19. Under the Freedom of Information Act,
    a. agencies must refuse to disclose documents that fall in an "exempt" category established by the FOIA.
    b. plaintiffs who successfully appeal an agency's denial of an FOIA request may recover their attorney's fees.
    c. private individuals are entitled to inspect files that agencies maintain on them and to request that erroneous or incomplete records be corrected.
    d. all of the above are true.

20. The Occupational Safety and Health Administration (OSHA) was created by Congress to regulate workplace conditions that could cause illness, injury, or death. If OSHA were to promulgate a rule stating that workers with more than two children should be given a preference in employers' hiring decisions, the rule could be be attacked as being:
    a. *de novo.*
    b. *de minimis.*
    c. *ultra vires.*
    d. *sua sponte.*

21. Business tycoon Dewey Cheatem is the respondent in an adjudicative proceeding brought by a federal administrative agency, which alleges that Cheatem violated a certain legislative rule of the agency. Assume that if Cheatem is found to have violated the rule, the sole remedy that the agency may impose is a cease and desist order. When called to testify at the initial hearing, Cheatem refused to answer questions dealing with the issues presented by the proceeding. He cited his Fifth Amendment privilege against compulsory testimonial self-incrimination as the basis for his refusal. Was Cheatem entitled to invoke his Fifth Amendment privilege? Why or why not?

22. Identify the three methods of administrative agency rulemaking and note the advantages and disadvantages of each.

23. What four requirements must a plaintiff satisfy before he can obtain judicial review of agency actions?

CHAPTER 47

THE FEDERAL TRADE COMMISSION AND CONSUMER PROTECTION LAWS

True-False:Circle T for True or F for False.

T F 1. A debt collector subject to the provisions of the Fair Debt Collection Practices Act cannot contact the employer of the debtor.

T F 2. The Consumer Product Safety Commission is empowered to bring an appropriate suit in federal court in an effort to eliminate the dangers associated with any hazardous product.

T F 3. When the Truth in Lending Act applies, the creditor must disclose that the creditor will be acquiring a security interest in the debtor's property to secure the debt, if that is the case.

T F 4. The Fair Credit Billing Act is primarily aimed at transactions in which consumers have leased goods on credit and are making installment payments during the term of the lease.

T F 5. A credit practice that seems neutral on its face may still violate the Equal Credit Opportunity Act if statistics show that the practice has an adverse impact on one of the statute's protected classes.

T F 6. Although certain extensions of closed-end credit may trigger application of the Truth in Lending Act, open-end credit is outside the scope of the TILA's provisions.

T F 7. When the provisions of the Magnuson-Moss Warranty Act apply, the warrantor must disclose any attempt by the warrantor to limit the purchaser's remedies or to eliminate consequential damages.

T F 8. Because FTC trade regulation rules and industry guides have the force of law, the knowing violation of either will provide a proper basis for an FTC adjudicative proceeding against the violator.

T F 9. The Consumer Product Safety Commission has the power to issue a rule amounting to an outright ban on a product when the necessary legal standard is met.

T F 10. Besides imposing certain duties on consumer reporting agencies, the Fair Credit Reporting Act imposes certain disclosure duties on those who procure and use credit reports.

Multiple Choice: Circle the best answer.

11. An FTC adjudicative proceeding:
   a. occurs when the FTC files suit against a defendant in an appropriate federal district court.
   b. may be brought by a consumer or competitor who was injured by another party's deceptive business practice.
   c. may result in an FTC order whose propriety and terms can provide the basis of an appeal that takes the case into the federal court system.
   d. is inappropriate if the allegedly wrongful practice of the respondent took place in a context other than advertising.

12. Which of the following is *not* an accurate statement about the Truth in Lending Act?
   a. Loans for agricultural puposes are not covered by the TILA.
   b. The TILA would apply to a bank's $20,000 loan to an individual person if he borrowed the money for use in his business.
   c. The TILA may apply to a creditor whose primary business is not the extension of credit.
   d. A credit transaction that exceeds $25,000 in amount is nonetheless subject to the TILA if the creditor takes, as part of the transaction, a security interest in the debtor's real property.

11. In an adjudicative proceeding brought by the FTC against an advertiser who allegedly engaged in conduct that violated Section 5 of the FTC Act,

a. the FTC will not prove the elements of its case if it demonstrates only that the advertising was unfair and is unable to show that the advertising was also deceptive.

b. the FTC will not win the case if it demonstates only that the advertiser violated an FTC trade regulation rule.

c. the advertiser's statement that his product is "great" almost certainly will be found to be deceptive if the advertiser has no consumer survey results or scientific test results supporting the claim of greatness.

d. the FTC may still prevail even if it is unable to prove that any consumers actually were deceived by the advertiser's allegedly deceptive advertising.

14. The Magnuson-Moss Warranty Act:

a. requires certain sellers of consumer goods to give written warranties to purchasers.

b. requires some sellers of consumer products to make certain warranty-related information available to the consumer buyer before the sale takes place.

c. does not apply to written warranties for consumer products if the products cost more than $15.

d. is satisfied by a seller subject to its provisions if the seller makes the required warranty-related information available to the buyer either before or immediately after the sale takes place.

15. The following statements pertain to the notion that in order for the FTC to attack advertising as deceptive, the advertiser's misrepresentation or omission must have been *material*. Which of the statements is/are accurate?

a. Unless the misrepresentation or omission pertained to the physical qualities of the product being advertised, the misrepresentation or omission was not material.

b. Under the FTC's current approach, an advertisement's express statements of alleged fact will be presumed to be material unless demonstrated to the contrary.

c. The advertiser's misrepresentation or omission will be considered material if what was misstated or omitted would be likely to influence reasonable consumers' decisions to choose the advertised product or service.

d. Both b and c.

16. Wendell and Wendy Waffler entered into a contract with Biltrong Construction Co. Under the contract, Biltrong was to perform $33,000 worth of remodeling at the Wafflers' home. As it often did in transactions involving consumers, Biltrong agreed to allow the contract price to be paid in installment payments over a period of years. The parties' agreement also provided that in order to secure the Wafflers' payment of the contract price, Biltrong would take a mortgage on the Wafflers' home. The mortgage in favor of Biltrong was to be a second mortgage, inferior in priority to the first mortgage that the Wafflers had granted years earlier to the local bank when it loaned them the money to purchase their home. On the day the Wafflers and Biltrong entered into their agreement, the Wafflers had second thoughts. That same day, they hand-delivered to Biltrong's president a written notice stating that they wished to rescind the contract in its entirety. Biltrong's president insisted that they had no right to do so. Is the president correct?

a. No, because the Wafflers properly exercised the rescission right granted to them by the Truth in Lending Act.

b. Yes, because the fact that the transaction involved more than $25,000 means that the Wafflers were not entitled to the rescission right contained in the TILA.

c. Yes, because the rescission right contained in the TILA does not apply to transactions in which the creditor is to take a mortgage on the property.

d. No, because of the operation of the 10-day cooling off period set out in the Fair Credit Billing Act.

17. The FTC has initiated an adjudicative proceeding against Grotesque Corp. The allegation seving as the basis of the FTC action is that Grotesque engaged in deceptive advertising. Assume that the evidence presented during the adjudicative proceeding convinces the administrative law judge (ALJ) to conclude that certain consumers could be deceived by Grotesque's advertising, but that the only consumers likely to be deceived would be the exceedingly naive and ignorant. If she applies the FTC's 1983 policy statement on deceptiveness, how should the ALJ rule?

   a. Adversely to Grotesque, because the FTC's role as consumer watchdog includes a duty to protect all consumers, including naive and ignorant ones.

   b. In Grotesque's favor, because not all of the elements of deceptiveness, as specified in the 1983 policy statement, are present under the facts.

   c. Adversely to Grotesque, because the 1983 policy statement expanded the scope of what constitutes deceptiveness.

   d. In Grotesque's favor, because nothing in the facts indicates that the advertising was proved to be unfair as well as deceptive.

18. Which of the following is an accurate statement about remedies that the FTC may impose on a party found to have engaged in deceptive advertising?

   a. A corrective advertising order would be impermissible because ordering the party to say certain things in its advertisement would violate the First Amendment.

   b. The FTC is allowed to assess punitive damamges against the party in order to deter future misconduct of a similar nature.

   c. Neither a nor b.

   d. Both a and b.

19. The Equal Credit Opportunity Act:

   a. applies to the extension of consumer credit but not to business or commercial loans.

   b. does not apply to denials of credit based on the applicant's age.

   c. allows for government enforcement of its provisions but not for private suits by aggrieved parties.

   d. originally barred credit discrimination because of sex or marital status but now covers other grounds as well.

20. Assume that the FTC has received numerous complaints about certain insurance companies' marketing strategies that, the complainants allege, are designed to manipulate the elderly and the infirm into purchasing special types of insurance policies and coverages they do not really need. In view of the applicable law concerning the FTC's authority to regulate unfair practices and in view of the FTC's current policy concerning whether to act with regard to an alleged unfair practice, which of the following statements is accurate?

   a. Regardless of whether any elderly or infirm persons actually have purchased unnecessary polies as a result of the insurance companies' practices, the FTC may proceed against the pertinent companies on an unfairness theory, so long as the FTC believes it is likely that such persons could be led to purchase policies they do not need.

   b. Even if the insurance companies' practices arguably were unfair, the FTC has no authority to proceed against the companies involved unless the practices were both unfair and deceptive; it would violate the insurance companies' first amendment rights if the FTC proceeded solely on an unfairness basis.

   c. If the allegedly unfair practices of the insurance companies actually have caused elderly or infirm persons to purchase policies they did not need, those purchasers have suffered economic injury that could support an FTC decision to proceed against the pertinent insurance companies on an unfairness theory.

   d. The FTC cannot proceed against the insurance companies on an unfairness theory for two reasons: first, the allegedly unfair practices obviously could not have caused anyone to experience physical injury; and second, the FTC has authority to regulate unfair practices with regard to the sale of goods only, and insurance policies are not goods.

21. Grover owed a large past-due balance on a charge account at Nonpareil, a local clothing store. A Nonpareil employee who had the responsibility of following up on past-due accounts began telephoning Grover while he was at work to discuss the debt, even though Grover had informed her that he was not to receive personal calls at work. The Nonpareil employee also called Grover at approximately midnight on more than one occasion to discuss the debt. In addition, she threatened to make public statements that Grover could not be trusted to pay his debts. Grover filed suit against Nonpareil, claiming that through the acts of its employee, Nonpareil violated the Fair Debt Collection Practices Act. Discuss the strength of Grover's case.

22. Why does FTC regulation of deceptive advertising pose few First Amendment problems? Why might FTC regulation of unfair advertising be potentially more troublesome in that regard?

23. Earl Solid applied for a loan at Perpetual Infidelity Savings & Loan (PISL). He later received notice that his application was denied. A credible source later told Solid that PISL had denied his application because a credit report on him stated that he had declared bankruptcy three years earlier. Solid claims that the bankruptcy information was untrue. What rights does Solid have under the circumstances?

CHAPTER 48

ANTITRUST: THE SHERMAN ACT

True-False:Circle T for True or F for False.

T F 1. If a manufacturer suggests a retail price for the goods it supplies to retailers, the manufacturer has committed a per se violation of Sherman Act Section 1.

T F 2. Under the Sherman Act, courts have the power to order companies to divest themselves of the stock or assets of other companies.

T F 3. The presumption of harm to competition from competitors' joint ventures is so strong that such ventures receive per se treatment when they become the basis for a plaintiff's suit under Sherman Act Section 1.

T F 4. In order to determine whether a party possesses monopoly power, the court must examine that party's share of the market for its specific product, as well as the availability of close substitutes for the product.

T F 5. Recent developments in antitrust law have indicated that not all group boycotts are automatic violations of Sherman Act Section 1.

T F 6. Even activity that occurs solely within the borders of a single state may be subject to the federal antitrust laws if the activity nonetheless has a significant impact on interstate commerce.

T F 7. Sherman Act Section 2 makes monopolies unlawful.

T F 8. A single firm may unilaterally refuse to deal with another party without violating Sherman Act Section 1.

T F 9. There was no tying agreement, for Sherman Act Section 1 purposes, if the two elements allegedly tied together were merely components of a larger product, service, or way of doing business.

T F 10. Chicago School advocates tend to regard concentration in the American economy as inherently undesirable.

Multiple Choice: Circle the best answer.

11. In each of a through d, below, an alleged violation of Sherman Act Section 1 is discussed. Which of the statements is accurate?

   a. If a manufacturer and various retail dealers of the manufacturer's products agreed to fix maximum prices to be charged by the dealers but did not agree to fix minimum prices, the agreement will be subjected to rule of reason analysis.

   b. If a retailer deliberately parallels the pricing policies of a competitor, the retailer has committed a per se violation of Section 1.

   c. If a manufacturer and the wholesale dealers of its products entered into an agreement fixing the minimum price that the wholesalers would charge when reselling the manufacturer's products, the agreement is a per se violation of Section 1.

   d. If various competing retailers agreed to fix maximum prices (but not minimum prices) that they would charge for the same goods, the retailers will be given an opportunity to prove, when an antitrust suit is brought against them, that their agreement benefited consumers.

12. The following statements pertain to a private plaintiff's suit against an alleged violator of Sherman Act Section 1. Which one is accurate?

    a. If the plaintiff is an indirect purchaser of goods as to which prices were fixed, he normally will have standing to pursue a Section 1 claim.

    b. The plaintiff will prevail in the suit by proving that the defendant's unilateral action constituted a significant restraint of trade.

    c. If the plaintiff wins the suit, she will be awarded three times her actual damages.

    d. If the defendant's anticompetitive behavior is given rule of reason treatment, the defendant will not be given an opportunity to prove that its behavior also benefited competition in some sense.

13. Exclusive dealing contracts:

    a. may be attacked under either Sherman Act Section 1 or Clayton Act Section 3 if they pertain to commodities.

    b. are per se violations of Sherman Act Section 1 because they inherently limit competition.

    c. between manufacturers and retail dealers are automatic violations of Sherman Act Section 1 but not of Clayton Act Section 3.

    d. cannot violate Sherman Act Section 1 because they merely reflect each contracting party's unilateral refusal to deal with anyone else.

14. The following statements pertain either to the *per se* approach used by courts in some Sherman Act Section 1 cases or to the *rule of reason* approach employed by courts in other cases involving an alleged violation of Section 1. Which of the statements is/are accurate?

    a. When the plaintiff proves that the defendant engaged in behavior triggering true per se treatment, it is conclusively presumed that the defendant's actions violated Section 1.

    b. Among the reasons the per se approach was developed was that it gives businesspersons guidance concerning the sorts of behavior that will be considered violative of Section 1.

    c. When the court employs the rule of reason approach, it will determine whether there were legitimate justifications for the defendant's actions, which otherwise could be regarded as violative of Section 1.

    d. All of the above.

15. Acme Co. and two of its competitors, Bogus Corp. and Marginal, Inc., manufacture widgets. The three competitors have been named as defendants in a civil antitrust suit in which they are alleged to have entered into an agreement limiting the quantities of widgets that each will produce. Assuming the evidence indicates that the three in fact entered into the agreement,

    a. they will not be held to have violated Sherman Act Section 1 because their agreement was merely an ancillary restraint.

    b. the court will apply the rule of reason analysis, because the agreement amounted to a vertical restraint on distribution.

    c. the court will apply the per se approach because the agreement will be considered horizontal price-fixing.

    d. they will be given an opportunity to demonstrate that there were legitimate reasons for the agreement.

16. Which of the following statements about antitrust law is accurate?
    a. If the defendant enters a *nolo contendere* plea in a criminal proceeding brought because of an alleged violation of the Sherman Act, evidence of that plea cannot be used by the plaintiff in a civil suit brought against the same defendant on the basis of the same conduct that gave rise to the criminal proceeding.
    b. When the government brings a criminal proceeding because of an alleged violation of the Sherman Act, the government must prove that the defendant possessed a specific intent to violate the antitrust laws.
    c. Chicago School thinkers generally maintain that economic efficiency should not be a goal of our antitrust laws.
    d. Chicago School thinkers often characterize the traditional approach to antitrust law as having done too much to protect competitition and too little to protect individual competitors.

17. The following statements deal with alleged violations of Sherman Act Section 1. Which statement is *inaccurate*?
    a. Even though group boycotts necessarily restrain competition, not of all them are per se violations of Section 1.
    b. A manufacturer's unilateral setting of a retail price for the resale of its goods is a per se violation of Section 1.
    c. Even though vertical restraints on distribution may harm intrabrand competition, they do not necessarily violate Section 1.
    d. Tying agreements are given full rule of reason treatment by the courts.

18. Section 2 of the Sherman Act:
    a. does not impose liability on a defendant who intentionally acquired monopoly power but has not abused it since acquiring it.
    b. allows for the imposition of liability on a defendant whose rise to a position of monopoly power stemmed from the defendant's possession and use of business skills that were superior to those of the defendant's competitors.
    c. cannot be used to impose liability on a defendant whose actions appear to be attempted monopolization, if the defendant has not yet acquired monopoly status.
    d. differs from Section 1 of the Sherman Act in that under Section 2, unilateral action by the defendant may be enough to make the defendant liable.

19. Elite Corp. manufactures joy buzzers. It has concluded that many of its dealers charge such a low retail price for the joy buzzers that the high-class image of the product is being eroded. The following statements purport to state the legal consequences of possible courses of action that Elite might take. Which of the statement is accurate?
    a. If Elite and its dealers agree that the dealers will charge a certain minimum price as well as a certain maximum price, and if Elite is sued for an alleged violation of Sherman Act Section 1, the fixing of the minimum price will be a per se violation but the fixing of the maximum price will be given rule of reason treatment.
    b. Elite will violate Sherman Act Section 1 if it unilaterally refuses to deal with dealers who fail to charge Elite's suggested retail price.
    c. If Elite and its dealers agree that the dealers will charge certain prices, and if Elite is later sued for an alleged violation of Sherman Act Section 1, the horizontal nature of the relationship between Elite and its dealers means that the court will apply the rule of reason analysis to the agreement.
    d. None of the above.

20. Average Corp., Mediocre, Inc., and Ordinary Co. are competitors engaged in the manufacturing and sale of trash compactors. They have entered into an agreement under which the entire United States has been divided into sales territories along geographic lines. Under the agreement, each of the three companies has its own exclusive sales territory. The agreement prohibits each of the companies from selling trash compactors in any area except the area assigned to it. Because of the agreement, Average, Mediocre, and Ordinary have been sued by another one of their competitors in an action brought under Sherman Act Section 1. Which of the following is a correct statement concerning the suit?

   a. Assuming the court takes the approach being taken in recent years by some federal courts, the court will give the agreement per se treatment if it was a naked restraint, but will apply the rule of reason analysis if it was an ancillary restraint.

   b. If the court follows the rule the Supreme Court prescribed in the *Topco* case for treatment of competitors' agreed divisions of markets, the court will apply the rule of reason analysis to the parties agreement.

   c. The defendants' agreement amounted to vertical price-fixing; therefore, the court will employ the per se approach.

   d. None of the above.

Short Essay

21. The U.S. government has filed suit against Belligerent Corp. on the theory that Belligerent violated Sherman Act Section 2 by engaging in monopolization. Belligerent maintains that the suit should be dismissed because none of the actions about which the government complains were joint actions. If Belligerent's characterization of its actions is correct, is Belligerent entitled to a dismissal on that basis? Explain your reasoning.

22. Numerous manufacturers of widgets agreed to fix prices. As a result, the manufacturers sold widgets to retailers at an artificially high price. Percy purchased numerous widgets from one of the retailers whose widgets had been acquired from a manufacturer at the fixed price. Once he acquired information tending to show the price-fixing that had taken place, Percy brought an antitrust suit against the manufacturers. His claim was that the retailers, in all likelihood, passed along their increased costs (resulting from their having to purchase widgets from the manufacturers at the high fixed price) to customers such as him, and that he therefore was injured by the manufacturers' price-fixing agreement. What is the biggest obstacle to Percy's winning the suit? Why?

23. Shoddy Co., a manufacturer, and several of its authorized retail dealers entered into an agreement under which each dealer was given a geographic area where that retailer was to be the exclusive dealer of Shoddy products. Each retailer subject to the agreement agreed to honor the territorial restrictions and to refrain from infringing upon another Shoddy dealer's designated sales territory. A proper plaintiff has now sued Shoddy, alleging that the agreement just described violated Sherman Act Section 1. What treatment will the court give the agreement? Why? What is the effect of that treatment?

CHAPTER 49

THE CLAYTON ACT, THE ROBINSON-PATMAN ACT, AND ANTITRUST EXEMPTIONS AND IMMUNITIES

True-False: Circle T for True or F for False.

T F 1. When defining the relevant product market for purposes of deciding a merger-challenging suit under Clayton Act Section 7, the court will consider not only the products produced by the acquired and acquiring firms, but also the reasonably interchangeable products produced by other companies.

T F 2. The *Noerr-Pennington* doctrine is based on the notion that the right to petition the government must be subordinated to the antitrust policy of preserving free competition.

T F 3. The statutory exemption from antitrust liability for the "business of insurance" does not insulate all insurance company activities from antitrust scrutiny.

T F 4. When the quantitative substantiality test is applied to an exclusive dealing contract, the court focuses more on the percentage of sales tied up by the contract in the effective area of competition than it does on the dollar amount of sales tied up by the contract.

T F 5. In a suit brought to challenge the validity of a merger under Clayton Act Section 7, the plaintiff will generally have more difficulty prevailing if the court defines the relevant market broadly than if the court defines the relevant market narrowly.

T F 6. Supreme Court precedent indicates that if a horizontal merger produces a firm with a market share of greater than 33 percent, the merger is conclusively presumed to be in violation of Clayton Act Section 7.

T F 7. If a seller charged a buyer a discriminatorily low price that violated Robinson-Patman Act Section 2(a) and the buyer received the benefit of the price while knowing that it was discriminatorily low, both the seller and the buyer may be held to have violated the Robinson-Patman Act.

T F 8. Labor unions' statutory exemption from antitrust liability allows them to avoid antitrust liability for agreements with nonlabor groups to restrain trade.

T F 9. Both the Clayton Act and the Robinson-Patman Act require only a probable anticompetitive effect, rather than an actual anticompetitive effect, as a precondition to liability for violations of their respective provisions.

T F 10. Under the Justice Department's 1984 amended merger guidelines, economic efficiency is a stronger argument for the legality of a vertical merger than it is for the legality of a horizontal merger.

T F 11. Although a patent holder, in licensing a manufacturer to make and sell the patented item, may control the price at which the manufacturer sells the item, the patent holder cannot control the price at which the patented item is resold by distributors who purchased the patented item directly from the patent holder.

T F 12. With regard to the legality of exclusive dealing contracts under Clayton Act Section 3, the Supreme Court's most recent indication was that the legality or illegality should be determined on the basis of the dollar amount of commerce involved.

T F 13. Price discrimination at the tertiary level exists if a chain store operator induces a supplier to sell it certain goods at a lower price than what the supplier charges others for the same goods, thus enabling the chain store operator to undersell its competitors.

Multiple Choice: Circle the best answer.

14. In which of the following alternative fact situations would there *not* be a violation of the Robinson-Patman Act's provisions on price discrimination and indirect price discrimination?

    a. The owner of the state's largest television repair business charges certain customers a lower per-hour rate for repair services than she charges other customers for the same repair services.

    b. A manufacturer of goods sold by many retailers sells the goods to retailer #1 at a price of $10 per item. Concerning the same goods, the manufacturer quotes a price of $8 per item to retailer #2, but no sale takes place between the manufacturer and retailer #2.

    c. A manufacturer of certain goods sold by many retailers makes certain payments in the nature of advertising allowances to one of its customers, but makes such payments available to its other customers on a proportionately equal basis.

    d. a, b, and c.

15. The Clayton Act:

    a. contains provisions calling for civil liability for violators, but does not contain provisions making it a crime to violate the act.

    b. reflects a stronger focus on whether there has been actual harm to competition than on whether there is a probability of harm to competition.

    c. does not prohibit a tying agreement or exclusive dealing agreement if the agreement involves commodities.

    d. prohibits any two companies that have been or are competitors from having the same individual serve as a director of one company and an officer of the other.

16. Wondrous Widget Co. sells its widgets to retailers across the country at a price of $1.25 per widget. Recently, Wondrous learned that one of its competitors, Widgetworks, Inc., is selling the same type of widget at a price of $1.10 per widget to all retailers in Oklahoma. Wondrous would like to respond appropriately to the actions of Widgetworks. Which of the following accurately states a way in which Wondrous may respond without potentially running afoul of the Robinson-Patman Act?

    a. Wondrous may begin selling widgets at $1.10 apiece to retailers in Oklahoma, but if it does so it must lower the price to $1.10 for retailers outside Oklahoma.

    b. Wondrous may begin selling widgets at $1.10 apiece to retailers in Oklahoma, without lowering its $1.25 charge to retailers outside Oklahoma.

    c. Wondrous may begin selling widgets at a price of $1.07 apiece to retailers in Oklahoma, while keeping the price at $1.25 for retailers outside Oklahoma.

    d. None of the above.

17. Each of the following statements pertains either to a type of merger or to the level of scrutiny courts give to a type of merger in a case in which the plaintiff claims that the merger violated Clayton Act Section 7. Which of the statements is *inaccurate*?

    a. A merger between one manufacturer of farm implements and another manufacturer of comparable farm implements would be classifed as horizontal in nature.

    b. In determining whether there has been a violation of Section 7, a court is likely to give more rigorous scrutiny to a conglomerate merger than it would give to a horizontal merger.

    c. A merger between a manufacturer of televisions and a manufacturer of television picture tubes would be considered vertical in nature regardless of whether the two manufacturers had ever had a customer-supplier relationship.

    d. In determining whether there has been a violation of Section 7, a court is likely to give less rigorous scrutiny to a vertical merger than it would give to a horizontal merger.

18. Of the following statements about the current version of Clayton Act Section 8, which is/are accurate?

    a. It does not necessarily bar a person from serving as a director of more than one corporation at the same time.

    b. It bars a person from serving simultaneously as an officer of two corporations that, besides meeting certain other statutory requirements, are or have been competitors.

    c. It bars a person from serving simultaneously as a director of two corporations that, besides meeting certain other statutory requirements, are or have been competitors.

    d. All of the above.

19. Gene's Jeans, Inc., a retail seller of jeans and other clothing items, has brought a Robinson-Patman Act suit against ZYX Co., a jeans manufacturer, on the theory that ZYX sold certain jeans to a retail competitor of Gene's at a price substantially below what ZYX charged Gene's for the same jeans. Of the following statements concerning the suit, which is *inaccurate*?

    a. Gene's will lose the suit if the sale to Gene's and the sale to the competitor were not fairly close in time.

    b. If the evidence shows that Gene's easily could have bought the same jeans from a wholesaler at the same price ZYX charged the competitor, Gene's probably will lose the suit.

    c. Gene's cannot win the suit unless it proves that ZYX engaged in the sort of practice referred to above with regard to various retailers other than Gene's, and thereby caused substantial actual harm to competition.

    d. If the incident described in the facts was only an isolated incident, it will be difficult for Gene's to win the suit.

20. Viable Corp. and Marginal Co. are competitors. Viable plans to purchase Marginal. Which of the following factors would make it most likely that the Justice Department would challenge the acquisition as a violation of Clayton Act Section 7?

    a. That Viable has not previously taken over a competitor.

    b. That Marginal is a failing company, the possible acquisition of which has not interested Viable's other competitors.

    c. That Viable has a 35 percent market share now and would only be increasing its market share by 10 percent in acquiring Marginal.

    d. That economic efficiencies are highly likely to result if Viable acquires Marginal.

21. Which of the following is an accurate statement about the state action doctrine?

    a. It automatically insulates municipalities from adverse results in antitrust suits brought against them.

    b. It protects the states from antitrust liability unless their actions were taken in their sovereign capacities.

    c. It causes states to be subject to antitrust liability on the grounds that private individuals and companies are held liable.

    d. It protects a state from liability for what otherwise could be a violation of antitrust law if the state action was clearly articulated as state policy and was actively supervised by the state.

22. PDQ Co. has acquired XYZ, Inc. in a conglomerate merger. Which of the following factors would help bolster a conclusion that the merger violates Clayton Act Section 7?

    a. That XYZ's competitors had feared PDQ's entry into the market for a significant period of time.

    b. That none of XYZ's competitors would have been suitable toeholds by which PDQ could have entered the market involving XYZ and its competitors.

    c. That PDQ could not realistically have entered the market involving XYZ and its competitors by starting its own competing company from "scratch" instead of by acquiring XYZ.

    d. None of the above.

23. Which of the following is an accurate statement about the Robinson-Patman Act?

    a. It allows the "meeting competition" privilege to be used as a means of acquiring a new customer, in addition to merely using it to keep an existing customer.

    b. It prohibits the primary level price discrimination that results when a wholesaler who has received a functional discount from a manufacturer passes along the savings to retail customers.

    c. It expressly labels manufacturer-to-wholesaler functional discounts as unlawful.

    d. It prohibits the tertiary level price discrimination that occurs when a chain store with substantial bargaining power deliberately induces a seller to charge it a discriminatorily low price.

Short Essay

24. Haney Co., the manufacturer of polygraph machines and a myriad of other items, refused to sell polygraph machines to retailers and wholesalers unless they also agreed to purchase computer diskettes (for use in connection with ordinary computers, and not in connection with the polygraph machines). Various retailers and wholesalers agreed to do so in order to acquire the polygraph machines. A proper plaintiff later sued Haney on the theory that the agreements just described were tying arrangements prohibited by Clayton Act Section 3. The evidence produced at trial revealed that Haney possessed sufficient power concerning polygraph machines to enable it to effectively compel purchasers to purchase computer diskettes from it as well. In addition, the evidence showed that in view of the large size of the computer diskette market, the volume of computer diskette sales from which the Haney arrangement foreclosed other sellers of compute diskettes was rather small, both in dollar amount and in percentage terms. Address the following questions:

    a. What are the different approaches courts take with regard to the elements of a prohibited tying agreement under Clayton Act Section 3?

    b. Under which of the approaches is the plaintiff likely to prevail in the suit against Haney, and why?

25. Bogus Co. and Sham, Inc. are competitors in the production of widgets. Both firms are Indiana corporations. They do business in Indiana, Illinois, and Iowa. Bogus is planning to acquire Sham. If the acquisition is challenged un der Clayton Act Section 7, why might the court determine that the relevant geographic market is not as broad as the Indiana-Illinois-Iowa area?

26. Jesfair, Inc. sells its canned green beans to Wrongway Co., which then sells the green beans in the nationwide chain of Wrongway grocery stores. In addition, Jesfair sells green beans to various other grocery store chains. The green beans sold by Jesfair to Wrongway are packaged by Jesfair under the Wrongway label. The green beans sold by Jesfair to the other grocery store chains are packaged by Jesfair under the Jesfair label. Despite the two different names, however, the green beans sold by Jesfair under the two labels are the same in quality. The price at which Jesfair sells the green beans to Wrongway is significantly lower then the price at which it sells the green beans to the other chains. One of the other chains has now brought a Robinson-Patman Act suit against Jesfair on the theory that Jesfair engaged in price discrimination. Jesfair argues that Robinson-Patman does not apply here because "Wrongway" green beans and "Jesfair" green beans effectively are not the same product and would not be perceived as the same by consumers. Should Jesfair succeed with this argument? Why or why not?

CHAPTER 50

EMPLOYMENT LAW

True-False: Circle T for True or F for False.

T F 1. Current American law requires employers to assist in several ways in ensuring that their employees receive financial protection after termination of the employment relation.

T F 2. An unemployed person who refuses an offer of a suitable job loses his right to unemployment compensation.

T F 3. The Employee Retirement Income Security Act of 1974 (ERISA) requires employers to establish and fund pension benefit plans.

T F 4. "Yellow dog" contracts, which require employees not to join a union, are no longer enforceable.

T F 5. The Equal Pay Act permits different rates of pay based upon any factor besides gender.

T F 6. Workers' compensation laws subject the employer to strict liability for employee injuries arising out of and in the course of employment.

T F 7. Under workers' compensation laws, the employer gives up the right to use the defenses of contributory negligence, assumption of risk, and the fellow-servant rule, and the employee gives up the right to sue the employer for negligence.

T F 8. Because workers' compensation is the employee's sole remedy, the employee may not sue either the employer or third parties for his injuries.

T F 9. The Age Discrimination in Employment Act protects employees over 40 years of age against age discrimination in favor of both younger and older individuals.

T F 10. OSHA inspectors are not required to obtain a search warrant even if the employer objects to a warrantless search.

Multiple Choice: Circle the best answer.

11. Which of the following is an accurate statement about the Fair Labor Standards Act?
    a. Its protections do not apply to employees engaged in interstate commerce.
    b. Employees who are executive, administrative, or professional in nature, or are involved in outside sales, are now protected by the FLSA.
    c. Covered employees must be paid at the regular hourly rate for the first 48 hours of work during a week, and then at a time-and-a-half rate for work in excess of 48 hours during the week.
    d. None of the above.

12. The Equal Pay Act:
    a. covers executive, administrative, and professional employees.
    b. does not cover state and local government employees.
    c. covers gender-based pay discrimination against women but permits such discrimination against men.
    d. requires that two employees possess equal skills before the employees must be paid at an equal rate.

13. Which of the following employer actions violates the Equal Pay Act?
    a. Paying employees with six months experience a bonus that is not paid to new employees.
    b. Paying blacks less than whites.
    c. Lowering the pay of all employees to the lowest pay rate after having been found to discriminate among employees.
    d. Each of the above.

14. According to ERISA,
    a. a corporation that fails to provide a pension plan for its employees is subject to civil penalties.
    b. an employer whose pension plan does not reflect the minimum benefit levels established by the statute is subject to civil penalties.
    c. pension plan managers must normally diversify the plan's investments to minimize the risk of large losses.
    d. employers cannot delay an employee's right to participate in the plan.

15. According to OSHA,
    a. inspectors may inspect the workplace without a warrant unless the employer objects.
    b. inspectors having a proper warrant may inspect the workplace despite the objection of the employer.
    c. neither of the above is true.
    d. both of the above are true.

16. Which of the following is an unfair labor practice under the Labor-Management Relations Act?
    a. A union's conducting a strike.
    b. A union's restraining an employee's right to refrain from joining a union.
    c. An employer's domination of a labor union.
    d. Each of the above.

17. For purposes of Title VII, a "bona fide occupational qualification" may:
    a. include race or color in certain situations.
    b. be based upon the preferences of customers.
    c. contain a specific gender requirement.
    d. be based upon stereotypes if they are prevalent.

18. Title VII prohibits religious discrimination:
    a. against atheists.
    b. on the basis only of membership in an established religious denomination.
    c. under any and all circumstances.
    d. only against adherents to "minority" religions.

19. Title VII's ban on sex discrimination:
    a. protects homosexuality as well as gender.
    b. prohibits gender-based discrimination against both men and women.
    c. prohibits even voluntary employer programs that favor women in hiring or promotion over men.
    d. is not necessarily violated by an employer's establishing being of a particular sex as a job requirement.

20. The employment at will doctrine:
    a. has been completely destroyed by the passage of various federal and state employment laws.
    b. prevents an employer from meeting changing business conditions by eliminating superfluous employees.
    c. does not apply to a discharge that violates public policy.
    d. provides a contract remedy, but not a remedy in tort.

21. Insolvent Airlines, Inc. will not hire males to serve food and drinks on Insolvent's flights within the United States. Larry Livid, who was denied such employment at Insolvent because of this policy, has brought a Title VII suit against Insolvent. In defense, Insolvent asserts that being female is a BFOQ for this job because according to actual surveys of passengers on its flights, passengers overwhelmingly prefer stewardesses to stewards. Should Insolvent succeed with the BFOQ defense? Why or why not?

22. What two types of sexual harassment are actionable under Title VII, and how do they differ?

23. Norton, an employee of Gargantua Corp., was injured at the company's factory while working on an assembly line. At the time of his injury, Norton was not wearing the safety goggles that employees were required to wear, even though the shift foreman had repeatedly told him to do so. Norton's injuries resulted to a significant extent from his failure to wear the goggles. Is Gargantua liable to Norton under the state's workers' compensation statute? Why or why not?

CHAPTER 51

ENVIRONMENTAL REGULATION

True-False - Circle T for True and F for False.

T F 1. An environmental impact statement must be prepared for every major federal project significantly affecting the quality of the environment so that a federal agency will have considered the environmental impact of such projects before they are undertaken.

T F 2. A state must decide which activities must be regulated or curtailed so that air pollution emissions for a given air quality region do not exceed national ambient air quality standards.

T F 3. The Clean Air Act requires that new stationary sources of air pollution install the best available technology for reducing that pollution.

T F 4. The primary responsibility for enforcing air quality standards lies with the federal government.

T F 5. Up to this time, federal and state regulatory efforts have dealt only with outdoor air pollution, and indoor air pollution is as yet unregulated.

T F 6. Both the Environmental Protection Agency and the Nuclear Regulatory Commission have jurisdiction over the control of radioactive substances.

T F 7. Under the Clean Water Act, the federal government has the primary responsibility for preventing, reducing, and eliminating water pollution.

T F 8. A private citizen may sue either another citizen or the EPA if either fails to observe the requirements of the Clean Water Act.

T F 9. The Clean Water Act regulates dredging or filling in wetlands, even where those wetlands are privately owned and the activity is being carried out by the landowner.

T F 10. Persons who dispose of hazardous waste in violation of the Resource Conservation and Recovery Act may be criminally, as well as civilly, liable.

Multiple Choice - Circle the best answer.

11. Superfund legislation requires that:
    a. a state prevent future environmental problems on sites which have been cleaned up.
    b. responsible parties reimburse the EPA for its costs of cleaning up a hazardous waste site.
    c. those responsible for contaminating a site be jointly and severally liable for the cost of cleanup.
    d. All of the above

12. Under the Clean Air Act, the *primary* ambient air-quality standards protect:
    a. the public health.
    b. the economic vitality of the local region.
    c. the vegetation and animal life of the U.S.
    d. the climate and visibility.

13. An environmental impact statement must reveal:
    a. irreversible commitments of resources under the proposed project.
    b. the alternatives to the proposed project.
    c. the differences between the short-term and the long-term environmental impacts of the project.
    d. all of the above matters.

14. Superfund cleanup activity is financed primarily by:
    a. a tax on chemicals and feedstocks.
    b. permitting fees.
    c. court judgments in environmental lawsuits.
    d. local and state tax levies.

15. The Resource Conservation and Recovery Act:
    a. provides a comprehensive scheme for dealing with air pollution.
    b. regulates disposal of hazardous waste.
    c. establishes a comprehensive framework for controlling water pollution.
    d. provides a mechanism for identifying and cleaning up the most hazardous uncontrolled waste sites.

16. The use of agricultural chemicals:
    a. has vastly increased the productivity of the American farmer.
    b. has proved fatal to certain species of wildlife.
    c. presents a danger to those who apply the chemicals.
    d. All of the above

17. When the EPA administrator has reason to believe that continued use of a particular pesticide poses an imminent hazard, the most appropriate action pursuant to the Federal Insecticide, Fungicide, and Rodenticide Act would be to:
    a. compel manufacturer registration of the pesticide.
    b. initiate a cancellation of registration proceeding.
    c. suspend the registration of the pesticide and remove it from the market.
    d. set limits on the pesticide residue permitted on crops that provide food for people or animals.

18. The genetic manipulation of organisms through the use of biotechnology:
    a. is not as yet regulated by U.S. environmental laws.
    b. is regulated by the states.
    c. is regulated jointly by several federal agencies.
    d. is reviewed after it occurs, not before it takes place.

19. Which federal environmental statute does not permit private citizen lawsuits?
    a. Resource Conservation and Recovery Act
    b. Clean Air Act
    c. Clean Water Act
    d. All of these statutes permit private lawsuits.

20. Nuisance actions:
    a. are ideally suited to dealing with widespread pollution problems.
    b. permit courts to order the owner or operator of a piece of property to stop using it in a way that unreasonably interferes with public or private property or health.
    c. provide a comprehensive, across-the-board approach to pollution problems.
    d. are no longer permitted, as this area of the common law has been preempted by federal environmental law.

21. Describe the scheme for enforcing the national ambient air quality standards established by the Environmental Protection Agency pursuant to the Clean Air Act.

22. What are "wetlands," and how are they regulated under the Clean Water Act?

23. Why did Congress create the Environmental Protection Agency?

CHAPTER 52

THE LEGAL ENVIRONMENT FOR INTERNATIONAL BUSINESS

True-False - Circle T for True and F for False.

T F   1.   Generally, the law governing international business transactions in situations where choice of law is not spelled out in the parties' contract is the law of the country in which the seller's place of business is located.

T F   2.   The 1980 Vienna Convention on Contracts for the International Sale of Goods is designed to provide a uniform code of rules to govern international contracts.

T F   3.   The most common form of international transaction engaged in by U.S. firms is the export of products manufactured by the firms in the U.S.

T F   4.   Under the Uniform Customs and Article 5 of the Uniform Commercial Code, the promises made by the issuing bank and the confirming bank in a documentary irrevocable letter of credit transaction are dependent upon the seller's satisfactory performance of its obligation under the underlying sales contract.

T F   5.   A *force majeure* clause in a distribution agreement states which language is to be used in interpreting the distribution agreement.

T F   6.   In international contracts, arbitration is often the forum of choice.

T F   7.   Legal action by a U.S. firm in response to the expropriation of its facilities by the host government seldom results in compensation for the loss.

T F   8.   An arbitration tribunal has no power to order the use of the host government's property to satisfy the claim of a U.S. firm whose property has been expropriated by that government.

T F   9.   U.S. firms that are unwilling to make a long-term commitment should not consider making a major investment in countries that place limits on the repatriation of earnings and investments.

T F 10.   A "most favored nation clause" eliminates most discrimination among countries on the basis of tariffs and duties.

Multiple Choice - Circle the best answer.

    11.   A documentary irrevocable letter of credit transaction:
       a.   ensures that the seller of goods on the international market will strictly perform its contract obligations.
       b.   involves two parties—the U.S. seller and its foreign customer.
       c.   performs a function similar to that performed by the indorsement of a note.
       d.   removes the need for a sales contract between the seller and buyer.

    12.   A distribution agreement between a U.S. firm and a distributor abroad:
       a.   is primarily governed by contract law.
       b.   has as its forum of choice the U.S. court system.
       c.   is exempt from U.S. and foreign antitrust laws.
       d.   is unenforceable in the U.S. courts.

    13.   The biggest worry of a U.S. firm which establishes a manufacturing operation abroad is:
       a.   repatriation.
       b.   *force majeure.*
       c.   expropriation.
       d.   tariffs.

14. "Dumping":
    a. involves goods that are economically supported by the government of their country of origin and can therefore be sold for less than goods produced in the native market.
    b. involves the selling of goods at unfairly low prices.
    c. involves a tax or duty assessed on goods when they are imported into a country for the purpose of restricting imports and protecting domestic sales.
    d. involves the seizure of a U.S. firm's manufacturing facilities by the host government without compensation.

15. Obstacles to the extraterritorial application of U.S. antitrust laws:
    a. are nonexistent in most of the major trading nations.
    b. can be easily overcome by the use of exclusive dealing agreements.
    c. include the requirement that the acts challenged be shown to have had a substantial effect on U.S. commerce.
    d. are eased by the doctrine of comity.

16. An exclusive licensing agreement between a U.S. firm and an EEC firm:
    a. can have a signficant negative impact on interbrand competition.
    b. can be exempted from Article 85 of the Treaty of Rome by a notification procedure similar to that used for exclusive distributorship agreements.
    c. is less likely to be exempt from EEC antitrust laws if the product in question is not currently being imported into the Common Market in significant quantities.
    d. poses a significant risk of illegality under U.S. antitrust laws.

17. A letter of credit in a documentary irrevocable letter of credit transaction:
    a. should be received by the seller prior to shipment of the goods to the buyer.
    b. is issued by the confirming bank pursuant to an agreement between it and the buyer.
    c. protects the buyer by assuring that the goods will not be paid for unless the issuing bank determines that they conform to the sales contract.
    d. obligates the issuing bank to pay for the goods upon delivery of the goods to the confirming bank.

18. An exclusive dealing provision in a distribution agreement between a U.S. firm and a foreign distributor:
    a. poses no risk of liability under U.S. antitrust laws because all sales occur outside the U.S.
    b. will be governed by Section 3 of the Clayton Act.
    c. will be governed primarily by the Sherman Act.
    d. is mainly intended to benefit the foreign distributor.

19. Which is *not* a concern for U.S. firms who establish manufacturing facilities abroad?
    a. Local regulation of technology transfer
    b. Local labor laws
    c. Local limits on repatriation of earnings and investments
    d. Expropriation

20. Countries impose import and export controls by:
    a. using tariffs.
    b. controlling the licensing of technology.
    c. limiting exports of militarily sensitive technology.
    d. all of the above methods.

21. Why is arbitration on the increase in international business transactions?

22. What is the difference between repatriation and expropriation?

23. What are the goals of licensing regulations in developing countries?

CHAPTER 53

COMPUTER LAW

True-False - Circle T for True and F for False.

T F 1. It is likely that a license of mass-produced and mass-marketed software which is sold over the counter will be considered to be a sale of goods for purposes of the U.C.C.

T F 2. The use of "box top licenses" by software manufacturers raises the possibility that the limitations of liability contained therein are unenforceable.

T F 3. Most written computer contracts contain merger clauses that operate to exclude from the contract any presale representations or statements which are not included in the writing.

T F 4. A tort remedy is often more profitable for the buyer of hardware or software than remedies available for breach of contract or warranty.

T F 5. The standard of care expected of computer designers and programmers is well-defined and can often be used as the basis for a malpractice claim.

T F 6. Strict liability claims are more useful in computer cases than claims for breach of warranty.

T F 7. One of the biggest problems in punishing and deterring computer crime is that traditional criminal statutes frequently do not address the crimes that can be committed through the use of computers.

T F 8. The "object code," or instructions included in a computer program which can be read only by the computer and not by humans, is not subject to copyright protection because it is not a literary work as required by the Copyright Act.

T F 9. As a general rule, when software is acquired along with hardware, the transaction will be considered a sale of goods.

T F 10. The tort cause of action for invasion of privacy adequately prevents the widespread collection, storage, and dissemination of information by computers.

Multiple Choice - Circle the best answer.

11. Copyright law provides limited protection to computer programs because:
    a. the process of obtaining copyright protection is so slow and expensive.
    b. program instructions written in object code are not subject to copyright protection.
    c. copyrights do not protect the basic idea behind a software program, merely the form in which it is expressed, and most computer programs' value lies in their ideas rather than in the way in which the ideas are expressed.
    d. the program must be kept secret in order for copyright protection to be available.

12. To be protected as a trade secret, a software program must be:
    a. kept secret.
    b. protected by a "box top license."
    c. written in object code.
    d. patentable.

13. A buyer who has been induced to enter a computer contract by the seller's misrepresentations of material fact might be able to sue the seller based on:
    a. fraud.
    b. misrepresentation.
    c. Both a and b
    d. Neither a nor b

14. The UCC applies to a computer purchase contract if:
    a. the goods were the primary factor in the contract.
    b. the services were the primary factor in the contract.
    c. the tangible goods supplied were incidental to the services provided under the contract.
    d. the customer bargained primarily for services.

15. Factors considered by a court in deciding whether a computer contract is unconscionable include:
    a. contract clauses that are extremely advantageous to the seller.
    b. exploitation of the buyer's inferior bargaining power.
    c. the fact that the buyer is a consumer and a first-time computer user.
    d. each of the above

16. When a computer system proves to be defective, a buyer may seek a remedy for breach of which warranty or warranties?
    a. Express warranties resulting from statements found on the boxes in which the computer arrives
    b. The implied warranty of merchantability, assuming that the seller is a merchant
    c. The implied warranty of fitness for a particular purpose if the computer was custom-designed for the buyer
    d. The buyer could seek a remedy for breach of all of the warranties mentioned above.

17. Software licensing agreements:
    a. are designed to preserve secrecy by restricting the licensee's disclosure of the program.
    b. permit the licensee to copy the program.
    c. provide consequential damages in lieu of replacement or repair of the software.
    d. All of the above

18. Some courts have increased the copyright protection of software by:
    a. holding that a program's structure, sequence, and organization are a part of the ideas it expresses.
    b. holding that a program's structure, sequence, and organization are part of the form in which ideas are expressed.
    c. holding that copyright protection only protects the duplication of the object code of the program.
    d. holding that copyright protection only protects the duplication of the source code of the program.

19. With regard to the patenting of computer software:
    a. an invention including a computer program is not patentable.
    b. the software need not meet the usual tests for patentability.
    c. an invention including a computer program is patentable.
    d. a patent on the software would give its producer the exclusive right to make it, but not to sell it.

20. Categorizing computer crime as theft:
    a. is an easy matter.
    b. requires computer data to be defined as property.
    c. is impossible under current criminal laws.
    d. is not possible under state law.

21. Paul uses the Big State University computer without authorization to write his doctoral dissertation. BSU asks that he be prosecuted for theft, which is defined in that state as "the knowing or intentional assertion of unauthorized control over property of another with intent to deprive the other person of any part of its use or value." What would be Paul's best defense to this charge?

22. How might a software manufacturer legally protect its software from copying by a competitor?

23. What factors make computer-assisted crime so hard to handle under current law?